PEARSON CUSTOM
ANTHROPOLOGY

Dr. McKether's Anthropology
The University of Toledo

Managing Editor
Jeffrey H. Cohen
Ohio State University

Associate Editor
Douglas E. Crews
Ohio State University

Contributing Editors–Cultural Anthropology
Randal Allison
Blinn College

Lee Cronk
Rutgers (New Brunswick)

Donald C. Wood
Akita University Medical School

Contributing Editors–Biological/Physical Anthropology
Susan Kirkpatrick-Smith
Kennesaw State University

James Stewart
Columbus State Community College

PEARSON

ISBN 10: 1-269-23927-9
ISBN 13: 978-1-269-23927-1

Table of Contents

The Importance of Anthropology

From Chapter 1 of *Human Culture*, Second Edition. Carol R. Ember, Melvin Ember. Copyright © 2012 by Pearson Education, Inc. All rights reserved.

The Importance of Anthropology

((•—[Listen to the **Chapter Audio** on **myanthrolab.com**   [◉—[Read on **myanthrolab.com**

What is anthropology and what can it do? The term **anthropology** comes from the Greek *anthropos* for "man, human" and *logos* for "study." Anthropologists seek answers to an enormous variety of questions about humans. They are interested in both universals and differences in human populations. They want to discover when, where, and why humans appeared on the earth, how and why they have changed since then, and how and why modern human populations vary in their biological and cultural features. Anthropology has a practical side too. Applied and practicing anthropologists put anthropological methods, information, and results to use, in efforts to solve practical problems.

Defining anthropology as the study of human beings is not complete, however, for such a definition would appear to incorporate a whole catalog of disciplines: sociology, psychology, political science, economics, history, human biology, and perhaps even the humanistic disciplines of philosophy and literature. There must, then, be something unique about anthropology—a reason for its having developed as a separate discipline and for its having retained a separate identity over the last 100 years.

The Scope of Anthropology

Anthropologists are often thought of as individuals who travel to little-known corners of the world to study exotic peoples or who dig deep into the earth to uncover the fossil remains or the tools and pots of people who lived long ago. These views, though clearly stereotyped, do indicate how anthropology differs from other disciplines concerned with humans. Anthropology is broader in scope, both geographically and historically. Anthropology is concerned explicitly and directly with all varieties of people throughout the world, not just those close at hand. Anthropologists are also interested in people of all periods. Beginning with the immediate ancestors of humans, who lived a few million years ago, anthropology traces the development of humans until the present.

Anthropologists have not always been as global and comprehensive in their concerns as they are today. Traditionally, they concentrated on non-Western cultures and left the study of Western civilization to other disciplines. In recent years, however, this division of labor among the disciplines has begun to disappear. Now anthropologists work in their own and other complex societies.

What induces anthropologists to study humans so broadly? In part, they are motivated by the belief that any suggested generalization about human beings should be shown to apply to many times and places of human existence. If a generalization does not prove to apply widely, anthropologists are entitled or even obliged to be skeptical about it. The skeptical attitude, in the absence of persuasive evidence, is our best protection against accepting invalid ideas about humans.

For example, when American educators discovered in the 1960s that African American schoolchildren rarely drank milk, they assumed that lack of money or education was the cause. But evidence from anthropology suggested a different explanation. Anthropologists had known for years that people do not drink fresh milk in many parts of the world where milking animals are kept; rather, they sour it before they drink it, or they make it into cheese. Why they do so is now clear. Many people lack the enzyme lactase that is necessary for breaking down lactose, the sugar in milk. When such people drink regular milk, it actually interferes with digestion. Not only is the lactose in milk not digested, but other nutrients are less likely to be digested as well; in many cases, drinking milk will cause cramps, stomach gas, diarrhea, and nausea.[1] Milk intolerance is common in adulthood among Asians, southern Europeans, Arabs and Jews, West Africans, North and South American native peoples, as well as African Americans. Because anthropologists are acquainted with human life in an enormous variety of geographic and historical settings, they are often able to correct mistaken beliefs about different groups of people.

The Holistic Approach

Another distinguishing feature of the discipline is its **holistic**, or multifaceted, approach to the study of human beings. Anthropologists study not only all varieties of people but many aspects of human experience. For example, when describing a group of people, an anthropologist might discuss the history of the area in which the people live, the physical environment, the organization of family life, the general features of their language, the group's settlement patterns, political and economic systems, religion, and styles of art and dress.

In the past, individual anthropologists tried to cover as many subjects as possible. Today, as in many other disciplines, so much information has been accumulated that anthropologists tend to specialize. Thus, one anthropologist may investigate the physical characteristics of some of our prehistoric ancestors. Another may study the biological effect of the environment on a human population over time. Still another will concentrate on many customs of a particular group of people. Despite this specialization, however, the discipline of anthropology retains its holistic orientation in that its many different specialties, taken together, describe many aspects of human existence, both past and present.

The Anthropological Curiosity

Thus far, we have described anthropology as being broader in scope, both historically and geographically, and more holistic in approach than other disciplines concerned with human beings. But this statement again implies that anthropology is the all-inclusive human science. How, then, is anthropology really different from the other disciplines? We suggest that anthropology's distinctiveness lies principally in the kind of curiosity it arouses.

Individuals may provide information to anthropologists, but the anthropological curiosity mostly focuses on the typical characteristics (traits, customs) of human groups and how to understand and explain them. For example, whereas economists take a monetary system for granted and study how it operates, anthropologists would ask how frequently monetary systems are found, why they vary, and why only some societies during the last few thousand years used money. This is not to imply that anthropologists are not interested in variation within human groups, but their focus is usually on typical characteristics of human groups—how and why populations and their characteristics have varied around the globe and throughout the ages.

Fields of Anthropology

Different anthropologists concentrate on different characteristics of societies. Some are concerned primarily with *biological* or *physical characteristics* of human populations; others are interested principally in what we call *cultural characteristics*. Hence, there are two broad classifications of

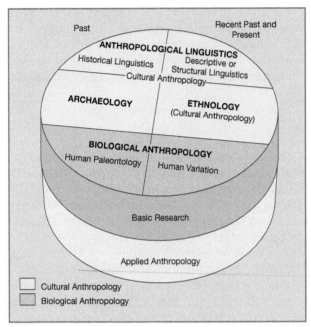

Figure 1 The Subdivisions of Anthropology
The four major subdisciplines of anthropology (in bold type) may be classified according to subject matter (biological or cultural) and according to the period with which each is concerned (distant past versus recent past and present). There are applications of anthropology in all four subdisciplines.

subject matter in anthropology: *biological (physical) anthropology* and *cultural anthropology*. Biological anthropology is one major field of anthropology. Cultural anthropology is divided into three major subfields: *archaeology, linguistics,* and *ethnology*. Ethnology, the study of recent cultures, is now usually referred to by the parent name, cultural anthropology (see Figure 1). Crosscutting these four fields is a fifth, *applied* or *practicing anthropology.*

Biological Anthropology

Biological (physical) anthropology, which deals with the biological or physical characteristics of humans, seeks to answer two distinct sets of questions. The first set is about the emergence of humans and their later evolution (this focus is called **human paleontology** or **paleoanthropology**). The second set is about how and why contemporary human populations vary biologically (this focus is called **human variation**).

To reconstruct human evolution, human paleontologists search for and study the buried, hardened remains or impressions—known as **fossils**—of humans, prehumans, and related animals. Paleontologists working in East Africa, for instance, have excavated the fossil remains of humanlike beings that lived more than 4 million years ago. These findings have suggested the approximate dates when our ancestors began to develop two-legged walking, very flexible hands, and a larger brain.

In attempting to clarify evolutionary relationships, human paleontologists may use not only the fossil record but also geological information on the succession of climates, environments, and plant and animal populations. Moreover, when reconstructing the past of humans, paleontologists are also interested in the behavior and evolution of our closest relatives among the mammals—the prosimians, monkeys, and apes, which, like ourselves, are members of the order of **Primates**. Anthropologists, psychologists, and biologists who specialize in the study of primates are called **primatologists**. The various species of primates are observed in the wild and in the laboratory. One especially popular subject of study is the chimpanzee, which bears a close resemblance to humans in behavior and physical appearance, has very similar genes, and is susceptible to many of the same diseases.[2]

The second major focus of biological anthropology, the study of human variation, investigates how and why contemporary human populations differ in biological or physical characteristics. All living people belong to one species, ***Homo sapiens***, for all can successfully interbreed.

Birute Galdikas works with two orangutans in Borneo.

Yet, much varies among human populations. Investigators of human variation ask such questions as: Why are some peoples taller than others? How have human populations adapted physically to their environmental conditions? Are some peoples, such as Inuit, better equipped than other peoples to endure cold? Does darker skin color offer special protection against the tropical sun?

To understand better the biological variations observable among contemporary human populations, biological anthropologists use the principles, concepts, and techniques of at least three other disciplines: human genetics (the study of human traits that are inherited), population biology (the study of environmental effects on, and interaction with, population characteristics), and epidemiology (the study of how and why diseases affect different populations in different ways). Research on human variation, therefore, overlaps research in other fields.

Cultural Anthropology

Cultural anthropology is concerned with how and why cultures vary or are similar in the past and present. But what is culture? Briefly, the term *culture* refers to the customary ways that a particular population or society thinks and behaves. The culture of a social group includes many things—from the language that people speak, the way children are brought up, the roles assigned to males and females, religious beliefs and practices, and preferences in music. Anthropologists are interested in all of these and other learned behaviors and ideas that have come to be widely shared or customary in the group. The three main branches of cultural anthropology are **archaeology** (the study of past cultures, primarily through their material remains), **anthropological linguistics** (the anthropological study of languages), and **ethnology** (the study of existing and recent cultures), now usually referred to by the parent name, *cultural anthropology.*

The Importance of Anthropology

In urban areas before new construction begins, archaeologists may be called upon to excavate and record information on historical sites, as shown here in New York City.

Archaeology Archaeologists seek not only to reconstruct the daily life and customs of peoples who lived in the past but also to trace cultural changes and to offer possible explanations for those changes. This concern is similar to that of historians, but archaeologists reach much farther back in time. Historians deal only with societies that left written records and are therefore limited to the last 5,000 years of human history. Human societies, however, have existed for more than a million years, and only a small proportion in the last 5,000 years had writing. Lacking written records for study, archaeologists must try to reconstruct history from the remains of human cultures. Some of these remains are as grand as the Mayan temples discovered at Chichén Itzá in Yucatán, Mexico. More often, they are as ordinary as bits of broken pottery, stone tools, and garbage heaps.

To collect the data they need to understand how and why ways of life have changed through time in different parts of the world, archaeologists use techniques and findings borrowed from other disciplines, as well as what they can infer from anthropological studies of recent and contemporary cultures. For example, to guess where to dig for evidence of early toolmaking, archaeologists rely on geology to tell them where sites of early human occupation are likely to be found, because of erosion and uplifting, near the surface of the earth. To infer when agriculture first developed, archaeologists date the relevant excavated materials by a process originally developed by chemical scientists. To try to understand why cities first emerged, archaeologists may use information from historians, geographers, and others about how recent and contemporary cities are related economically and politically to their hinterlands. If we can discover what recent and contemporary cities have in common, we can speculate on why cities developed originally. Thus, archaeologists use information from the present and recent past in trying to understand the distant past.

Anthropological Linguistics Anthropological linguistics is another branch of cultural anthropology. Linguistics, or the study of languages, is a somewhat older discipline than anthropology, but the early linguists concentrated on the study of languages that had been written for a long time—languages such as English that had been written for nearly a thousand years. Anthropological linguists began to do fieldwork in places where the language was not yet written. This meant that anthropologists could not consult a dictionary or grammar to help them learn the language. Instead, they first had to construct a dictionary and grammar. Then they could study the structure and history of the language.

Like biological anthropologists, linguists study changes that have taken place over time, as well as contemporary variation. Some anthropological linguists are concerned with the emergence of language and also with the divergence of languages over thousands of years. The study of how languages change over time and how they may be related is known as **historical linguistics**. Anthropological linguists are also interested in how contemporary languages differ, especially in their construction. This focus of linguistics is generally called **descriptive (structural) linguistics**. The study of how language is used in social contexts is called **sociolinguistics**.

In contrast with human paleontologists and archaeologists, who have physical remains to help them reconstruct change over time, historical linguists deal only with languages—and usually unwritten ones at that. (Remember that writing is only about 5,000 years old, and most languages since then have not been written.) Because unwritten languages must be heard to be studied, they do not leave any trace once speakers have died. Linguists interested in reconstructing the history of unwritten languages must begin in the present, with comparisons of contemporary languages. On the basis of these comparisons, they draw inferences about the kinds of change in language that may have occurred in the past and that may account for similarities and differences observed in the present. Historical linguists typically ask such questions as these: Did two or more contemporary languages diverge from a common ancestral language? If they are related, how far back in time did they begin to differ?

Unlike historical linguists, descriptive (or structural) linguists are typically concerned with discovering and recording the principles that determine how sounds and words are put together in speech. For example, a structural description of a particular language might tell us that the sounds *t* and *k* are interchangeable in a word without causing a difference in meaning. In American Samoa, one could say *Tutuila* or *Kukuila* as the name of the largest island, and everyone, except perhaps newly arrived anthropologists who know little yet about the Samoan language, would understand that the same island was being mentioned.

Sociolinguists are interested in the social aspects of language, including what people speak about and how they interact conversationally, their attitudes toward speakers of other dialects or languages, and how people speak differently in different social contexts. In English, for example, we do not address everyone we meet in the same way. "Hi, Sandy" may be the customary way a person greets a friend. But we would probably feel uncomfortable addressing a doctor by a first name; instead, we would probably say, "Good morning, Dr. Brown." Such variations in language use, which are determined by the social status of the people being addressed, are significant for sociolinguists.

Ethnology Ethnologists, usually called "cultural anthropologists" nowadays, try to understand how and why peoples today and in the recent past differ or are similar in their customary ways of thinking and acting. How and why do cultures develop and change? How does one aspect of culture affect others? The aim of ethnologists is largely the same as that of archaeologists. However, ethnologists generally use data collected through observation and interviews of living peoples. Archaeologists, on the other hand, must work with fragmentary remains of past cultures, on the basis of which they can only make inferences about the customs of prehistoric peoples.

The Importance of Anthropology

One type of ethnologist, **ethnographers**, usually spend a year or so living with, talking to, and observing the people whose customs they are studying. This fieldwork provides the data for a detailed description (an **ethnography**) of customary behavior and thought. Ethnographers vary in the degree to which they strive for completeness in their coverage of cultural and social life. Earlier ethnographers tended to strive for holistic coverage; more recent ethnographers have tended to specialize or focus on narrower realms such as ritual healing or curing, interaction with the environment, effects of modernization or globalization, or gender issues. Ethnographies often go beyond description; they may address current anthropological issues or try to explain some aspect of culture.

Many cultures have undergone extensive change in the recent past so trying to understand what life was like in earlier times is important. Ethnographers can ask older people what life was like when they were young, and information about the past may be contained in historical documents usually not written by anthropologists. An **ethnohistorian** studies how the ways of life of a particular group of people have changed over time. Ethnohistorians investigate written documents such as missionary accounts, reports by traders and explorers, and government records to try to establish the cultural changes that have occurred. Unlike ethnographers, who rely mostly on their own observations and interviewing, ethnohistorians rely on the reports of others. Often, they must attempt to piece together and make sense of widely scattered, and even apparently contradictory, information. Thus, the ethnohistorian's research is very much like that of a historian, except that ethnohistorians are usually concerned with the history of a people who did not themselves leave written records.

Ethnographic and ethnohistorical research is very time-consuming, and it is rare for one person to study more than a few cultures. The **cross-cultural researcher** (who may be a cultural anthropologist or some other kind of social scientist) is interested in discovering general patterns about cultural traits—what is universal, what is variable, why traits vary, and what the consequences of the variability might be. Why, for example, is there more gender inequality in some societies than in others? Is family violence related to aggression in other areas of life? What are the effects of living in a very unpredictable environment? In testing possible answers to such questions, cross-cultural researchers use data from samples of cultures (usually described initially by ethnographers) to try to arrive at explanations or relationships that hold across cultures. Archaeologists may find the results of cross-cultural research useful for making inferences about the past, particularly if they can discover material indicators of cultural variation.

Because ethnologists may be interested in many aspects of customary behavior and thought—from economic behavior to political behavior to styles of art, music, and religion—ethnology overlaps with disciplines that concentrate on some particular aspect of human existence, such as sociology, psychology, economics, political science, art, music, and comparative religion. But the distinctive feature of cultural anthropology is its interest in how all these aspects of human existence vary from society to society, in all historical periods, and in all parts of the world.

Applied Anthropology

In the physical and biological sciences, it is well understood that technological breakthroughs like DNA splicing, spacecraft docking in outer space, and the development of miniscule computer chips could not have taken place without an enormous amount of basic research to uncover the laws of nature in the physical and biological worlds. If we did not understand fundamental principles, the technological achievements we are so proud of would not be possible. Researchers are often simply driven by curiosity, with no thought to where the research might lead, which is why such research is sometimes called *basic research.* The same is true of the social sciences. If a researcher finds out that societies with combative sports tend to have more wars, it may lead to other inquiries about the relationships between one kind of aggression and another. The knowledge acquired may ultimately lead to discovering ways to correct social problems, such as family violence and war.

Whereas basic research may ultimately help to solve practical problems, applied research is more explicit in its practical goals. Today, more than half of all professional anthropologists are applied, or practicing, anthropologists.[3] **Applied (practicing) anthropology** is explicit in its concern with making anthropological knowledge useful.[4] Applied anthropologists may be trained in any or all of the subfields of anthropology. In contrast to basic researchers, who are almost always employed in colleges, universities, and museums, applied anthropologists are commonly employed in settings outside traditional academia, including government agencies, international development agencies, private consulting firms, businesses, public health organizations, medical schools, law offices, community development agencies, and charitable foundations.

APPLIED ANTHROPOLOGY ● ● ● ● ● ● ● ● ●

Getting Development Programs to Notice Women's Contributions to Agriculture

When Anita Spring first did fieldwork in Zambia in the 1970s, she was not particularly interested in agriculture. Rather, medical anthropology was her interest. Her work focused on customary healing practices, particularly involving women and children. She was surprised at the end of the year when a delegation of women came to tell her that she didn't understand what it meant to be a woman. "To be a woman is to be a farmer," they said. She admits that it took her a while to pay attention to women as farmers, but then she began to participate in efforts to provide technical assistance to them. Like many others interested in women in development, Spring realized that all too often development agents downplay women's contributions to agriculture.

How does one bring about change in male-centered attitudes and practices? One way is to document how much women actually contribute to agriculture. Beginning with the influential writing of Ester Boserup in *Woman's Role in Economic Development* (1970), scholars began to report that in Africa south of the Sahara, in the Caribbean, and in parts of Southeast Asia, women were the principal farmers or agricultural laborers. Moreover, as agriculture became more complex, it required more work time in the fields, so the women's contribution to agriculture increased.

In addition, men increasingly went away to work, so women had to do much of what used to be men's work on the farms.

In the 1980s, Spring designed and directed the Women in Agricultural Development Project in Malawi, funded by the Office of Women in the U.S. Agency for International Development. Rather than focusing just on women, the project aimed to collect data on both female and male agriculturalists and how development agents treated them. The project did more than collect information; mini-projects were set up and evaluated so that successful training techniques could be passed on to development agents in other regions. Spring points out that the success of the program was due not just to the design of the project. Much of the success depended on the interest and willingness of Malawi itself to change. It didn't hurt that the United Nations and other donor organizations increasingly focused attention on women. It takes the efforts of many to bring about change. Increasingly, applied anthropologists like Anita Spring are involved in these efforts from beginning to end, from the design stage to implementation and evaluation.

Sources: Spring 1995; 2000b.

Forensic anthropology is one kind of applied anthropology. Kathy Reichs is a forensic anthropologist working in a medical examiner's office.

Biological anthropologists may be called upon to give forensic evidence in court, or they may work in public health, or they may design clothes and equipment to fit human anatomy. Archaeologists may be involved in preserving and exhibiting artifacts for museums and in doing contract work to find and preserve cultural sites that might be damaged by construction or excavation. Linguists may work in bilingual educational training programs or may work on ways to improve communication. Ethnologists may work in a wide variety of applied projects ranging from community development, urban planning, health care, and agricultural improvement to personnel and organizational management and assessment of the impact of change programs on people's lives.[5]

The Relevance of Anthropology

The idea that it is impossible to account for human behavior scientifically, either because our actions and beliefs are too individualistic and complex or because human beings are understandable only in otherworldly terms, is a self-fulfilling notion. We cannot discover general principles explaining human behavior if we neither believe such principles exist nor bother to look for them. People who do not believe that there can be general principles of human behavior will be reinforced by their finding none. If we are to increase our understanding of human beings, we first have to believe it is possible to do so.

If we aim to understand humans, it is essential that we study humans in all times and places. We must study ancient humans and modern humans. We must study their cultures and their biology. How else can we understand what is true of humans generally or how they are capable of varying? If we study just our own society, we may come up only with explanations that are culture-bound, not general or applicable to most or all humans. Anthropology is useful, then, to the degree that it contributes to our understanding of human beings everywhere.

In addition, anthropology is relevant because it helps us avoid misunderstandings between peoples. If we can understand why other groups are different from ourselves, we might have less reason to condemn them for behavior that appears strange to us. We may then come to realize that many differences between peoples are products of physical and cultural adaptations to different environments. For example, someone who first finds out about the San as they lived in the Kalahari Desert of southern Africa in the 1950s might assume that the San were "backward." The San wore little clothing, had few possessions, lived in meager shelters, and enjoyed none of our technological niceties like radio and computers. But let us reflect on how a typical North American community might react if it awoke to find itself in an environment similar to that in which the San lived. The people would find that the arid land makes both agriculture and animal husbandry impossible, and they might have to think about adopting a nomadic existence. They might then discard many of their material possessions so that they could travel easily, to take advantage of changing water and food supplies. Because of the extreme heat and the lack of extra water for laundry, they might find it more practical to be almost naked than to wear clothes. They would undoubtedly find it impossible to build elaborate homes. For social security, they might start to share the food brought into the group. Thus, if they survived at all, they might end up looking and acting far more like the San looked than like typical North Americans.

As the world becomes increasingly interconnected or globalized, the importance of understanding and trying to respect cultural and physical differences becomes more and more important. Minor misunderstandings can escalate quickly into more serious problems. Even when powerful countries think they are being helpful, they may convey that other countries are inferior. They may also unknowingly promote behaviors that are not in the best interest of the people they are trying to help. At the extreme, misunderstandings can lead to violent confrontations. In today's world, going to war with modern weapons of mass destruction can kill more people than ever before.

Knowledge of our past may bring both a feeling of humility and a sense of accomplishment. If we are to attempt to deal with the problems of our world, we must be aware of our vulnerability so that we do not think that problems will solve themselves. But we also have to think enough of our accomplishments to believe that we can find solutions to problems. Much of the trouble we get into may be a result of feelings of self-importance and invulnerability—in short, our lack of humility. Knowing something about our evolutionary past may help us to understand and accept

A large number of emigrants from the former Soviet Union, particularly from Black Sea cities and towns such as Odessa, live in the Brighton Beach neighborhood of Brooklyn. Migrant and immigrant communities, such as "Little Odessa," are an increasing focus of anthropological study.

The Importance of Anthropology

our place in the biological world. Just as for any other form of life, there is no guarantee that any particular human population, or even the entire human species, will perpetuate itself indefinitely. The earth changes, the environment changes, and humanity itself changes. What survives and flourishes in the present might not do so in the future.

Yet, our vulnerability should not make us feel powerless. We have many reasons to feel confident about the future. Consider what we have accomplished so far. By means of tools and weapons fashioned from sticks and stones, we were able to hunt animals larger and more powerful than ourselves. We discovered how to make fire, and we learned to use it to keep ourselves warm and to cook our food. As we domesticated plants and animals, we gained greater control over our food supply and were able to establish more permanent settlements. We mined and smelted ores to fashion more durable tools. We built cities and irrigation systems, monuments and ships. We made it possible to travel from one continent to another in a single day. We conquered some illnesses and prolonged human life.

In short, human beings and their cultures have changed considerably over the course of history. Human populations have often been able to adapt to changing circumstances. Let us hope that humans continue to adapt to the challenges of the present and future.

✓—Study and Review on myanthrolab.com

Summary

1. Anthropology is literally the study of human beings. It differs from other disciplines concerned with people in that anthropology is: (a) concerned with humans in all places of the world and it traces human evolution and cultural development from millions of years ago to the present day; (b) holistic, that is, studies all aspects of peoples' experiences; and (c) concerned with identifying and explaining typical characteristics (traits, customs) of particular human populations.

2. Biological (physical) anthropology, one of the major fields of anthropology, studies the emergence of humans and their later physical evolution (human paleontology) and how and why contemporary human populations vary biologically (human variation).

3. Cultural anthropology has three subfields: archaeology, anthropological linguistics, and ethnology (now usually referred to by the parent name, cultural anthropology). All the subfields deal with aspects of human culture, that is, with the customary ways of thinking and behaving of particular societies.

4. Archaeologists seek to reconstruct and explain the daily life and customs of prehistoric peoples from the remains of human cultures.

5. Anthropological linguists are concerned with the emergence of language and with the divergence of languages over time (historical linguistics) as well as how contemporary languages differ, both in construction (descriptive or structural linguistics) and in actual speech (sociolinguistics).

6. The ethnologist (now often called a cultural anthropologist) seeks to understand how and why peoples of today and the recent past differ in their customary ways of thinking and acting. There are three major types of cultural anthropologists: ethnographers, ethnohistorians, and cross-cultural researchers.

The Importance of Anthropology

7. In all four major subdisciplines of anthropology, there are applied anthropologists, people who apply anthropological knowledge to achieve more practical goals.

8. By showing us why other people are the way they are, both culturally and physically, anthropology may make us more tolerant. Knowledge of our past may bring us both a feeling of humility and a sense of accomplishment.

Glossary Terms

anthropological linguistics
anthropology
applied (practicing)
   anthropology
archaeology
biological (physical)
   anthropology
cross-cultural researcher
cultural anthropology

descriptive (structural)
   linguistics
ethnographer
ethnography
ethnohistorian
ethnology
fossils
historical linguistics
holistic

Homo sapiens
human paleontology
human variation
paleoanthropology
Primates
primatologists
sociolinguistics

Critical Questions

1. Why study anthropology? What are its goals and how is it useful?

2. How does anthropology differ from other fields of study you've encountered that deal with humans? (Compare with psychology, sociology, political science, history, or biology, among others.)

3. What did you think anthropology was about before you read this chapter? Did your ideas change? Why or why not?

Read the Original Source on myanthrolab.com

Read the chapter by Terence E. Hays, "From Ethnographer to Comparativist and Back Again," on MyAnthroLab, and answer the following questions.

1. Many researchers find that their interests change when they go to the field. What did Hays start out studying? What did he get more interested in?

2. Explain why Hays thinks that you need both ethnography and comparison.

Photo Credits

Glossary

Anthropological linguistics The anthropological study of languages.

Anthropology A discipline that studies humans, focusing on the study of differences and similarities, both biological and cultural, in human populations. Anthropology is concerned with typical biological and cultural characteristics of human populations in all periods and in all parts of the world.

Applied (practicing) anthropology The branch of anthropology that concerns itself with applying anthropological knowledge to achieve practical goals, usually in the service of an agency outside the traditional academic setting.

Archaeology The branch of anthropology that seeks to reconstruct the daily life and customs of peoples who lived in the past and to trace and explain cultural changes. Often lacking written records for study, archaeologists must try to reconstruct history from the material remains of human cultures. See also Historical archaeology.

Biological (physical) anthropology The study of humans as biological organisms, dealing with the emergence and evolution of humans and with contemporary biological variations among human populations.

Cross-cultural researcher An ethnologist who uses ethnographic data about many societies to test possible explanations of cultural variation to discover general patterns about cultural traits—what is universal, what is variable, why traits vary, and what the consequences of the variability might be.

Cultural anthropology The study of cultural variation and universals in the past and present. Also refers to the subfield ethnology, one of the three subfields of cultural anthropology (the other subfields are anthropological linguistics and archaeology).

Descriptive (structural) linguistics The study of how languages are constructed.

Ethnographer A person who spends some time living with, interviewing, and observing a group of people to describe their customs.

Ethnography A description of a society's customary behaviors and ideas.

Ethnohistorian An ethnologist who uses historical documents to study how a particular culture has changed over time.

Ethnology The study of how and why recent cultures differ and are similar.

Fossils The hardened remains or impressions of plants and animals that lived in the past.

Historical linguistics The study of how languages change over time.

Holistic Refers to an approach that studies many aspects of a multifaceted system.

Homo sapiens All living people belong to one biological species, *Homo sapiens*, which means that all human populations on earth can successfully interbreed. The first *Homo sapiens* may have emerged about 200,000 years ago.

Human paleontology The study of the emergence of humans and their later physical evolution. Also called *paleoanthropology.*

Human variation The study of how and why contemporary human populations vary biologically.

Paleoanthropology See Human paleontology.

Primate A member of the mammalian order Primates, divided into the two suborders of prosimians and anthropoids.

Primatologists Researchers who study primates.

Sociolinguistics The study of cultural and subcultural patterns of speaking in different social contexts.

Notes

1. Durham 1991, 228–37; G.G. Harrison 1975.
2. Chimpanzee Sequencing and Analysis Consortium 2005.
3. Nolan 2003, 2.
4. Van Willigen 2002, 7.
5. Kedia and van Willigen 2005; Miracle 2009.

Bibliography

Chimpanzee Sequencing and Analysis Consortium. 2005. Initial sequence of the chimpanzee genome and comparison with the human genome. *Nature* 437 (September 1):69–87.

Durham, William H. 1991. *Coevolution: Genes, culture and human diversity.* Stanford, CA: Stanford University Press.

Harrison, Gail G. 1975. Primary adult lactase deficiency: A problem in anthropological genetics. *American Anthropologist* 77:812–35.

Kedia, Satish, and John van Willigen, eds. 2005. *Applied anthropology: Domains of application.* Wesport, CT: Praeger.

Miracle, Andrew W. 2009. A shaman to organizations. In MyAnthroLibrary, eds. C. R. Ember, M. Ember, and P. N. Peregrine. MyAnthroLibrary.com. Pearson.

Nolan, Riall W. 2003. Anthropology in practice: Building a career outside the academy. Boulder: Lynne Rienner.

Van Willigen, John. 2002. *Applied anthropology: An introduction.* 3rd ed. Westport, CT: Bergin & Garvey.

Applied and Practicing Anthropology

From Chapter 13 of *Human Culture*, Second Edition. Carol R. Ember, Melvin Ember. Copyright © 2012 by Pearson Education, Inc. All rights reserved.

Applied and Practicing Anthropology

CHAPTER OUTLINE

Ethics of Applied Anthropology

Evaluating the Effects of Planned Change

Difficulties in Instituting Planned Change

Cultural Resource Management

Forensic Anthropology

Medical Anthropology

((•—[Listen to the **Chapter Audio** on **myanthrolab.com**   [□•]—[Read on **myanthrolab.com**

Anthropology is no longer a merely academic subject. A large number of anthropologists in the United States are applied and practicing anthropologists. Some estimates suggest that more than half of those with graduate degrees in anthropology are now employed outside of colleges and universities.[1] The fact that so many organizations hire anthropologists suggests an increasing realization that anthropology, what it has discovered and can discover about humans, is useful. Anthropologists who call themselves applied or practicing anthropologists work for a large variety of organizations, government agencies, international development agencies, private consulting firms, public health organizations, medical schools, public interest law firms, community development agencies, charitable foundations, and profit-seeking corporations.

Applied or **practicing anthropology** as a profession is explicitly concerned with making anthropological knowledge useful. Applied or practicing anthropologists may be involved in one or more phases of a project: assembling relevant knowledge, developing plans and policies, assessing the likely social and environmental impacts, implementation, and evaluating the project and its effects.[2] Anthropologists are most often involved in gathering information, rather than constructing policy or initiating action.[3] The organizations that hire the applied anthropologists usually set policy and have staff to execute projects. However, anthropologists are increasingly finding themselves involved in policymaking and action. The field of applied or practicing anthropology is very diverse. Here, after focusing on general issues, we turn to some frequent types of applied work: *cultural resource management,* the "social impact" studies required in connection with many government or private programs, and *forensic anthropology,* the use of physical anthropology to help identify human remains and assist in solving crimes. We conclude with an extensive discussion of the application of anthropological knowledge to the study of health and illness.

Ethics of Applied Anthropology

Anthropologists have usually studied people who are disadvantaged—by imperialism, colonialism, and other forms of exploitation—and so it is no wonder that we care about the people's lives we have shared. But caring is not enough to improve others' lives. We may need basic research that allows us to understand how a condition might be successfully treated since a particular proposed "improvement" might actually not be an improvement; well-meaning efforts have sometimes produced harmful consequences. And even if we know that a change would be an improvement, there is still the problem of how to make that change happen. The people to be affected may not want to change. Is it ethical to try to persuade them? And, conversely, is it ethical *not* to try? Applied anthropologists must take all of these matters into consideration in determining whether and how to act in response to a perceived need.

Anthropology as a profession has adopted certain principles of responsibility. Above all, an anthropologist's first responsibility is to those who are being studied; everything should be done to ensure that their welfare and dignity will be protected. Anthropologists also have a responsibility to those who will read about their research; research findings should be reported openly and truthfully.[4] But because applied anthropology often deals with planning and implementing changes in some population, ethical responsibilities can become complicated. Perhaps the most important ethical question is: Will the change truly benefit the potentially affected population?

In May 1946, the Society for Applied Anthropology established a committee to draw up a specific code of ethics for professional applied anthropologists. After many meetings and revisions, a statement on ethical responsibilities was finally adopted in 1948, and in 1983, the

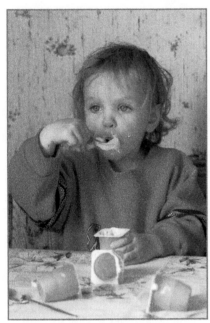

Businesses and consulting companies are doing more ethnographic research. Such research in the United States among families during the morning suggests that "breakfast" has become an intermittent series of snacks throughout the morning as families struggle with their time schedules and finding the right foods for their children.

statement was revised.[5] According to the code, the targeted community should be included as much as possible in the formulation of policy, so that people in the community may know in advance how the program will affect them. Perhaps the most important aspect of the code is the pledge not to recommend or take any action that is harmful to the interests of the community. The National Association for the Practice of Anthropology goes further: If the work the employer expects of the employee violates the ethical principles of the profession, the practicing anthropologist has the obligation to try to change those practices or, if change cannot be brought about, to withdraw from the work.[6]

Ethical issues are often complicated. Thayer Scudder described the situation of Gwembe Tonga villagers who were relocated after a large dam was built in the Zambezi Valley of central Africa. Economic conditions improved during the 1960s and early 1970s, as the people increasingly produced goods and services for sale. But then conditions deteriorated. By 1980, the villagers were in a miserable state; rates of mortality, alcoholism, theft, assault, and murder were up. Why? One reason was that they had cut back on producing their own food in favor of producing for the world market. Such a strategy works well when world market prices are high; however, when prices fall, so does the standard of living.[7] The situation described by Scudder illustrates the ethical dilemma for many applied anthropologists. As he said: "So how is it that I can still justify working for the agencies that fund such projects?" He points out that large-scale projects are almost impossible to stop. The anthropologist can choose to stand on the sidelines and complain or try to influence the project to benefit the affected population as much as possible.[8]

The problem described by Scudder comes about in part because the anthropologist is not often involved until after a decision is made to go ahead with a change program. This situation has begun to change as applied anthropologists are increasingly asked to participate in earlier stages of the planning process. Anthropologists are also increasingly asked to help in projects initiated by the affected party. Such requests may range from help in solving problems in corporate organizations to helping Native Americans with land claims. Because the project is consistent with the wishes of the affected population, the results are not likely to put the anthropologist into an ethical dilemma.

Evaluating the Effects of Planned Change

The decision as to whether a proposed change would benefit the affected population is not always easy to make. In certain cases, as when improved medical care is involved, the benefits offered to the target group would seem to be unquestionable—we all feel sure that health is better than illness. However, what about the long-term effects? Consider a public health innovation such as inoculation against disease. Once the inoculation program was begun, the number of children surviving would probably increase. But will there be enough food for the additional population? Given the level of technology, capital, and land resources possessed by the population, there might not be enough resources to feed more people. Thus, the death rate, because of starvation, might rise to its previous level and perhaps even exceed it. Without additional changes to increase the food supply, the inoculation program in the long term might merely change the causes of death. This example shows that, even if a program of planned change has beneficial consequences in the short run, a great deal of thought and investigation has to be given to its long-term effects.

Debra Picchi raised questions about the long-term effects on the Bakairí Indians of a program by the Brazilian National Indian Foundation (FUNAI) to produce rice with machine technology.[9] The Bakairí of the Mato Grosso region largely practice slash-and-burn horticulture in gallery forests along rivers, with supplementary cattle raising, fishing, and hunting. In the early part of the twentieth century, their population had declined to 150 people and they were given a relatively small reserve, much of it parched and infertile (cerrado). When the Bakairí population began to increase, FUNAI introduced a scheme to plant rice on formerly unused cerrado land, using machinery, insecticides, and fertilizer. FUNAI paid the costs for the first year and expected that the scheme would be self-supporting by the third year. The project did not go so well because FUNAI did not deliver all the equipment needed and did not provide adequate advice. Only half the expected rice was produced. Still, it was more food than the Bakairí had previously, so the program should have been beneficial to them.

But there were unanticipated negative side effects. Using cerrado land for agriculture reduced the area on which cattle could be grazed; cattle are an important source of high-quality protein. Mechanization also makes the Bakairí more dependent on cash for fuel, insecticides, fertilizer, and repairs. But cash is hard to come by. Only some individuals can be hired—usually men with outside experience who have the required knowledge of machinery. So the cash earned in the now-mechanized agriculture goes mainly to a relatively small number of people, creating new inequalities of income.

These failures were not the fault of anthropologists—indeed, most instances of planned change by governments and other agencies usually have begun without the input of anthropologists at all. Applied anthropologists have played an important role in pointing out the problems with programs like these that fail to evaluate long-term consequences. Such evaluations are an important part of convincing governments and other agencies to ask for anthropological help in the first place.

Difficulties in Instituting Planned Change

After numerous reforestation projects failed in Haiti, an anthropologist, Gerald Murray, was asked to help design a program that would work.[10] Understanding why previous projects failed was the first step in helping Murray design an effective project. One problem seems to have been that previous projects were run through the government's Ministry of Agriculture. The seedling trees that were given away were referred to as the "state's trees." In the project proposed by Murray, private voluntary organizations rather than the Haitian government were used to distribute trees and the farmers were told that they were the tree owners. Ownership included the right to cut the trees and sell the wood, just as they could sell crops. In the new plan, the tree seedlings given away were fast-growing species that matured in as little as 4 years. In addition, the new seedlings were very small and could be planted quickly. Perhaps most important of all, the new trees could be planted in borders or interspersed with other crops, interfering little with traditional crop patterns. To Murray's great surprise, by the end of 2 years, 2,500 Haitian households had planted

People cut down trees in Haiti for firewood and to clear fields, resulting in severe deforestation. The need for reforestation is clear, but how to bring about change was not so clear.

3 million seedlings. Over 20 years, the estimate is that over a 100 million trees were planted and over 350,000 farm families were involved in the project, more than 40 percent of rural households.[11] Because growing trees do not spoil, farmers were postponing their cutting and sales until they needed cash. So even though farmers were told that it was all right to cut down trees, a statement contrary to the message of previous reforestation projects, the landscape was filling up with trees.

Whether a program of planned change can be successfully implemented depends largely on whether the people want the proposed change and like the proposed program. Before an attempt can be made at cultural innovation, the innovators must determine whether the population is aware of the benefits of the proposed change. Lack of awareness can be a temporary barrier to solving the problem at hand. For example, health workers have often had difficulty convincing people that they were becoming ill because something was wrong with their water supply. Many people do not believe that disease can be transmitted by water. At other times, the population is perfectly aware of the problem. A case in point involved Taiwanese women who were introduced to family-planning methods beginning in the 1960s. The women knew they were having more children than they wanted or could easily afford, and they wanted to control their birth rate. They offered no resistance—they merely had to be given the proper devices and instructions, and the birth rate quickly fell to a more desirable, and more manageable, level.[12]

Overcoming Resistance

Not all proposed change programs are beneficial to the recipients. Sometimes resistance is rational. Applied anthropologists have pointed to cases where the judgment of the affected population has been better than that of the agents of change. One such example occurred during a Venezuelan government–sponsored program to give infants powdered milk. The mothers rejected the milk, even though it was free, on the grounds that it implied that the mothers' milk was no good.[13] But who is to say that the resistance was not in fact intuitively smart, reflecting an awareness that such a milk program would not benefit the children? Medical research now indicates quite clearly that mothers' milk is far superior to powdered milk or formula. First, human milk best supplies the nutrients needed for human development. Second, it is now known that the mother, through her milk, is able to transmit antibodies (disease resistances) to the baby. And third, nursing delays ovulation and usually increases the spacing between births.[14]

The switchover to powdered milk and formula in many underdeveloped areas has been nothing short of a disaster, resulting in increased malnutrition and misery. For one thing, powdered milk must be mixed with water, but if the water and the bottles are not sterilized, more sickness is introduced. Then, too, if powdered milk has to be purchased, mothers without cash are forced to dilute the milk to stretch it. And if a mother feeds her baby formula or powder for even a short time, the process is tragically irreversible, for her own milk dries up and she cannot return to breast-feeding even if she wants to.

As the Venezuelan example suggests, individuals may be able to resist proposed medical or health projects because acceptance is ultimately a personal matter. Large development projects planned by powerful governments or agencies rarely are stoppable, but even they can be resisted successfully. The Kayapo of the Xingu River region of Brazil were able to cancel a plan by the Brazilian government to build dams along the river for hydroelectric power. The Kayapo gained international attention when some of their leaders appeared on North American and European television and then successfully organized a protest in 1989 by members of several tribal groups. Their success seemed to come in part from their ability to present themselves to the international community as guardians of the rain forest—an image that resonated with international environmental organizations that supported their cause. Although to outsiders it might seem that the Kayapo want their way of life to remain as it was, the Kayapo are not opposed to all change. In fact, they want greater access to medical care, other government services, and manufactured goods from outside.[15]

Even if a project is beneficial to a population, it may still meet with resistance. Factors that may hinder acceptance can be divided roughly into three, sometimes overlapping, categories: *cultural, social,* and *psychological* barriers.

Cultural barriers are shared behaviors, attitudes, and beliefs that tend to impede the acceptance of an innovation. For example, members of different societies may view gift giving in different ways. Particularly in commercialized societies, things received for nothing are often believed to be worthless. When we discuss approaches to AIDs prevention later, we will see that certain beliefs about sex make it difficult for people to follow medical guidelines for safer sex. It is very important for agents of change to understand what the shared beliefs and attitudes are. For instance, in a program in Haiti to prevent child mortality from diarrhea, change agents used the terminology for traditional native herbal tea remedies (*rafrechi,* or cool refreshment) to identify the new oral rehydration therapy, which is a very successful medical treatment. In native belief, diarrhea is a "hot" illness and people believe that appropriate remedies have to have cooling properties.[16]

The acceptance of planned change may also depend on social factors. Research suggests that acceptance is more likely if the change agent and the target or potential adopter are similar socially. But change agents may have higher social status and more education than the people they are trying to influence. So change agents may work more with higher-status individuals because they are more likely to accept new ideas. If lower-status individuals also have to be reached, change agents of lower status may have to be employed.[17]

Finally, acceptance may depend on psychological factors—that is, how the individuals perceive both the innovation and the agents of change. In the course of

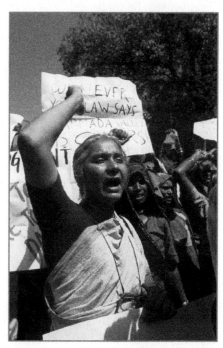

Medha Patkar leading a protest rally in New Delhi against Narmada dams.

trying to encourage women in the southeastern United States to breast-feed rather than bottle-feed their infants, researchers discovered a number of reasons why women were reluctant to breast-feed their infants, even though they heard it was healthier. Many women did not have confidence that they would produce enough milk for their babies; they were embarrassed about breast-feeding in public; and their family and friends had negative attitudes.[18] In designing an educational program, change agents may have to address such psychological concerns directly.

Discovering and Utilizing Local Channels of Influence

In planning a project involving cultural change, the administrator of the project should find out what the normal channels of influence are in the population. In most communities, there are preestablished networks for communication, as well as people of high prestige or influence who are looked to for guidance and direction. An understanding of such channels of influence is extremely valuable when deciding how to introduce a program of change. In addition, it is useful to know at what times, and in what sorts of situations, one channel is likely to be more effective in spreading information and approval than another.

An example of the effective use of local channels of influence occurred when an epidemic of smallpox broke out in the Kalahandi district of the state of Orissa in India. The efforts of health workers to vaccinate villagers against the disease were consistently resisted. The villagers, naturally suspicious and fearful of these strange men with their equally strange medical equipment, were unwilling to offer themselves, and particularly their babies, to the peculiar experiments the strangers wished to perform. Afraid of the epidemic, the villagers appealed for help to their local priest, whose opinions on such matters they trusted. The priest went into a trance, explaining that the illness was the result of the goddess Thalerani's anger with the people. She could be appeased, he continued, only by massive feasts, offerings, and other demonstrations of the villagers' worship of her. Realizing that the priest was the village's major opinion leader, at least in medical matters, the frustrated health workers tried to get the priest to convince his people to undergo vaccination. At first, the priest refused to cooperate with the strange men, but when his favorite nephew fell ill, he decided to try any means available to cure the boy. He thereupon went into another trance, telling the villagers that the goddess wished all her worshipers to be vaccinated. Fortunately, the people agreed, and the epidemic was largely controlled.[19]

If channels of influence are not stable, using influential people in a campaign can sometimes backfire. In the educational campaign in Haiti to promote the use of oral rehydration therapy to treat diarrhea in children, Madame Duvalier, the first lady of Haiti at the time, lent her name to the project. Because there were no serious social or cultural barriers to the treatment and mothers reported that children took to the solutions well, success was expected. But in the middle of the campaign, Haiti became embroiled in political turmoil and the first lady's husband was overthrown. Some of the public thought that the oral rehydration project was a plot by the Duvaliers to sterilize children, and this suspicion fueled resistance.[20] As the earlier discussion of Haiti deforestation shows, people in Haiti were suspicious of any government-sponsored program.

Cultural Resource Management

Large-scale programs of planned change have an impact not only on living people, they can also have an impact on the archaeological record left by the ancestors of living people. Recovering and preserving the archaeological record before programs of planned change disturb or destroy it is called **cultural resource management (CRM).** CRM work is carried out by archaeologists who are often called "contract archaeologists" because they typically work under contract to a government agency, a private developer, or a native group.

What kinds of impact can programs of planned change have on the archaeological record? In the 1960s, a large number of hydroelectric dam projects were initiated to provide flood control and to bring a stable source of electrical power to developing nations. In Egypt, a dam was built on the Nile River at a site called Aswan. Archaeologists realized that once the dam was in place a huge lake would form behind it, submerging thousands of archaeological sites, including the massive temple of Rameses II. Something needed to be done; the archaeological record had to be salvaged or protected. In the language of CRM, there needed to be a *mitigation plan* put into action. And there was. As the Aswan dam was being built, archaeologists went to work excavating sites that would be flooded. Archaeologists and engineers designed a way to take apart the temple of Rameses II and rebuild it, piece by piece, on higher ground where it would not be flooded. By the time the dam was completed in 1965, hundreds of sites had been investigated and two entire temple complexes moved.

Large-scale development projects are not the only projects that involve CRM archaeologists. In many nations, including the United States and Canada, historic preservation laws require any project receiving federal funds to ensure that archaeological resources are protected or their damage mitigated. Virtually all highway projects rely on federal funding, and before a highway can be built, a complete archaeological survey of the proposed right-of-way has to be made. A CRM archaeologist will work with the construction company, the state archaeologist, and perhaps a federal archaeologist to decide on the best course of action. In some cases, the archaeological site will be excavated. In others, the right-of-way may be moved. In still others, the decision is to allow the archaeological site to be destroyed because it would be too costly to excavate or the site may not be significant enough to warrant excavation.

CRM archaeologists do not work only for state or federal agencies. In many nations today, CRM archaeologists are also working with native peoples to protect, preserve, and manage archaeological materials for them. Indeed, archaeologist John Ravesloot recently stated that "the future of American archaeology is with Indian communities functioning as active, not passive, participants in the interpretation, management, and preservation of their rich cultural heritage."[21] One example of such a working relationship is the Zuni Heritage and Historic Preservation Office. During the 1970s, the Pueblo of Zuni decided it needed to train tribal members in archaeology to ensure that Zuni cultural resources and properties were managed properly. It hired three professional archaeologists and, with additional assistance from the National Park Service and the Arizona State Museum, initiated a program to train and employ tribal members in cultural resource management. Working with these non-Zuni archaeologists, the Pueblo of Zuni were able to establish their own historic preservation office that today manages and coordinates all historic preservation on the Zuni reservation, a task that the federal government managed until 1992. The Pueblo also established the Zuni Cultural Resource Enterprise, a Zuni-owned CRM business that employs both Zuni and non-Zuni archaeologists and carries out contract archaeology projects both on and off the Zuni reservation.[22]

Cultural resource management accounts for the majority of archaeology jobs in the United States.[23] As development and construction projects continue to affect the archaeological record, the need for well-trained CRM archaeologists is likely to persist.

Forensic Anthropology

Many of us are fascinated by detective stories. We are interested in crimes and why they occur, and we like to read about them, fictional or not. **Forensic anthropology** is the specialty in anthropology that is devoted to helping solve crimes and identifying human remains, usually by applying knowledge of physical anthropology.[24] It is attracting increasing attention by the public, and

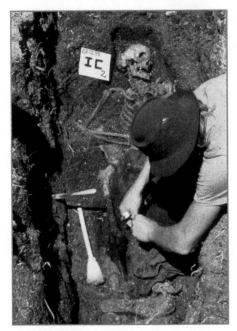

A forensic anthropologist digs out a body, apparently a victim of state-sponsored violence in Argentina between 1976 and 1983.

an increasing number of practitioners. One forensic anthropologist says she is called "the bone lady" by law enforcement personnel.[25] Like others in her line of work, she is asked to dig up or examine human bones to help solve crimes. Narrowing down identification is one of the first priorities, but it is not as simple as on television shows. Are these the bones of a man or woman? How old was the person? How well the forensic anthropologist can answer these seemingly simple questions depends on whether the remains include most bones of the skeleton. Identification of an adult's sex from remains is easier if the pelvis is present, but establishing sex in nonadult remains is not reliable from skeletal remains.[26] With regard to estimating age, only a wide age range can be estimated for adults, but a much narrower range can be estimated for nonadult remains. Forensic anthropologists are often asked for "race" as well. "Race" is not a useful biological category when applied to humans, but it is a significant social category. Forensic anthropologists can estimate with fairly high accuracy whether a person's ancestors came from Asia, Europe, or Africa, but they cannot detect skin color.[27] The police files may suggest that an adult male with Asian ancestry disappeared 5 years ago. The forensic anthropologist could say with a high probability that the remains were of an Asian male adult. Dental, surgical, or hospital records from that individual might lead to unique features that could be matched for more precise identification. Sometimes the forensic anthropologist can suggest the cause of death when the law enforcement people are stumped.

Some cultural anthropologists have also done forensic work, often in connection with legal cases involving Native Americans. For example, in 1978, Barbara Joans was asked to advise the defense in a trial of six older Bannock-Shoshoni women from the Fort Hall reservation who were accused of fraud. They had received "supplemental security income (SSI)," which the social service agency claimed they had no right to receive because they had not reported receiving rent money on land that they owned. Joans presented evidence that the women, although they spoke some English, did not have enough proficiency to understand the nuances of what the SSI people told them. The judge agreed with the defense and ruled that the SSI would have to use a Bannock-Shoshoni interpreter in the future when they went to the reservation to describe the requirements of the program.[28]

In recent years, Clyde Snow and other forensic anthropologists have been called on to confirm horrendous abuses of human rights. Governments have been responsible for the systematic killing of their citizens, and forensic anthropologists have helped to bring the perpetrators to justice. For example, Snow and other forensic anthropologists helped to confirm that the military dictatorship in Argentina in the 1980s was responsible for the deaths of many Argentine civilians who had "disappeared." The forensic anthropologists were also able to determine the location of mass graves and the identity of victims of state-organized brutality in Guatemala. In addition to bringing the perpetrators to justice, confirming the massacres and identifying the victims help the families of the "disappeared" put their anguish behind them.

Medical Anthropology

Illness and death are significant events for people everywhere. No one is spared. So it should not be surprising that how people understand the causes of illness and death, how they behave, and what resources they marshal to cope with these events are extremely important parts of culture. Some argue that we will never completely understand how to treat illness effectively until we understand the cultural behaviors, attitudes, values, and the larger social and political milieu in which people live. Others argue that society and culture have little to do with the outcome of illness—the reason that people die needlessly is that they do not get the appropriate medical treatment.

But anthropologists, particularly those in **medical anthropology,** who are actively engaged in studying health and illness, are increasingly realizing that biological *and* social factors need to be considered if we are to reduce human suffering. For instance, some populations have an appalling incidence of infant deaths due to diarrhea. The origin of this situation is mostly biological, in the sense that the deaths are caused by bacterial infection. But why are so many infants exposed to those bacteria? Usually, the main reason is social. The affected infants are likely to be poor. Because they are poor, they are likely to live with infected drinking water. Similarly, malnutrition may be the biological result of a diet poor in protein, but such a diet is usually also a cultural phenomenon, reflecting a society with classes of people with very unequal access to the necessities of life. In many ways, therefore, medical anthropology, and anthropology in general, are developing in the direction of a "biocultural synthesis."[29]

Cultural Understandings of Health and Illness

Medical researchers and medical practitioners in the United States and other Western societies do not exist in a social vacuum. Many of their ideas and practices are influenced by the culture in which they live. We may think of medicine as purely based on "fact," but it is clear on reflection that many ideas stem from the culture in which the researchers reside. Consider the recent shift in attitudes toward birth. Not so long ago in the United States, fathers were excluded from the birth, hospitals whisked the baby away from the mother and only brought the baby to her infrequently, and visitors (but not attending nurses and doctors) had to wear masks when holding the baby. Rationalizations were given for those practices, but looking back at them, they do not appear to be based on scientific evidence. Many medical anthropologists now argue that the *biomedical paradigm* (the system in which physicians are trained) itself needs to be understood as part of the culture.

Discovering the health-related beliefs, knowledge, and practices of a cultural group—its **ethnomedicine**—is one of the goals of medical anthropology. How do cultures view health and illness? What are their theories about the causes of illness? Do those theories impact on how illnesses are treated? What is the therapeutic process? Are there specialized medical practitioners, and how do they heal? Are there special medicines, and how are they administered? These are just some of the questions asked by the anthropological study of ethnomedicine.

Concepts of Balance or Equilibrium Many cultures have the view that the body should be kept in equilibrium or balance. The balance may be between hot and cold, or wet and dry, as in many cultures of Latin America and the Caribbean.[30] The notion of balance is not limited to opposites. For example, the ancient Greek system of medicine, stemming from Hippocrates, assumed that there were four "humors"—blood, phlegm, yellow bile, and black bile—that must be kept in balance. These humors have hot and cold as well as wet and dry properties. The Greek medical system was widely diffused in Europe and spread to parts of the Islamic world.

In China and elsewhere, tai chi exercises are believed to bring harmony and balance.

In Europe, the humoral medical system was dominant until the germ theory replaced it in the 1900s.[31] In the Ayurvedic system, whose practice dates back 4,000 years in North India, Pakistan, Bangladesh, Sri Lanka, and in the Arab world, there are three humors (phlegm, bile, and flatulence), and a balance between hot and cold is also important.[32] The Chinese medical system, which dates back about 3,500 years, initially stressed the balance between the contrasting forces of *yin* and *yang* and later added the concept of humors, which were six in number in Chinese medicine.[33]

The concepts of hot and cold and *yin* and *yang* are illustrated in Emily Ahern's ethnographic description of the medical system of the Taiwanese Hokkien.[34] The body requires both hot and cold substances; when the body is out of balance, a lack of one substance can be restored by eating or drinking the missing substance. So, for example, when Ahern was faint with heat, she was told to drink some bamboo shoot soup because it was "cold." In the winter, you need more hot substances; in the summer, you want fewer. Some people can tolerate more imbalance than others; people who are older, for instance, can tolerate imbalance less than those who are young. A loss of blood means a loss of heat. So, for a month after childbirth, women eat mostly a soup made of chicken, wine, and sesame oil—all "hot" ingredients. Hot things to eat are generally oily, sticky, or come from animals; cold things tend to be soupy, watery, or made from plants.

Supernatural Forces The Taiwanese Hokkien believe that most illnesses have natural or physiological causes, but around the world, it is more common to believe that illnesses are caused by supernatural forces. In fact, in a cross-cultural study of 139 societies, George P. Murdock found that only two societies did not have the belief that gods or spirits could cause illness, making such a belief a near universal. And 56 percent of those sample societies thought that gods or spirits were the major causes of illness.[35] Sorcery and witchcraft are common in the world's societies. Although humans practice both sorcery and witchcraft for good or evil, making people ill is one of their major uses. Illness can also be thought of as caused by the loss of one's soul, fate, retribution for violation of a taboo, or contact with a polluting or tabooed substance or object. Sorcery is believed to be a cause of illness by most societies on all continents; retribution because of violation of a taboo is also very frequent in all but one region of the world. The belief that soul loss can cause illness is absent in the area around the Mediterranean, uncommon in Africa, infrequent in the New World and the Pacific, and has its highest frequency in Eurasia.[36]

On Chuuk (Truk), an atoll in the central Pacific, serious illnesses and death are mainly believed to be the work of spirits. Occasionally, the spirits of relatives are to blame, although they usually do not cause serious damage. More often, illness is caused by the spirit of a particular locality or a ghost on a path at night.[37] Nowadays, one of two therapeutic options or their combination is often chosen: hospital medicine or Chuuk medicine. Chuuk medical treatment requires a careful evaluation of symptoms by the patient and the patient's relatives, because different spirits inflict different symptoms. If the symptom match is clear, the patient may choose an appropriate Chuuk medical formula to cure the illness. The patient may also ask whether he or she has done something wrong, and if so, what might point to the appropriate spirit and countervailing formula. For example, there is a taboo on having sexual relations before going to sea. If a person who violated this prohibition becomes ill, the reef spirits will be suspected. The Chuuk medical formula is supposed to cure illness quickly and dramatically. For this reason, Chuuk patients ask for a discharge from a hospital if their condition does not improve quickly. If treatment fails, the Chuukese believe that they need to reevaluate the diagnosis, sometimes with the aid of a diviner.[38] In contrasting their theories of illness to the American germ theory, the people of Chuuk point out that, although they have seen ghosts, they have never seen the germs that Americans talk about. Using both methods, some people recover and some do not, so the ultimate cause is a matter of faith.[39]

The Biomedical Paradigm In most societies, people simply think that their ideas about health and illness are true. Often people are not aware that there may be another way of viewing things until they confront another medical system. Western medical practice has spread widely. People with other medical systems have had to recognize that Western practitioners may consider their ideas about health and illness to be deficient, so they often need to decide which course (Western or non-Western) to follow in dealing with illness. Change, however, is not entirely one-way. For example, for a long time, the Western medical profession disparaged the Chinese practice of acupuncture, but now more medical practitioners are recognizing that acupuncture may provide effective treatment of certain conditions.

Most medical anthropologists use the term **biomedicine** to refer to the dominant medical paradigm in Western cultures today, with the *bio* part of the word emphasizing the biological emphasis of this medical system. As Robert Hahn points out, biomedicine appears to focus on specific diseases and cures for those diseases. Health is not the focus, as it is thought to be the *absence* of disease. Diseases are considered to be purely natural, and there is relatively little interest in the person or the larger social and cultural systems. Doctors generally do not treat the whole body but tend to specialize, with the human body partitioned into zones that belong to different specialties. Death is seen as a failure, and biomedical practitioners do everything they can to prolong life, regardless of the circumstances under which the patient would live life.[40]

Treatment of Illness

Anthropologists who study diseases in this and other cultures can be roughly classified into two camps. First, there are those, the more relativistic, who think that the culture so influences disease symptoms, incidence, and treatment that there are few if any cultural universals about any illness. If each culture is unique, we should expect its conception and treatment of an illness to be unique too, not like beliefs and practices in other cultures. Second, there are those, the more universalistic, who see cross-cultural similarities in the conception and treatment of illness, despite the unique qualities of each culture. For example, native remedies may contain chemicals that are the same as, or similar in effect to, chemicals used in remedies by Western biomedicine.[41] The reality might be that a given culture is very much like other cultures in some respects but unique in other respects.

In their extensive research on Maya ethnomedicine, Elois Ann Berlin and Brent Berlin make a strong case that, although studies of the Maya have emphasized beliefs about illness that are based on supernatural causes, a good deal of Maya ethnomedicine is about natural conditions, their signs and symptoms, and the remedies used to deal with those conditions. In regard to

A Dayak woman in Malaysia collects herbal medicine.

gastrointestinal diseases, the Berlins found that the Maya have a wide-ranging and accurate understanding of anatomy, physiology, and symptoms. Furthermore, the remedies they use, including recommendations for food, drink, and herbal medicines, have properties that are not that different from those of the biomedical profession.[42]

Carole Browner also suggests that the emphasis on "hot-cold" theories of illness in Latin America has been over-emphasized, to the neglect of other factors that influence choices about reproductive health and female health problems. In a study of the medical system in a highland Oaxacan community, Browner finds that certain plants are used to expel substances from the uterus—to facilitate labor at full term, to produce an abortion, or to induce menstrual flow. Other plants are used to retain things in the uterus—to prevent excess blood loss during menstruation, to help healing after delivery, and to prevent miscarriage. Most of these plant remedies appear to work.[43]

The biomedical establishment has become increasingly aware of the value of studying the "traditional" medicinal remedies discovered or invented by people around the world. In studying the indigenous medicines of the Hausa of Nigeria, Nina Etkin and Paul Ross asked individuals to describe the physical attributes of more than 600 plants and their possible medicinal uses, more than 800 diseases and symptoms, and more than 5,000 prepared medicines. Although many medicines were used for treating sorcery, spirit aggression, or witchcraft, most medicines were used for illnesses regarded by the Hausa as having natural causes. Malaria is a serious endemic medical problem in the Hausa region, as in many areas of Africa. The Hausa use approximately 72 plant remedies for conditions connected with malaria—among them anemia, intermittent fever, and jaundice. Experimental treatment of malaria in laboratory animals supports the efficacy of many of the Hausa remedies. But perhaps the most important part of the Etkin and Ross findings is the role of diet. Although most medical research does not consider the possible medical efficacy of the *foods* that people eat in combating illness, food is, of course, consumed in much larger quantities and more often than medicine. It is noteworthy, therefore, that the Hausa eat many plants with antimalarial properties; in fact, dietary consumption of these plants appears to be greatest during the time of year when the risk of malarial infection is at its highest. Recent research has also discovered that foods and spices like garlic, onions, cinnamon, ginger, and pepper have antiviral or antibacterial properties.[44]

Medical Practitioners In our society, we may be so used to consulting a full-time medical specialist (if we do not feel better quickly) that we tend to assume that biomedical treatment is the only effective medical treatment. If we are given a medicine, we expect it to have the appropriate medical effect and make us feel better. Therefore, many in the biomedical system, practitioners and patients alike, are perplexed by the seeming effectiveness of other medical systems that are based in part on symbolic or ritual healing. Yet there is increasing evidence that the *form* of treatment may be just as important as the *content* of treatment.[45]

Applied and Practicing Anthropology

Illness may be viewed as being due to something in one's social life being out of order. The cause could be retribution for one's own bad behavior or thoughts, or the work of an angry individual practicing sorcery or witchcraft. Or a bad social situation or a bad relationship may be thought of as provoking physical symptoms because of anxiety or stress. In societies with occupational specialization, priests, who are formally trained full-time religious practitioners, may be asked to convey messages or requests for healing to higher powers.[46] Societies with beliefs in sorcery and witchcraft as causes of illness typically have practitioners who are believed to be able to use magic in reverse—that is, to undo the harm invoked by sorcerers and witches. Sometimes sorcerers or witches themselves may be asked to reverse illnesses caused by others. However, they may not be sought out because they are often feared and have relatively low status.[47] Shamans are perhaps the most important medical practitioners in societies lacking full-time occupational specialization.

After working with shamans in Africa, E. Fuller Torrey, a psychiatrist and anthropologist, concluded that they use the same mechanisms and techniques to cure patients as psychiatrists and achieve about the same results. He isolated four categories used by healers the world over:

1. **The naming process.** If a disease has a name—"neurasthenia" or "phobia" or "possession by an ancestral spirit" will do—then it is curable; the patient realizes that the doctor understands his case.

2. **The personality of the doctor.** Those who demonstrate some empathy, nonpossessive warmth, and genuine interest in the patient get results.

3. **The patient's expectations.** One way of raising the patient's expectations of being cured is the trip to the doctor; the longer the trip—to the Mayo Clinic, Menninger Clinic, Delphi, or Lourdes—the easier the cure. An impressive setting (the medical center) and impressive paraphernalia (the stethoscope, the couch, attendants in uniform, the rattle, the whistle, the drum, the mask) also raise the patient's expectations. The healer's training is important. And high fees also help to raise a patient's expectations. (The Paiute doctors always collect their fees before starting a cure; if they don't, it is believed that they will fall ill.)

4. **Curing techniques.** Drugs, shock treatment, conditioning techniques, and so on have long been used in many different parts of the world.[48]

Biomedical research is not unaware of the effect of the mind on healing. In fact, considerable evidence has accumulated that psychological factors can be very important in illness. Patients who believe that medicine will help them often recover quickly even if the medicine is only a sugar pill or a medicine not particularly relevant to their condition. Such effects are called *placebo effects*.[49] Placebos do not just have psychological effects. Although the mechanisms are not well understood, they may also alter body chemistry and bolster the immune system.[50]

Shamans may coexist with medical doctors. Don Antonio, a respected Otomi Indian shaman in central Mexico, has many patients, perhaps not as many as before modern medicine, but still plenty. In his view, when he was born, God gave him his powers to cure, but his powers are reserved for removing "evil" illnesses (those caused by sorcerers). "Good" illnesses can be cured by herbs and medicine, and he refers patients with those illnesses to medical doctors; he believes that doctors are more effective than he could be in those cases. The doctors, however, do not seem to refer any patients to Don Antonio or other shamans.[51]

The most important full-time medical practitioner in the biomedical system is the physician, and the patient-physician relationship is central. In the ideal scheme of things, the physician is viewed as having the ability, with some limits, of being able to treat illness, alleviate suffering, and

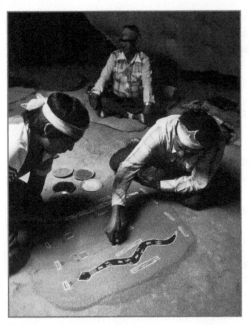

A Navajo medicine man performs a healing ceremony involving a snake painted on the ground.

prolong the life of the patient, as well as offering promises of patient confidentiality and privacy. The patient relies on the physician's knowledge, skill, and ethics. Consistent with the biomedical paradigm, doctors tend to treat patients as having "conditions" rather than as complete people. Because patients commonly go to physicians to solve a particular condition or sickness, physicians tend to try to do something about it even in the face of uncertainty. Physicians tend to rely on technology for diagnoses and treatment and place relatively low value on talking with patients. In fact, physicians tend to give patients relatively little information, and they may not listen very well.[52]

Despite the importance of physicians in biomedicine, patients do not always seek physician care. In fact, one-third of the population of the United States regularly consults with alternative practitioners, such as acupuncturists or chiropractors, often unbeknownst to the physician. Somewhat surprisingly, individuals with more education are more likely to seek alternative care.[53]

Political and Economic Influences on Health

People with more social, economic, and political power in a society are generally healthier.[54] Inequality in health in socially stratified societies is not surprising. The poor usually have more exposure to disease because they live in more crowded conditions. And the poor are more likely to lack the resources to get quality care. For many diseases, health problems, and death rates, incidence or relative frequency varies directly with social class. In the United Kingdom, for example, people in the higher social classes are less likely to have headaches, bronchitis, pneumonia, heart disease, arthritis, injuries, and mental disorders, to name just a few of the differences.[55] Ethnic differences also predict health inequities. In South Africa under apartheid, the 14 percent minority population, referred to as "white," controlled most of the income of the country and most of the high-quality land. "Blacks" were restricted to areas with shortages of housing, inadequate housing, and little employment. To get a job, families often had to be disrupted; usually the husband would have to migrate to find work. "Blacks" lived, on average, about 9 years less than "whites" in 1985, and "black" infants died at about seven times the rate of "white" infants. In the United States recently, the differences between African Americans and European Americans in health are not as stark as in South Africa, but those favoring European Americans are still substantial. As of 2001, the difference in life expectancy was about 5–6 years, and African American infant mortality was almost three times the rate for European American infants. Robert Hahn has estimated that poverty accounts for about 19 percent of the overall mortality in the United States.[56]

Inequities, because of class and ethnicity, are not limited to within-society differences. Power and economic differentials *between* societies also have profound health consequences. Over the course of European exploration and expansion, indigenous peoples died in enormous numbers from introduced diseases, wars, and conquests; they had their lands expropriated and diminished in size and quality. When incorporated into colonial territories or into countries, indigenous people usually become minorities and they are almost always very poor. These conditions of life not only affect the incidence of disease, they also tend to lead to greater substance abuse, violence, depression, and other mental pathologies.[57] Medical anthropologists have studied an enormous variety of conditions. What follows is only a small sampling.

AIDS

We may think that epidemics are a thing of the past. But the recent and sudden emergence of the disease we call **AIDS (acquired immune deficiency syndrome)** reminds us that new diseases, or new varieties of old diseases, can appear at any time. Like all other organisms, disease-causing organisms also evolve. The human immunodeficiency virus (HIV) that causes AIDS emerged only recently. Viruses and bacteria are always mutating, and new strains emerge that are initially a plague on our genetic resistance and on medical efforts to contain them.

Millions of people around the world already have the symptoms of AIDS, and millions more are infected with HIV but do not know they are infected. As of December 2007, 33 million adults and children in the world were living with HIV/AIDS.[58] There are a few signs of improvement since 2001. The percentage of people infected globally is now stable; some countries have improved with prevention efforts, and the number of new cases each year has gone down. However, AIDS is the major cause of death in sub-Saharan Africa and is still a leading cause of death worldwide.[59] There is still no cure. AIDS is a frightening epidemic not only because of its death toll. It is also frightening because it takes a long time (on average, 4 years) after exposure for symptoms to appear. This means that many people who have been infected by HIV but do not know they are infected may continue, unknowingly, to transmit the virus to others.[60]

Transmission occurs mostly via sexual encounters, through semen and blood. Drug users may also transmit HIV by way of contaminated needles. Transmission by blood transfusion has been virtually eliminated in this and other societies by medical screening of blood supplies. In many countries, however, there is still no routine screening of blood prior to transfusions. HIV may be passed from a pregnant woman to her offspring through the placenta and after birth through her breast milk. The rate of transmission between a mother and her baby is 20–40 percent. Children are also at great risk because they are likely to be orphaned by a parent's death from AIDS. At the turn of the twenty-first century, approximately 14 million children were parentless because of AIDS.[61]

Millions of children in sub-Saharan Africa are orphaned because of AIDS. These orphaned children in Uganda look on during a visit by Britain's Queen Elizabeth to their center.

Many people think of AIDS as only a medical problem that requires only a medical solution, without realizing that behavioral, cultural, and political issues need to be addressed as well. It is true that developing a vaccine or a drug to prevent people from getting AIDS and finding a permanent cure for those who have it will finally solve the problem. But, for a variety of reasons, we can expect that the medical solution alone will not be sufficient, at least not for a while. First, to be effective worldwide, or even within a country, a vaccine has to be inexpensive and relatively easy to produce in large quantities; the same is true of any medical treatment. Second, governments around the world have to be willing and able to spend the money and hire the personnel necessary to manage an effective program.[62] Third, future vaccination and treatment will require the people at risk to be willing to get vaccinated and treated, which is not always the case. Witness the fact that the incidence of measles is on the rise in the United States because many people are not having their children vaccinated.

There are now expensive drug treatments that significantly reduce the degree of HIV infection, but we do not know if an effective and inexpensive vaccine or treatment will be developed soon. In the meantime, the risk of HIV infection can be reduced only by changes in social, particularly sexual, behavior. But to persuade people to change their sexual behavior, it is necessary to find out exactly what they do sexually, and why they do what they do.

Research so far suggests that different sexual patterns are responsible for HIV transmission in different parts of the world. In the United States, England, northern Europe, Australia, and Latin America, the recipients of anal intercourse, particularly men, are the most likely individuals to acquire HIV infection; vaginal intercourse can also transmit the infection, usually from the man to the woman. Needle sharing can transmit the infection, too. In Africa, the most common mode of transmission is vaginal intercourse, and so women get infected more commonly in Africa than elsewhere.[63] In fact, in Africa there are slightly more cases of HIV in women as compared with men.[64]

As of now, there are only two known ways to reduce the likelihood of sexual HIV transmission. One way is to abstain from sexual intercourse; the other is to use condoms. Male circumcision now appears to decrease the risk of HIV infection, but studies have not yet evaluated long-term effects.[65] Educational programs that teach how AIDS spreads and what one can do about it may reduce the spread somewhat, but such programs may fail where people have incompatible beliefs and attitudes about sexuality. For example, people in some central African societies believe that deposits of semen after conception are necessary for a successful pregnancy and generally enhance a woman's health and ability to reproduce. It might be expected then that people who have these beliefs about semen would choose not to use condoms; after all, condoms in their view are a threat to public health.[66] Educational programs may also emphasize the wrong message. Promiscuity may increase the risk of HIV transmission, so hardly anyone would question the wisdom of advertising to reduce the number of sexual partners. And, at least in the homosexual community in the United States, individuals report fewer sexual partners than in the past. What was not anticipated, however, was that individuals in monogamous relationships, who may feel safe, are less likely to use condoms or to avoid the riskiest sexual practices. Needless to say, sex with a regular partner who is infected is not safe![67] In what may seem like something of a paradox, the United Nations observed that, for most women in the world today, the major risk factor for being infected with HIV is being married.[68] It is not marriage, *per se,* that heightens the risk of HIV infection; rather, the proximate cause may be the lower likelihood of condom use or less abstinence by a married couple.

Undernutrition

What people eat is intrinsically connected to their survival and the ability of a population to reproduce itself, so we would expect that the ways people obtain, distribute, and consume food have been generally adaptive.[69] For example, the human body cannot synthesize eight amino acids. Meat can provide all of these amino acids, and combinations of particular plants can also provide them for a complete complement of protein. The combination of maize and beans in many traditional Native American diets, or *tortillas* and *frijoles* in Mexico, can provide all the needed amino acids. In places where wheat (often made into bread) is the staple, dairy products combined with wheat also provide complete protein.[70] Even the way that people have prepared for scarcity, such as breaking up into mobile bands, cultivating crops that can better withstand drought, and preserving food in case of famine, are probably adaptive practices in unpredictable environments. Geneticists have proposed that populations in famine-prone areas may have had genetic selection for "thrifty genes"—genes that allow individuals to need a minimum of food and store the extra in fatty tissue to get them past serious scarcity.[71] Customary diets and genetic changes may have been selected over a long stretch of time, but many serious nutritional problems observed today are due to rapid culture change. For instance, although "thrifty genes" may be adaptive during famine, they may become maladaptive when food is readily available. The high prevalence of diabetes and obesity in many populations today may be linked to such genes.

Often the switch to commercial or cash crops has harmful effects in another direction—creating undernutrition. For example, when the farmer-herders of the arid region in northeastern Brazil started growing sisal, a drought-resistant plant used for making twine and rope, many of them abandoned subsistence agriculture. The small landholders used most of their land for sisal growing and, when the price of sisal fell, they had to work as laborers for others to try to make ends meet. Food then had to be mostly bought, but if a laborer or sisal grower didn't earn enough, there was not enough food for the whole family.

Analysis of allocation of food in some households by Daniel Gross and Barbara Underwood suggests that the laborer and his wife received adequate nutrition, but the children often received much less than required. Lack of adequate nutrition usually results in retarded weight and height in children. As is commonly the case when there is substantial social inequality, the children from lower-income groups weigh substantially less than those from higher-income groups. But even though there were some economic differences before sisal production, the effects on nutrition appeared negligible before, judging from the fact that there was little or no difference in weight among adults from higher and lower socioeconomic positions who grew up prior to sisal production. But more recently, 45 percent of the children from lower economic groups were undernourished as compared with 23 percent of those children from the higher economic groups.[72]

This is not to say that commercialization is always deleterious to adequate nutrition. For example, in the Highlands of New Guinea, there is evidence that the nutrition of children improved when families started growing coffee for sale. However, in this case, the families still had land to grow some crops for consumption. The extra money earned from coffee enabled them to buy canned fish and rice, which provided children with higher amounts of protein than the usual staple of sweet potatoes.[73]

Nutritional imbalances for females have a far-reaching impact on reproduction and the health of the infants they bear. In some cultures, the lower status of women has a direct bearing on their access to food. Although the custom of feeding males first is well known, it is less often realized that females end up with less nutrient-dense food such as meat. Deprivation of food sometimes starts in infancy where girl babies, as in India, are weaned earlier than boy babies.[74] Parents may be unaware that their differential weaning practice has the effect of reducing the amount of high-quality protein that girl infants receive. Indeed, in Ecuador, Lauris McKee found that parents thought that earlier weaning of girls was helpful to them. They believed that mothers' milk transmitted sexuality and aggression, both ideal male traits, to their infants and so it was important that girl babies be weaned early. Mothers weaned their

APPLIED ANTHROPOLOGY ● ● ● ● ● ● ● ●

Eating Disorders, Biology, and the Cultural Construction of Beauty

Cultures differ about what they consider beautiful, including people. In many cultures, fat people are considered more beautiful than thin people. Melvin Ember did fieldwork years ago on the islands of American Samoa. When he returned to the main island after 3 months on a distant island, he ran into a Samoan acquaintance, a prominent chief. The chief said: "You look good. You gained weight." In reality, he had lost 30 pounds! The chief may not have remembered how heavy the anthropologist had been, but he clearly thought that fat was better than thin. Among the Azawagh Arabs of Niger, fatness was not merely valued and considered beautiful; great care was taken to ensure that young girls became fat by insisting and sometimes forcing them to drink large quantities of milk-based porridge.

Around the world, fatness is generally considered more desirable than thinness, particularly for women. Fatness is widely valued in these cultures not only because it is considered more beautiful, but also because it is thought to be a marker of health, fertility, and higher status in societies with social stratification. This view is in strong contrast to the ideal in the United States and many other Western societies, where fatness is thought to be unattractive and to reflect laziness, a lack of self-control, and poor health. Thinness, particularly in the upper classes, is considered beautiful. How can we explain these differences in what is considered beautiful?

Recent cross-cultural research suggests that the picture is more complicated. It appears that societies with unpredictable resources actually value thinness, particularly in societies that have no way of storing food. At first glance, this seems puzzling. Shouldn't an individual who stores calories on the body be better off than an individual who is thin when facing starvation, particularly if there is no food storage? Perhaps. But 10 thin individuals will generally consume less than 10 heavier people, so perhaps there is a group advantage to being thin. Indeed, many societies with frequent episodes of famine encourage fasting or eating very light meals, as among the Gurage of Ethiopia. The strongest cross-cultural predictor of valuing fatness in women is what is often referred to as "machismo" or "protest masculinity." Societies with a strong emphasis on male aggression, strength,

and sexuality are the most likely to value fatness in women; those with little machismo value thinness. Why machismo is associated with valuing fatness in women is far from clear. One suggestion is that machismo actually reflects male insecurity and fear of women. Such men may not be looking for closeness or intimacy with their wives, but they may want to show how potent they are by having lots of children. If fatness suggests fertility, men may look for wives who are fatter. Consistent with this idea, the ideal of thinness in women became more common in North America with the rise of women's movements in the 1920s and late 1960s. Consider that Marilyn Monroe epitomized beauty in the 1950s; she was well rounded, not thin. Thin became more popular only when women began to question early marriage and having many children. Behaviors associated with machismo became less acceptable at those times.

Cultural beliefs about what is considered a beautiful body can impose enormous pressures on females to achieve the ideal body type—whether it be fat or thin. In the United States and other Western countries, the effort to be thin can be carried to an extreme, resulting in the eating disorders anorexia nervosa and bulimia. If you suffer from these often fatal illnesses, you may regularly eat little and you may regularly force yourself to throw up, thus depriving your body of nutrients in your quest to be thinner and thinner. The irony of "thinness" being idealized in the United States and other Western countries is that obesity is becoming more common in those societies. In 2001, the incidence of obesity increased in the United States to 31 percent, and medical researchers worried about the increase in heart disease and diabetes resulting from obesity. Whether or not obesity is a result of an eating disorder (in the psychological sense) is more debatable. Researchers are finding biological causes of obesity, such as resistance to the hormone leptin, which regulates appetite, suggesting that much of the obesity "epidemic" has biological causes. Still, fast food, increasing sedentariness, and extremely large portion sizes are probably contributing factors also.

Sources: J. L. Anderson et al. 1992; P. J. Brown 1997, 100; C. R. Ember et al. 2005: Friedman 2003; Loustaunau and Sobo 1997, 85; Popenoe 2004; N. Wolf 1991.

girls at about 11 months and their boys at about 20 months, a 9-month difference. McKee found that girl infants had a significantly higher mortality than boy infants in their second year of life, suggesting that the earlier weaning time for girls and their probable undernutrition may have been responsible.[75]

Applied and practicing anthropologists are not the only ones interested in solving problems. Many researchers in anthropology and the other social sciences do *basic research* on social problems. Such research may involve fieldwork to get a broad understanding of cultural ideas and practices about health, illness, or violence. Or basic research may involve testing theories about the possible causes of specific problems. The results of such tests could suggest solutions to the problems if the causes, once discovered, can be reduced or eliminated.

✓●─[Study and **Review** on **myanthrolab.com**

Summary

1. Applied or practicing anthropology as a profession is explicitly concerned with making anthropological knowledge useful. Applied or practicing anthropologists may be involved in one or more phases of programs that are designed to change peoples' lives: assembling relevant knowledge, constructing alternative plans, assessing the likely social and environmental impact of particular plans, implementing the programs, and monitoring the programs and their effects.

2. Applied or practicing anthropologists work for a large variety of organizations, government agencies, international development agencies, private consulting firms, public health organizations, medical schools, public interest law firms, community development agencies, charitable foundations, and profit-seeking corporations.

3. The code of ethics for those who work professionally as applied anthropologists specifies that the target population should be included as much as possible in the formulation of policy, so that people in the community may know in advance how the program may affect them. But perhaps the most important aspect of the code is the pledge not to be involved in any plan whose effect will not be beneficial. It is often difficult to evaluate the effects of planned changes. Long-term consequences may be detrimental even if the changes are beneficial in the short run.

4. Even if a planned change will prove beneficial to the targeted population, the people may not accept it. And if the proposed innovation is not utilized by the intended population, the project cannot be considered a success. Affected populations may reject or resist a proposed innovation for cultural, social, or psychological reasons. It is important to understand what the reasons are. The population may also resist the proposed change because they unconsciously or consciously know it is not good for them. To be effective, change agents may have to discover and use the traditional channels of influence in introducing their projects.

5. Cultural resource management usually takes the form of "contract archaeology" to record and/or conserve the archaeology of a building site.

6. Forensic anthropology is the specialty in anthropology that is devoted to helping solve crimes and identifying human remains, usually by applying knowledge of physical anthropology.

7. Medical anthropologists suggest that biological and social factors need to be considered if we are to understand how to treat illness effectively and reduce the suffering in human life. Understanding ethnomedicine—the medical beliefs and practices of a society or cultural group—is one of the goals of medical anthropology.

8. Many cultures have the view that the body should be kept in equilibrium or balance. The balance may be between hot and cold, or wet and dry, or there may be other properties that need to be balanced. The belief that gods or spirits can cause illness is a near universal. The belief in sorcery or witchcraft as a cause of illness is also very common.

9. Some researchers are finding evidence that many of the plant remedies that indigenous peoples use contain chemicals that are the same as, or similar in effect to, chemicals used in Western biomedicine remedies.

10. People with more social, economic, and political power in a society are generally healthier. Power and economic differentials between societies also have had profound health consequences.

11. The enormous death toll of AIDS, the leading cause of adult death in many countries today, will be reduced when medical science develops effective and inexpensive medicines to treat victims of HIV or AIDS and a vaccine to prevent individuals from getting HIV. In the meantime, if the death toll from AIDS is to be reduced, changes in attitudes, beliefs, and practices regarding sexual activity are needed.

12. The ways that people obtain, distribute, and consume food have been generally adaptive. Geneticists have proposed that populations in famine-prone areas may have had genetic selection for "thrifty genes." Now these populations with regular food supplies may be prone to diabetes and obesity. Many of the serious nutritional problems of today are due to rapid culture change, particularly those making for an increasing degree of social inequality.

Glossary Terms

AIDS (acquired immune deficiency syndrome)
applied (or practicing) anthropology

biomedicine
cultural resource management (CRM)
ethnomedicine

forensic anthropology
medical anthropology

Critical Questions

1. What particular advantages do anthropologists have in trying to solve practical problems?
2. Is it ethical to try to influence people's lives when they have not asked for help? Explain your answer.
3. Why do native remedies often contain chemicals that are the same as, or similar in effect to, chemicals used in Western biomedicine remedies?
4. Why might people engage in sexual practices that increase their likelihood of contracting AIDS?

Read the **Original Source** on **myanthrolab.com**

Read the chapter by Andrew W. Miracle titled "A Shaman for Organizations" on MyAnthroLab. Answer the following questions.

1. Why does Miracle call himself a "shaman"?
2. According to Miracle, what skills are useful to an applied anthropologist? Why does he think so?

Photo Credits

Credits are listed in order of appearance.

Michael M. Horowitz; Hallgerd/Shutterstock; Thony Belizaire/AFP/Getty Images; Joerg Boethling/Photolibrary; Horacio Villalobos/Corbis; Tibor Bognar/Alamy; Nigel Dickinson/Photolibrary; Martha Cooper/Photolibrary; Jon Hursa/Pool/epa/Corbis.

E. Fuller Torrey, THE MIND GAME: Witchdoctors and Psychiatrists. Copyright (c) 1973 Bantam Books, a division of Random House, Inc. Reprinted with permission of the author.

Glossary

AIDS (acquired immune deficiency syndrome) A disease caused by the HIV virus.

Applied (practicing) anthropology The branch of anthropology that concerns itself with applying anthropological knowledge to achieve practical goals, usually in the service of an agency outside the traditional academic setting.

Biomedicine The dominant medical paradigm in Western societies today.

Cultural resource management (CRM) The branch of applied anthropology that seeks to recover and preserve the archaeological record before programs of planned change disturb or destroy it.

Ethnomedicine The health-related beliefs, knowledge, and practices of a cultural group.

Applied and Practicing Anthropology

Forensic anthropology The application of anthropology, usually physical anthropology, to help identify human remains and assist in solving crimes.

Medical anthropology The application of anthropological knowledge to the study of health and illness.

Practicing anthropology See **Applied (practicing) anthropology**.

Notes

1. Nolan 2003, 2.
2. Kushner 1991.
3. Van Willigen 2002, 10.
4. "Appendix C: Statements on Ethics . . . " 1971. 1991; "Appendix I: Revised Principles. . . " 1990. 1991.
5. Appendix A: Report of the Committee on Ethics . . . 2002; Appendix F: Professional and Ethical Responsibilities . . . 2002.
6. Appendix H: National Association of Practicing Anthropologists' Ethical Guidelines . . . 1988. 1991.
7. Scudder 1978.
8. Ibid., 204ff.
9. Picchi 1991, 26–38; for a more general description of the Bakairí, see Picchi 2009.
10. Murray and Bannister 2004; Wulff and Fiste 1987.
11. Ibid.
12. Niehoff 1966, 255–67.
13. G. M. Foster 1969, 8–9.
14. Jelliffe and Jelliffe 1975.
15. W. H. Fisher 1994.
16. Coreil 1989, 149–50.
17. Rogers 1983, 321–31.
18. Bryant and Bailey 1990.
19. Niehoff 1966, 219–24.
20. Coreil 1989, 155.
21. Ravesloot 1997, 174.
22. Anyon and Ferguson 1995.
23. Society for American Archaeology 2009.
24. Komar and Buikstra 2008, 11–12.
25. Manhein 1999.
26. Komar and Buikstra 2008, 126–45.
27. Brace 1995.
28. Joans 1997.
29. A. H. Goodman and Leatherman 1998; Kleinman, Das, and Lock, 1997.
30. Loustaunau and Sobo 1997, 80–81; Rubel and Haas 1996, 120.
31. Loustaunau and Sobo 1997, 82–83, referring to Magner 1992, 93.
32. Loustaunau and Sobo 1997, referring to Gesler 1991, 16.
33. Loustaunau and Sobo 1997, referring to G. M. Foster 1994, 11; C. Leslie 1976, 4.
34. Ahern 1975, 92–97, as appearing in eHRAF World Cultures, 2000.
35. Murdock 1980, 20.
36. C. C. Moore 1988.
37. T. Gladwin and Sarason 1953, 64–66.
38. Mahony 1971, 34–38, as seen in eHRAF World Cultures, 2000.
39. Gladwin and Sarason 1953, 65.
40. Hahn 1995, 133–39.
41. For an exhaustively documented presentation of the more universalistic approach, see E. A. Berlin and Berlin 1996; see also Browner 1985, 13–32; Rubel et al. 1984.
42. E. A. Berlin and B. Berlin 1996.
43. Browner 1985; Ortiz de Montellano and Browner 1985.
44. Etkin and Ross 1997.
45. Moerman 1997, 240–41.
46. Loustaunau and Sobo 1997, 98–101.
47. Winkelman 1986a.
48. Torrey 1972.

49. Loustaunau and Sobo 1997, 101–02; Moerman 1997.
50. Loustaunau and Sobo 1997, 102.
51. Dow 1986, 6–9, 125.
52. Hahn 1995, 131–72.
53. Ibid., 165.
54. For a discussion of some of the relevant research, see Hahn 1995, 80–82.
55. Mascie-Taylor 1990, 118–21.
56. See references in Hahn 1995, 82–87; for more recent statistics: Shrestha 2006; Singh and van Dyck. n.d.
57. A. Cohen 1999.
58. UNAIDS 2007, 1.
59. Ibid., 4–6.
60. Bolton 1989.
61. Reported in Carey et al. 2004, 462.
62. Bolton 1989.
63. Carrier and Bolton 1991; Schoepf 1988, 625, cited in Carrier and Bolton 1991.
64. Simmons, Farmer, and Schoepf, 1996, 64.
65. Altman 2008.
66. Schoepf 1988, 637–38.
67. Bolton 1992.
68. Farmer 1997, 414. Married men in Thailand are gradually turning away from commercial sex and having affairs with married women who are believed to be safe; see Lyttleton 2000, 299.
69. Quandt 1996, 272–89.
70. McElroy and Townsend 2002.
71. See discussion in Leslie Lieberman 2004.
72. Gross and Underwood 1971.
73. McElroy and Townsend 2002, 187, referring to Harvey and Heywood 1983, 27–35.
74. Quandt 1996, 277.
75. McKee 1984, 96.

Bibliography

Ahern, Emily M. 1975. Sacred and secular medicine in a Taiwan village: A study of cosmological disorders. In *Medicine in Chinese cultures: Comparative studies of health care in Chinese and other societies,* eds. A. Kleinman et al. Washington, DC: U.S. Department of Health, Education, and Welfare, National Institutes of Health.

Altman, Lawrence K. 2008. Protective effects of circumcision are shown to continue after trials' end. *New York Times,* August 12. http://www.nytimes.com.

Anyon, Roger, and T. J. Ferguson. 1995. Cultural resources management at the Pueblo of Zuni, New Mexico, USA. *Antiquity* 69:913–30.

Appendix A: Report of the Committee on Ethics, Society for Applied Anthropology. 2002. In *Ethics and the profession of anthropology,* ed. C. Fluehr-Lobban. Philadelphia: University of Pennsylvania Press.

Appendix C: Statements on Ethics: Principles of Professional Responsibility, Adopted by the Council of the American Anthropological Association, May 1971. 1991. In *Ethics and the profession of anthropology,* ed. C. Fluehr-Lobban. Philadelphia: University of Pennsylvania Press.

Appendix F: Professional and Ethical Responsibilities, SfAA. 2002. In *Ethics and the profession of anthropology,* ed. C. Fluehr-Lobban. Philadelphia: University of Pennsylvania Press.

Appendix H: National Association of Practicing Anthropologists' Ethical Guidelines for Practitioners, 1988. 1991. In *Ethics and the profession of anthropology,* ed. C. Fluehr-Lobban. Philadelphia: University of Pennsylvania Press.

Appendix I: Revised Principles of Professional Responsibility, 1990. 1991. In *Ethics and the profession of anthropology,* ed. C. Fluehr-Lobban. Philadelphia: University of Pennsylvania Press.

Berlin, Elois Ann, and Brent Berlin. 1996. *Medical ethnobiology of the highland Maya of Chiapas, Mexico: The gastrointestinal diseases.* Princeton, NJ: Princeton University Press.

Bolton, Ralph. 1989. Introduction: The AIDS pandemic, a global emergency. *Medical Anthropology* 10:93–104.

Bolton, Ralph. 1992. AIDS and promiscuity: Muddled in the models of HIV prevention. *Medical Anthropology* 14:145–223.

Brace, C. Loring. 1995. Region does not mean "race"—reality versus convention in forensic anthropology. *Journal of Forensic Sciences* 40:171–75.

Browner, Carole H. 1985. Criteria for selecting herbal remedies. *Ethnology* 24:13–32.

Applied and Practicing Anthropology

Bryant, Carol A., and Doraine F. C. Bailey. 1990. The use of focus group research in program development. In *Soundings,* eds. J. van Willigen and T. L. Finan. NAPA Bulletin No. 10. Washington, DC: American Anthropological Association.

Carey, James W., Erin Picone-DeCaro, Mary Spink Neumann, Devorah Schwartz, Delia Easton, and Daphne Cobb St. John. 2004. HIV/AIDS research and prevention. In *Encyclopedia of medical anthropology: Health and illness in the world's cultures,* vol. 1, eds. C. R. Ember and M. Ember, 462–79. New York: Kluwer Academic/Plenum Press.

Carrier, Joseph, and Ralph Bolton. 1991. Anthropological perspectives on sexuality and HIV prevention. *Annual Review of Sex Research* 2:49–75.

Cohen, Alex. 1999. *The mental health of indigenous peoples: An international overview.* Geneva: Department of Mental Health, World Health Organization.

Coreil, Jeannine. 1989. Lessons from a community study of oral rehydration therapy in Haiti. In *Making our research useful,* eds. J. van Willigen, B. Rylko-Bauer, and A. McElroy. Boulder, CO: Westview Press.

Dow, James. 1986. *The shaman's touch: Otomi Indian symbolic healing.* Salt Lake City: University of Utah Press.

eHRAF World Cultures. http://ehrafworldcultures.yale.edu. Accessed 2000.

Etkin, Nina L., and Paul J. Ross. 1997. Malaria, medicine, and meals: A biobehavioral perspective. In *The anthropology of medicine,* eds. L. Romanucci-Ross, D. E. Moerman, and L. R. Tancredi, 169–209. Westport, CT: Bergin & Garvey.

Farmer, Paul. 1997. Ethnography, social analysis, and the preven-tion of sexually transmitted HIV infection among poor women in Haiti. In *The anthropology of infectious disease,* eds. M. C. Inhorn and P. J. Brown, 413–38. Amsterdam: Gordon and Breach.

Fisher, William H. 1994. Megadevelopment, environmentalism, and resistance: The institutional context of Kayapo indigenous politics in central Brazil. *Human Organization* 53:220–32.

Foster, George M. 1969. *Applied anthropology.* Boston: Little, Brown.

Foster, George M. 1994. *Hippocrates' Latin American legacy: Humoral medicine in the New World.* Amsterdam: Gordon and Breach.

Gesler, Wilbert. 1991. *The cultural geography of health care.* Pittsburgh, PA: University of Pittsburgh Press.

Gladwin, Thomas, and Seymour B. Sarason. 1953. *Truk: Man in paradise.* New York: Wenner-Gren Foundation for Anthropological Research.

Goodman, Alan H., and Thomas L. Leatherman, eds. 1998. *Building a new biocultural synthesis: Political-economic perspectives on human biology.* Ann Arbor: University of Michigan Press.

Gross, Daniel R., and Barbara A. Underwood. 1971. Technological change and caloric costs: Sisal agriculture in northeastern Brazil. *American Anthropologist* 73:725–40.

Hahn, Robert A. 1995. *Sickness and healing: An anthropological perspective.* New Haven, CT: Yale University Press.

Harvey, Philip W., and Peter F. Heywood. 1983. Twenty-five years of dietary change in Simbu Province, Papua New Guinea. *Ecology of Food and Nutrition* 13:27–35.

Jelliffe, Derrick B., and E. F. Patrice Jelliffe. 1975. Human milk, nutrition, and the world resource crisis. *Science* 188 (May 9):557–61.

Joans, Barbara. 1997. Problems in Pocatello: A study in linguistic misunderstanding. In *Applying cultural anthropology: An introductory reader.* 3rd ed. eds. A. Podolefsky and P. J. Brown, 51–54. Mountain View, CA: Mayfield.

Kleinman, Arthur, Veena Das, and Margaret Lock, eds. 1997. *Social suffering.* Berkeley: University of California Press.

Komar, Debra A., and Jane E. Buikstra. 2008. *Forensic anthropology: Contemporary theory and practice.* New York: Oxford University Press.

Kushner, Gilbert. 1991. Applied anthropology. In *Career explorations in human services,* eds. W. G. Emener and M. Darrow. Springfield, IL: Charles C Thomas.

Leslie, Charles. 1976. Introduction. In *Asian medical systems: A comparative study,* ed. C. Leslie. Los Angeles: University of California Press.

Lieberman, Leslie Sue. 2004. Diabetes mellitus and medical anthropology. In *Encyclopedia of medical anthropology: Health and illness in the world's cultures,* vol. I, eds. Carol R. Ember and Melvin Ember, 335–53. New York: Kluwer Academic Press/Plenum Press.

Loustaunau, Martha O., and Elisa J. Sobo. 1997. *The cultural context of health, illness, and medicine.* Westport, CT: Bergin & Garvey.

Lyttleton, Chris. 2000. *Endangered relations: Negotiating sex and AIDS in Thailand.* Bangkok: White Lotus Press.

Magner, Lois. 1992. *A history of medicine.* New York: Marcel Dekker.

Mahony, Frank Joseph. 1971. *A Trukese theory of medicine.* Ann Arbor, MI: University Microfilms.

Manhein, Mary H. 1999. *The bone lady: Life as a forensic anthropologist.* Baton Rouge: Louisiana State University Press.

Mascie-Taylor, C. G. Nicholas. 1990. The biology of social class. In *Biosocial aspects of social class,* ed. C. G. N. Mascie-Taylor, 117–42. Oxford, UK: Oxford University Press.

McElroy, Ann, and Patricia Townsend. 2002. *Medical anthropology in ecological perspective.* 3rd ed. Boulder, CO: Westview Press.

McKee, Lauris. 1984. Sex differentials in survivorship and the customary treatment of infants and children. *Medical Anthropology* 8:91–108.

Moerman, Daniel E. 1997. Physiology and symbols: The anthropological implications of the placebo effect. In *The anthropology of medicine.* 3rd ed. eds. L. Romanucci-Ross, D. E. Moerman, and L. R. Tancredi, 240–53. Westport, CT: Bergin & Garvey.

Moore, Carmella C. 1988. An optimal scaling of Murdock's theories of illness data—An approach to the problem of interdependence. *Behavior Science Research* 22:161–79.

Murdock, George P. 1980. *Theories of illness: A world survey.* Pittsburgh, PA: University of Pittsburgh Press.

Murray, Gerald F., and M. E. Bannister. 2004. Peasants, agroforesters, and anthropologists: A 20-year venture in income-generating trees and hedgerows in Haiti. *Agroforestry Systems* 61:383–97.

Niehoff, Arthur H. 1966. *A casebook of social change.* Chicago: Aldine.

Nolan, Riall W. 2003. Anthropology in practice: Building a career outside the academy. Boulder: Lynne Rienner.

Ortiz de Montellano, Bernard R., and C. H. Browner. 1985. Chemical bases for medicinal plant use in Oaxaca, Mexico. *Journal of Ethnopharmacology* 13:57–88.

Picchi, Debra. 1991. The impact of an industrial agricultural project on the Bakairí Indians of central Brazil. *Human Organization* 50:26–38.

Picchi, Debra. 2009. Bakairí: The death of an Indian. In MyAnthroLibrary, eds. C. R. Ember, M. Ember, and P. N. Peregrine. MyAnthroLibrary.com. Pearson.

Quandt, Sara A. 1996. Nutrition in anthropology. In *Handbook of medical anthropology,* rev. ed., eds. C. F. Sargent and T. M. Johnson, 272–89. Westport, CT: Greenwood Press.

Ravesloot, John. 1997. Changing Native American perceptions of archaeology and archaeologists. In *Native Americans and archaeologists,* eds. N. Swidler, et al. Walnut Creek, CA: AltaMira Press.

Rogers, Everett M. 1983. *Diffusion of innovations.* 3rd ed. New York: Free Press.

Applied and Practicing Anthropology

Rubel, Arthur J., and Michael R. Hass. 1996. Ethnomedicine. In *Medical anthropology*, rev. ed., eds. C. F. Sargent and T. M. Johnson. Westport, CT: Praeger.

Rubel, Arthur J., Carl O'Nell, and Rolando Collado-Ardón (with the assistance of John Krejci and Jean Krejci). 1984. *Susto: A folk illness.* Berkeley: University of California Press.

Schoepf, Brooke. 1988. Women, AIDS and economic crisis in central Africa. *Canadian Journal of African Studies* 22:625–44.

Scudder, Thayer. 1978. Opportunities, issues and achievements in development anthropology since the mid-1960s: A personal view. In *Applied anthropology in America.* 2nd ed. eds. E. M. Eddy and W. L. Partridge. New York: Columbia University Press.

Shrestha, Laura B. 2006. Life Expectancy in the United States. CRS Report for Congress. Retrieved from: http://aging.senate.gov/crs/aging1.pdf on September 17, 2011.

Simmons, Janie, Paul Farmer, and Brooke G. Schoepf. 1996. A global perspective. In *Women, poverty, and AIDS: Sex, drugs, and structural violence,* eds. P. Farmer, M. Connors, and J. Simmons, 39–90. Monroe, ME: Common Courage Press.

Singh, Gopal K., and Peter C. van Dyck. n.d. Infant Mortality in the United States, 1935-2007: Over Seven Decades of Progress and Disparities. Retrieved from: http://www.hrsa.gov/healthit/images/mchb_infantmortality_pub.pdf on September 17, 2011.

Society for American Archaeology. 2009. FAQs for students. http://www.saa.org/ForthePublic/FAQs/ForStudents/tabid/101/Default.aspx (accessed August 26, 2009).

Torrey, E. Fuller. 1972. *The mind game: Witchdoctors and psychiatrists.* New York: Emerson Hall.

UNAIDS. 2007 (December). *AIDS epidemic update.* http://data.unaids.org/pub/EPISlides/2007/2007_epiupdate_en.pdf

Winkelman, Michael 1986a. Magico-religious practitioner types and socioeconomic conditions. *Behavior Science Research* 20:17–46.

Wulff, Robert, and Shirley Fiste. 1987. The domestication of wood in Haiti. In R. M. Wulff and S. J. Fiste, *Anthropological praxis.* Boulder, CO: Westview Press.

Explanation
and Evidence

Explanation and Evidence

((•━Listen to the **Chapter Audio** on **myanthrolab.com**   ▢▣━Read on **myanthrolab.com**

Anthropologists in the field try to arrive at accurate answers to descriptive questions. How do the people make a living? How do they marry? What gods do they believe in? But as important as accurate description is, it is not the ultimate goal of anthropology. Anthropologists want to *understand*—to know *why* people have certain customs or beliefs, not just to see that they *do* have them. As difficult as the *how* and *what* questions are to answer, the *why* questions are even harder. *Why* questions deal with explanations, which are harder to generate and harder to evaluate. In science, to understand is to explain, and so the major goal of science is to arrive at trustworthy explanations.[1]

For many anthropologists, the plausibility or persuasiveness of an explanation cannot be considered a sufficient reason to accept it. The explanation must also be tested and supported by objective evidence that could have falsified it. And even when it is supported, there still may be grounds for skepticism. According to the scientific orientation, all knowledge is uncertain and therefore subject to increasing or decreasing confirmation as new tests are made. This means that we will never arrive at absolute truth. On the other hand, and this is encouraging, we should be able to achieve more and more reliable understanding if we keep testing our theories.

Explanations

An **explanation** is an answer to a *why* question. There are many types of explanations, some more satisfying than others. For example, suppose we ask why a society thinks that a couple should abstain from sex for a year or so after the birth of a baby. If we say their tradition is to practice a long postpartum sex taboo, is this a satisfactory explanation? We would have to say no, because the thing to be explained (the taboo) is being explained by itself, by its prior existence. To explain something in terms of tradition is to say that people do it because they already do it, which is not informative. What kinds of explanations are more satisfactory, then? In science, there are two kinds of explanations that are sought: associations and theories.

Associations or Relationships

One way of explaining something (an observation, an action, a custom) is to say how it conforms to a general principle or relationship. So to explain why the water left outside in the basin froze, we say that it was cold last night and that water freezes at 32°F (0°C). The statement that water solidifies (becomes ice) at 32°F is a statement of a relationship or association between two **variables**—things or quantities that vary. In this case, variation in the state of water (liquid vs. solid) is related to variation in the temperature of the air (above vs. below 32°F). The truth of the relationship is suggested by repeated observations. In the physical sciences, such relationships are called **laws** when almost all scientists accept them. We find such explanations satisfactory because they allow us to predict what will happen in the future or to understand something that has happened regularly in the past.

In the social sciences, associations are usually stated *probabilistically;* that is, we say that two or more variables tend to be related in a predictable way, which means that there are usually some exceptions. For example, to explain why a society has a long postpartum sex taboo, we can point to the association (or correlation) that John Whiting found in a worldwide sample of societies: Societies with apparently low-protein diets tend to have long postpartum sex taboos.[2] We call the relationship between low-protein diets and the sex taboo a **statistical association**, which means that the observed relationship is unlikely to be due to chance.

Theories

Even though laws and statistical associations explain by relating what is to be explained to other things, we want to know more: why those laws or associations exist. Why does water freeze at 32°F? Why do societies with low-protein diets tend to have long postpartum sex taboos? Therefore, scientists try to formulate theories that will explain the observed relationships (laws and statistical associations).[3] **Theories** are explanations of laws and statistical associations. By way of example, let us return to the question of why some societies have long postpartum sex taboos. We have already seen that a known statistical association can be used to help explain it. In general (but not always), if a society has a low-protein diet, it will have a long postpartum sex taboo. But most people would ask additional questions: Why does a low-protein diet explain the taboo? What is the mechanism by which a society with such a diet develops the custom of a long postpartum sex taboo? A theory is intended to answer such questions.

John Whiting theorized that a long postpartum sex taboo may be an adaptation to certain conditions. Particularly in tropical areas, where the major food staples are low in protein, babies are vulnerable to the protein-deficiency disease called *kwashiorkor.* But if a baby could continue to nurse for a long time, it might have more of a chance to survive. The postpartum sex taboo might be adaptive, Whiting's theory suggests, because it increases the likelihood of a baby's survival. That is, if a mother puts off having another baby for a while, the first baby might have a better chance to survive because it can be fed mother's milk for a longer time. Whiting suggests that parents may be aware, whether unconsciously or consciously, that having another baby too soon might jeopardize the survival of the first baby, and so they might decide that abstaining from intercourse for more than a year after the birth of the first baby would be a good idea.

As this example of a theory illustrates, there are differences between a theory and an association. A theory is more complicated, containing a series of statements. An association usually states quite simply that there is a relationship between two or more measured variables. Another difference is that, although a theory may mention some things that are observable, such as the presence of a long postpartum sex taboo, parts of it are difficult or impossible to observe

The Yanomamö Indians of Brazil (*left*) depend on root crops. The Inuit of Nunavut (*right*) depend largely on sea mammals and fish.

directly. For example, with regard to Whiting's theory, it would be difficult to find out if people had deliberately or unconsciously decided to practice a long postpartum sex taboo because they recognized that babies would thereby have a better chance to survive. Then, too, the concept of adaptation—that some characteristic promotes greater reproductive success—is difficult to verify because it is difficult to find out whether different individuals or groups have different rates of reproduction because they do or do not practice the supposedly adaptive custom. Thus, some concepts or implications in a theory are unobservable (at least at the present time), and only some aspects may be observable. In contrast, statistical associations or laws are based entirely on observations.[4]

Why Theories Cannot be Proved

Many people think that the theories they learned in physics or chemistry courses have been proved. Unfortunately, many students get that impression because their teachers present "lessons" in an authoritative manner. Scientists and philosophers of science now generally agree that no theory can be said to be proved or unquestionably true, although some theories may have considerable evidence supporting them. This is because many of the concepts and ideas in theories are not directly observable and therefore not directly verifiable. For example, scientists may try to explain how light behaves by postulating that it consists of particles called photons, but photons cannot be observed, even with the most powerful microscope. So, exactly what a photon looks like and exactly how it works remain in the realm of the unprovable. The photon is a **theoretical construct**, something that cannot be observed or verified directly. Because all theories contain such constructs, theories cannot be proved entirely or with absolute certainty.[5]

Why should we bother with theories, then, if we cannot prove that they are true? Perhaps the main advantage of a theory as a kind of explanation is that it may lead to new under-standing or knowledge. A theory can suggest new relationships or imply new predictions that might be supported or confirmed by new research. For example, Whiting's theory about long postpartum sex taboos has implications that researchers could investigate. Because the theory discusses how a long postpartum sex taboo might be adaptive, we would expect that certain changes would result in the taboo's disappearance. For example, suppose people adopted either mechanical birth control devices or began to give supplementary high-protein foods to babies. With birth control, a family could space births without abstaining from sex, so we would expect the custom of postpartum abstinence to disappear. As well, we would expect it to disappear with protein supplements for babies because *kwashiorkor* would then be less likely to afflict the babies. Whiting's ideas might also prompt investigators to try to find out whether parents are consciously or unconsciously aware of the problem of close birth spacing in areas with low supplies of protein.

Although theories cannot be proved, they are rejectable. The method of **falsification**, which shows that a theory seems to be wrong, is the main way that theories are judged.[6] Scientists derive implications or predictions that should be true if the theory is correct. So, for example, Whiting predicted that societies with long postpartum sex taboos would be found more often in the tropics than in temperate regions and that they would be likely to have low-protein food supplies. Such predictions of what might be found are called **hypotheses**. If the predictions turn out not to be correct, the researcher is obliged to con-clude that something may be wrong with the theory or something wrong with the test of the theory. Theories that are not falsified are accepted for the time being because the available evidence seems to be consistent with them. But remember that no matter how much the available evidence seems to support a theory, we can never be certain it is true. There is always the possibility that some implication of it, some hypothesis derivable from it, will not be confirmed in the future.

Evidence: Testing Explanations

In any field of investigation, theories are generally the most plentiful commodity. It is necessary, then, for us to have procedures that enable us to select from among the many available theories those that are more likely to be correct. "Just as mutations arise naturally but are not all beneficial, so hypotheses [theories] emerge naturally but are not all correct. If progress is to occur, therefore, we require a superfluity of hypotheses and also a mechanism of selection."[7] In other words, generating a theory or interpretation is not enough. We need some reliable method of testing whether or not that theory is likely to be correct. If a theory is not correct, it may detract from our efforts to achieve understanding by misleading us into thinking the problem is already solved.

The strategy in all kinds of testing in science is to predict what one would expect to find if a particular theory were correct, and then to conduct an investigation to see if the prediction is generally consistent with the data. If the prediction is not supported, the investigator is obliged to accept the possibility that the theory is wrong. If, however, the prediction holds true, then the investigator is entitled to say that evidence supports the theory. Thus, conducting research designed to test expectations derived from theory allows researchers to eliminate some theories and to accept others, at least tentatively.

Operationalization and Measurement

To transform theoretical predictions into statements that might be verified, a researcher provides an **operational definition** of each of the concepts or variables mentioned in the prediction. An operational definition is a description of the procedure that is followed to measure the variable.[8]

Whiting predicted that societies with a low-protein diet would have a long postpartum sex taboo. Amount of protein in the diet is a variable; some societies have more, others have less. Length of the postpartum sex taboo is a variable; a society may have a short taboo or a long taboo. Whiting operationally defined the first variable, *amount of protein*, in terms of staple foods.[9] If a society depended mostly on root and tree crops (such as cassava and

A thermometer provides a way of comparing or measuring the "heat" of different locations or over different time periods. While the physical sciences often use physical instruments and the social sciences often use humans to observe, all measurements compare things on some scale of variation.

bananas), Whiting rated the society as having low protein. If the society depended mostly on cereal crops (such as wheat, barley, corn, and oats), he rated it as having moderate protein because cereal crops have more protein by weight than root and tree crops. If the society depended mostly on hunting, fishing, or herding for food, he rated it as having high protein. The other variable in Whiting's prediction, *length of postpartum sex taboo,* was operationalized as follows: A society was rated as having a long taboo if couples customarily abstained from sex for more than a year after the birth of a baby; abstention for a year or less was considered a short taboo.

Specifying an operational definition for each variable is extremely important because it allows other investigators to check a researcher's results.[10] Science depends on *replication,* the repetition of results. Only when many researchers observe a particular association can we call that association or relationship a law. Providing operational definitions is also extremely important because it allows others to evaluate whether a measure is appropriate. Only when we are told exactly how something was measured can we judge whether the measure reflects what it is supposed to reflect. Specifying measures publicly is so important in science that we are obliged to be skeptical of any conclusions offered by a researcher who fails to say how variables were measured.

To **measure** something is to say how it compares with other things on some scale of variation.[11] People often assume that a measuring device is always a physical instrument, such as a scale or a ruler, but *classification* is also a form of measurement. When we classify people as male or female or employed versus unemployed, we are dividing them into *sets.* Deciding which set they belong to is a kind of measurement because doing so allows us to compare them. We can also measure things by deciding which cases or examples have more or less of something (e.g., more or less protein in the diet). The measures employed in physical science are usually based on scales that allow us to assign numbers to each case; we measure height in meters and weight in grams, for example. However we measure our variables, the fact that we can measure them means that we can test our hypotheses to see if the predicted relationships actually exist, at least most of the time.

Sampling

After deciding how to measure the variables in some predicted relationship, investigators must decide how to select which cases to study to see if the predicted relationship holds. If the prediction is about the behavior of people, the sampling decision involves which people to observe. If the prediction is about an association between societal customs, the sampling decision involves which societies to study. No researcher can investigate all the possible cases, so choices must be made. Some choices are better than others. The best sample is almost always some kind of random sample in which all cases selected have an equal chance of being included in the sample or subset. Almost all statistical tests used to evaluate the results of research require random sampling because only results based on a random sample can be assumed to be probably true for some larger set or universe of cases.

Statistical Evaluation

When researchers have measured the variables of interest for all the sample cases, they are ready to see if the predicted relationship actually exists in the data. Remember, the results may not turn out to be what the theory predicts. Sometimes researchers construct a *contingency table,* like that shown in Table 1, to see if the variables are associated as predicted. In Whiting's sample of 172 societies, each case is assigned to a box, or cell, in the table, depending on how the society is measured on the two variables of interest. For example, a society that has a long postpartum sex taboo and a low-protein diet is placed in the third row of the Long Duration column. (In Whiting's sample [see Table 1], there are 27 such societies.) A society that has a short postpartum sex taboo and a low-protein diet is placed in the third row in the Short Duration column. (There are 20 such societies in the sample.) The statistical question is: Does the way the cases are distributed in the six central cells of the table generally support Whiting's prediction? If we looked just at the table, we might not know what to answer. Many cases appear to be in the expected places. For example, most of the high-protein cases (47 of 62) have short taboos, and most of the low-protein cases (27 of 47) have long taboos. But there are also many exceptions (e.g., 20 cases have low protein and a short taboo). So, although many cases appear to be in the expected places, there are also many exceptions. Do the exceptions invalidate the prediction? How many exceptions would compel us to reject the hypothesis? Here is where we resort to *statistical tests of significance.*

Statisticians have devised various tests that tell us how "perfect" a result has to be for us to believe that there is probably an association between the variables of interest, that one variable generally predicts the other. Essentially, every statistical result is evaluated in the same objective way. We ask: What is the chance that this result is purely accidental, that there is no association at all between the two variables? Although some of the mathematical ways of answering this question are complicated, the answer always involves a probability value (or p-value)—the likelihood that the observed result or a stronger one could have occurred by chance. The statistical test used by Whiting gives a p-value of less than .01 ($p < .01$) for the observed result. In other words, there is less than 1 chance out of 100 that the relationship observed is purely accidental. A p-value of less than .01 is a fairly low probability; most social scientists conventionally agree to call any result with a p-value of .05 or less (five or fewer chances out of 100) a statistically significant, or probably true, result. When describing relationships or associations, those doing the describing are almost always referring to results that have been found to be statistically significant.

But why should a probably true relationship have any exceptions? If a theory is really correct, shouldn't *all* the cases fit? There are many reasons why we can never expect a perfect result. First, even if a theory is correct (e.g., if a low-protein diet really does favor the adoption of a long postpartum sex taboo), there may still be other causes that we have not investigated. For example, societies that depend mostly on hunting for their food, and would therefore be classified as having a high-protein diet, may have a problem carrying infants from one campsite to another and may practice a long postpartum sex taboo so that two infants will not have to be carried at the same time.

TABLE 1 Association between Availability of Protein and Duration of Postpartum Sex Taboo

Availability of Protein	Duration of Postpartum Sex Taboo		
	Short (0–1 Year)	Long (More Than 1 Year)	Total
High	47	15	62
Medium	38	25	63
Low	20	27	47
Total	105	67	172
Source: Based on Whiting 1964, 520.			

Exceptions to the predicted relationship might also occur because of *cultural lag*.[12] Cultural lag occurs when change in one aspect of culture takes time to produce change in another aspect. Suppose that a society recently changed crops and is now no longer a low-protein society but still practices the taboo. This society would be an exception to the predicted relationship, but it might fit the theory if it stopped practicing the taboo in a few years. Measurement inaccuracy is another source of exception. Whiting's measure of protein, which is based on the major sources of food, is not a very precise measure of protein in the diet. It does not take into account the possibility that a "tree crop" society might get a lot of protein from fishing or raising pigs. So it might turn out that some supposedly low-protein societies have been misclassified, which may be one reason why there are 20 cases in the lowest cell in the left-hand column of Table 1. Measurement error usually produces exceptions.

Significant statistical associations that are predictable from a theory offer tentative support for the theory. But much more is needed before we can be fairly confident about the theory. Replication is needed to confirm whether other researchers can reproduce the predictions using other samples. Other predictions should be derived from the theory to see if they too are supported. The theory should be pitted against alternative explanations to see which theory works better. We may have to combine theories if alternative explanations also predict the relationship in question. The research process in science thus requires time and patience. Perhaps most important, it requires that researchers be humble. No matter how wonderful one's own theory seems, it is important to acknowledge that it may be wrong. If we don't test our theories, we can never tell the difference between a better or worse theory, and we will be saddled forever with our present ignorance.

Types of Research in Cultural Anthropology

Cultural anthropologists use several methods to conduct research. Each has certain advantages and disadvantages in generating and testing explanations. The types of research in cultural anthropology can be classified according to two criteria. One is the spatial scope of the study—analysis of a single society, analysis of societies in a region, or analysis of a worldwide sample of societies. The other criterion is the temporal scope of the study—historical versus nonhistorical. Combinations of these criteria are shown in Table 2.

Ethnography

Around the beginning of the twentieth century, anthropologists realized that, if they were to produce anything of scientific value, they would have to study their subject in depth. To describe cultures more accurately, they started to live among the people they were studying. They observed, and

TABLE 2 Types of Research in Cultural Anthropology

Scope	Nonhistorical	Historical
Single case	Ethnography/fieldwork	Ethnohistory
	Within-culture comparison	Within-culture comparison
Region	Controlled comparison	Controlled comparison
Worldwide sample	Cross-cultural research	Cross-historical research

even took part in, the important events of those societies and carefully questioned the people about their native customs. This method is known as **participant-observation**. Participant-observation always involves **fieldwork**, which is firsthand experience with the people being studied, but fieldwork may also involve other methods, such as conducting a census or a survey.[13]

Fieldwork, the cornerstone of modern anthropology, is the means by which most anthropological information is obtained. Regardless of other methods that anthropologists may use, participant-observation conducted usually for a year or more is regarded as fundamental. In contrast to the casual descriptions of travelers and adventurers, anthropologists' descriptions record, describe, analyze, and eventually formulate a picture of the culture, or at least part of it.[14] After doing fieldwork, an anthropologist may prepare an *ethnography*, a description and analysis of a single society.

How an anthropologist goes about doing long-term participant-observation in another culture—and, more important, doing it well—is not so straightforward. Much of it depends on the person, the culture, and the interaction between the two. Without a doubt, the experience is physically and psychologically demanding, comparable often to a rite of passage. Although it helps enormously to learn the local language before going, often it is not possible to do so, and so most anthropologists find themselves struggling to communicate in addition to trying to figure out how to behave properly. Participant-observation carries its own dilemma. Participation implies living like the people who are being studied, trying to understand subjectively what they think and feel by doing what they do, whereas observation implies a certain amount of objectivity and detachment.[15] Because participant-observation is such a personal experience, it is not surprising that anthropologists have begun to realize that *reflecting* on their experiences and their personal interaction with the people they live with is an important part of understanding the enterprise.

An essential part of the participant-observation process is finding some knowledgeable people who are willing to work with you (anthropologists call them *informants*), to help you interpret what you observe and tell you about aspects of the culture that you may not have a chance to see, or may not be entitled to see. For example, it is not likely that you will see many weddings in a village of

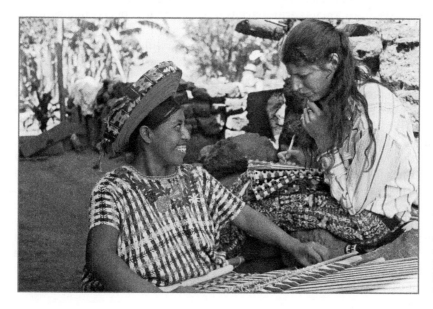

Anthropologist Margaret Kieffer conducts an ethnographic interview with a Mayan woman in Guatemala.

53

200 people in a year or two of fieldwork. So how can you know who will be a good informant? It is obviously important to find people who are easy to talk to and who understand what information you need. But how do you know who is knowledgeable? You can't just assume that the people you get along with have the most knowledge. (Besides, knowledge is often specialized; one person may know a whole lot more about some subjects than others.) At a minimum, you have to try out a few different people to compare what they tell you about a subject. What if they disagree? How do you know who is more trustworthy or accurate? Fortunately, formal methods have been developed to help anthropologists select the most knowledgeable informants. One method, called the "cultural consensus model," relies on the principle that those things that most informants agree on are probably cultural. After you establish which things appear to be cultural by asking a sample of informants the same questions about a particular cultural domain, it will be easy to discover which informants are very likely to give answers that closely match the cultural consensus. These individuals are your best bets to be the most knowledgeable in that domain.[16] It may seem paradoxical, but the most knowledgeable and helpful individuals are not necessarily "typical" individuals. Many anthropologists have pointed out that key informants are likely to feel somewhat marginal in their culture. After all, why would they want to spend so much time with the visiting anthropologist?[17]

Participant-observation is valuable for understanding some aspects of culture, particularly the things that are the most public, readily talked about, and most widely agreed upon. But more systematic methods are important too: mapping, house-to-house censuses, behavior observations (e.g., to determine how people spend their time), as well as focused interviews with a sample of informants.

Ethics in Fieldwork Anthropologists have many ethical obligations—to the people they study, their anthropological colleagues, to the public and world community, and even to their employers and their own and host countries. But anthropologists agree that, should a conflict arise in ethical obligations, the most important obligation is to protect the interests of the people they study. According to the profession's code of ethics, anthropologists should tell people in the field site (or, if they are archaeologists, people who are direct descendants of the prehistoric people they are studying) about the research, and they should respect the right of people to remain anonymous if they so choose.[18] For this reason, informants are often given "pseudonyms" or fake names; many anthropologists have extended this principle to using a fake name for the community as well. But the decision to create a fake name for a community is questionable in many circumstances.[19] First, anthropologists "stick out," and it is not hard for anyone interested to figure out where they lived and worked. Governments may have to be asked for research clearance, which means that they know where the anthropologist is going to do the fieldwork. Second, people who are studied are often proud of their place and their customs and they may be insulted if their community is called something else. Third, important geographic information is often vital to understanding the community. You have to reveal if it is located at the confluence of two major rivers, or if it is the trading center of the region. And lastly, it may be difficult for future anthropologists to conduct follow-up studies if the community is disguised. Of course, if a community were truly in danger, there would be no question that an anthropologist has an obligation to try to protect it.

Honest, objective reporting is also an obligation to the anthropological profession, to the public at large, and to the observed community. But suppose a custom or trait that appears perfectly reasonable to the observed community is considered objectionable by outsiders. Such customs could range from acts that outsiders consider criminal, such as infanticide, to those that are considered repugnant, such as eating dogs. Archaeologists have caused outrage by presenting evidence of cannibalism in ancient populations.[20] An anthropologist may believe that publication of the information could bring harm to the population. Kim Hill and Magdalena Hurtado faced this situation when they realized that infanticide rates were high in the group they studied in South America. They did not want to play up their findings, nor did they want to dissimulate. After they met with community leaders to discuss the situation, they agreed not to publish their findings in Spanish to minimize the possibility that the local media or neighboring groups might learn of their findings.[21]

Everyday decisions like how to compensate people for their time are not easy either. Nowadays, many if not most informants expect to be paid or receive gifts. But in the early days of anthropology, in places where money was not an important part of the native economy, the decision to pay people was not a clear ethical choice. If money is rare, paying people increases the importance of money in that economy. Even nonmonetary gifts can increase inequalities or create jealousies. On the other hand, doing nothing by way of compensation doesn't seem right either. As an alternative, some anthropologists try to find some community project that they can help with—that way, everyone benefits. This is not to say that the anthropologists are necessarily a burden on the community. People often like to talk about their customs, and they may want others to appreciate their way of life. And anthropologists are often amusing. They may ask "funny" questions, and when they try to say or do customary things, they often do them all wrong. Probably every anthropologist has been laughed at sometimes in the field.

Within-Culture Comparisons

Ethnographers could test a theory within one society if they decide to compare individuals, families, households, communities, or districts. The natural variability that exists can be used to create a comparison. Suppose we want to verify Whiting's assumption that longer postpartum taboos enhance the survival of babies in a society with a low-protein diet. Although almost all couples might practice a long postpartum sex taboo because it is customary, some couples might not adhere to the taboo consistently and some couples might not conceive quickly after the taboo is lifted. So we would expect some variation in spacing between births. If we collected information on the births of each mother and the survival outcome of each birth, we would be able to compare the survival rates of children born a short time after the mother's last pregnancy with those of children born after longer intervals. A significantly higher survival rate for the births after longer intervals would support Whiting's theory. What if some communities within the society had access to more protein than others? If Whiting's theory is correct, those communities with more protein should also have a higher survival rate for babies. If there were variation in the length of the postpartum sex taboo, the communities with more protein should have shorter taboos.

Regional Controlled Comparisons

In a regional controlled comparison, anthropologists compare ethnographic information obtained from societies found in a particular region—societies that presumably have similar histories and occupy similar environments. Anthropologists who conduct a regional comparison are apt to be familiar with the complex of cultural features associated with that region. These features may provide a good understanding of the context of the phenomenon that is to be explained.

Because some of the societies being compared will have the characteristic that is to be explained and some will not, anthropologists can determine whether the conditions hypothesized to be related are in fact related, at least in that region. We must remember, however, that two or more conditions may be related in one region for reasons peculiar to that region. Therefore, an explanation supported in one region may not fit others.

Cross-Cultural Research

The most common use of worldwide comparisons has been to test explanations. An example is Whiting's test of his theory about the adaptive functions of a long postpartum sex taboo. Recall that Whiting hypothesized that, if his theory were correct, variation in protein supplies in the adult diet should predict variation in the duration of the postpartum sex taboo. Cross-cultural researchers first identify conditions that should generally be associated if a particular theory is correct. Then they look at a worldwide sample of societies to see if the

APPLIED ANTHROPOLOGY

There is Nothing Like Evidence to Shake Mistaken Beliefs

Potatoes are widely grown in the Andean highlands of South America, and they may have been domesticated there or close by. It is often assumed therefore that the highlands are the best place to grow potatoes. But some scientists were skeptical. (After all, potatoes have been grown successfully at low altitudes elsewhere.) Perhaps, the scientists reasoned, potatoes are grown in the Andean highlands because other crops such as corn are not suited to the highlands. Potatoes grow in the ground, and the short Andean growing season or a frost won't kill them. They can stay in the ground for some time without rotting. Other crops such as corn could be grown in the highlands, but they grow more safely and productively in the warmer lowlands, which have a longer growing season and less risk of untimely frost. And corn would be the crop of choice in the lowlands particularly if there is adequate rainfall or the crop can be irrigated (as in the coastal river valleys of Peru that empty into the Pacific). Corn agriculture would leave little room for growing potatoes in the lowlands. By default, then, potatoes might have become the crop of choice in the highlands because little else could produce as many edible calories.

For many years the International Potato Center in Lima, Peru, has employed anthropologists to conduct research on how to increase potato production while protecting the environment and preserving biodiversity. To explore the possibilities, the anthropologists decided to investigate how and where potatoes were grown around the world, adopting the strategy of comparative research that was pioneered by the Human Relations Area Files (HRAF) to document cross-cultural variation and to test hypotheses about it. Data on potato production were obtained from 132 countries. Surprisingly, the data showed that the bulk of potatoes produced in developing countries were not grown in the tropical highlands, where the Potato Center had targeted most of its work, but rather in the lowland subtropical zones of Asia, where potatoes are typically rotated with rice or wheat. The Center discovered from its comparative study that its own development projects in tropical hilly areas of Asia (the Philippines, Indonesia, Thailand, and Sri Lanka) and Africa (Rwanda and Burundi) had disadvantageous consequences. They had degraded the environment because potatoes leave the slopes precariously exposed during periods of high rainfall. Furthermore, potatoes are often grown as a luxury crop for fast-food restaurants, tourist hotels, and airlines—not as food for the poor. Who would have thought that the potato could be a luxury crop?

The worldwide comparative research by the Potato Center's anthropologists became a model for other agricultural centers and programs that work on how to increase sustainable and safe production of other important world crops, such as rice, corn, wheat, and peanuts. Applied anthropology can "open eyes" and suggest possibilities because it looks worldwide at the human condition.

Sources: Rhoades 2001; 2005, 61–85.

expected association generally holds true. Most cross-culturalists choose a published sample of societies that was not constructed for any specific hypothesis test. Two of the most widely used samples are the Standard Cross-Cultural Sample (SCCS) of 186 societies and the HRAF Collection of Ethnography (much of which is available in eHRAF World Cultures online), an annually growing collection of original ethnographic books and articles on approximately 400 cultures past and present around the world.[22]

The advantage of cross-cultural research is that the conclusion drawn from it is probably applicable to most societies, if the sample used for testing has been more or less randomly selected and therefore is representative of the world. In other words, the results of a cross-cultural study are probably applicable to most societies and most regions, in contrast with the results of a regional comparison, which may or may not be applicable to other regions.

Historical Research

Ethnohistory consists of studies based on descriptive materials about a single society at more than one point in time. It provides the essential data for historical studies of all types, just as ethnography provides the essential data for all nonhistorical types of research. Ethnohistorical data may consist of

Ethnohistorians need to analyze pieces of information from a variety of sources such as the accounts of European explorers. Pictured here is a group of Roanoke Native Americans fishing in the late 1500s. It provides ethnohistorians with good information on how these people harvested fish.

Source: John White/Copyright The British Museum.

sources other than the ethnographic reports prepared by anthropologists—accounts by explorers, missionaries, traders, and government officials. Ethnohistorians, like historians, cannot simply assume that all the documents they find are simply descriptions of fact; they were written by very different kinds of people with very different goals and purposes. So they need to separate carefully what may be fact from what may be speculative interpretation. To reconstruct how a culture changed over hundreds of years, where the natives left few or no written accounts, anthropologists have to seek out travelers' accounts and other historical documents that were written by non-natives.

An important goal of ethnohistory, and of cultural anthropology in general, is to explain variation in cultural patterns, that is, to specify what conditions will favor one cultural pattern rather than another. Such specification requires us to assume that the supposed causal, or favoring, conditions antedated the pattern to be explained. Theories or explanations, then,

Explanation and Evidence

imply a sequence of changes over time, which are the stuff of history. Therefore, if we want to come closer to an understanding of the reasons for the cultural variations we are investigating, we should examine historical sequences. They will help us determine whether the conditions we think caused various phenomena truly antedated those phenomena and thus might more reliably be said to have caused them.

Sometime, we have strong suspicions about the determinants of cultural variation but other times we jut do not know or only dimly suspect. There is a good deal that we do not know or has not yet been adequately researched, Acknowledging what you don't know can help a field move forward.

✓—Study and Review on myanthrolab.com

Summary

1. Scientists try to achieve two kinds of explanations: associations (observed relationships between two or more variables) and theories (explanations of associations).

2. Theories are falsified by deriving hypotheses or predictions that should be true if the theory is correct. Evidence is gathered to see if the predictions are true or not. If the predictions are not borne out, the researcher is obliged to be skeptical of the theory.

3. Making satisfactory tests requires specifying how to measure the variables involved, deciding on appropriate samples of cases (preferable representative cases), and performing statistical analyses that assign probability values to the results.

4. Anthropologists use several different methods to conduct research. The types of research in anthropology can be classified according to two criteria: the spatial scope of the study (analysis of a single case, analysis of several or more cases in a region, or analysis of a worldwide sample of cases) and the temporal scope of the study (historical vs. nonhistorical). In cultural anthropology, the basic research methods, then, are ethnographic fieldwork and ethnohistory, historical and nonhistorical regional controlled comparisons, and historical and nonhistorical cross-cultural research.

Glossary Terms

explanation	laws	statistical association
falsification	measure	theoretical construct
fieldwork	operational definition	theories
hypotheses	participant-observation	variables

Explanation and Evidence

Critical Questions

1. Anthropological methods vary from single-case studies to broad comparisons across space and time. Compare the different strategies with respect to their usefulness in generating and testing explanations.

2. Are theories important? Explain why or why not.

3. If two ethnographers describing the same culture disagree, how do we decide who's right?

Read the **Original Source** on **myanthrolab.com**

Read the chapter by Carol R. Ember and Melvin Ember, "On Cross-Cultural Research," on MyAnthroLab and answer the following questions.

1. Give a few examples of questions that can be answered by cross-cultural research.
2. What are the basic assumptions and steps in a cross-cultural study?

Photo Credits

Glossary

Explanation An answer to a *why* question. In science, there are two kinds of explanation that researchers try to achieve: associations and theories.

Fieldwork Firsthand experience with the people being studied and the usual means by which anthropological information is obtained. Regardless of other methods that anthropologists may use (e.g., censuses, surveys), fieldwork usually involves participant-observation for an extended period of time, often a year or more. See Participant-observation.

Hypotheses Predictions, which may be derived from theories, about how variables are related.

Laws (scientific) Associations or relationships that almost all scientists accept.

Measure To describe how something compares with other things on some scale of variation.

Operational definition A description of the procedure that is followed in measuring a variable.

Participant-observation Living among the people being studied—observing, questioning, and (when possible) taking part in the important events of the group. Writing or otherwise recording notes on observations, questions asked and answered, and things to check out later are parts of participant-observation.

Statistical association A relationship or correlation between two or more variables that is unlikely to be due to chance.

Theoretical construct Something that cannot be observed or verified directly.

Theories Explanations of associations or laws.

Variable A thing or quantity that varies.

Notes

1. Hempel 1965: 139.
2. J. Whiting 1964.
3. Nagel 1961: 83–90.
4. Ibid., 83–90.
5. Ibid., 85. See also McCain and Segal 1988, 75–79.
6. McCain and Segal 1988, 62–64.
7. Caws 1969, 1378.
8. McCain and Segal 1988, 56–57, 131–32.
9. J. Whiting 1964, 519–20.
10. McCain and Segal 1988, 67–69.
11. Blalock 1972, 15–20; Thomas 1986, 18–28. See also M. Ember 1970, 701–03.
12. Ogburn 1922, 200–80.
13. Bernard 2001, 323.
14. Peacock 1986, 54.
15. Lawless, Sutlive, and Zamora 1983, xi–xxi; Peacock 1986, 54–65.
16. Romney, Weller, and Batchelder, 1986.
17. Bernard 2001, 190.
18. American Anthropological Association 1991.
19. Szklut and Reed 1991.
20. Lambert et al. 2000, 405.
21. Hill and Hurtado 2004.
22. See Murdock and White 1969 for a description of the SCCS sample; the HRAF Collection of Ethnography is described at www.yale.edu/hraf; for a description of many different cross-cultural samples, see C. R. Ember and M. Ember 2009.

Bibliography

American Anthropological Association. 1991. Revised principles of professional responsibility, 1990. In *Ethics and the profession of anthropology: Dialogue for a new era*, ed. Carolyn Fluehr-Lobban, 274–79. Philadelphia: University of Pennsylvania Press.

Bernard, H. Russell. 2001. *Research methods in cultural anthropology: Qualitative and quantitative approaches*. 3rd ed. Walnut Creek, CA: AltaMira Press.

Blalock, Hubert M. 1972. *Social statistics*. 2nd ed. New York: McGraw-Hill.

Caws, Peter. 1969. The structure of discovery. *Science* 166 (December 12):1375–80.

Ember, Carol R. and Melvin Ember. 2009a. On Cross-Cultural Research. In MyAnthroLibrary, eds. C. R. Ember, M. Ember, and P. N. Peregrine. MyAnthroLibrary.com. Pearson.

Ember, Melvin. 1970. Taxonomy in comparative studies. In *A handbook of method in cultural anthropology*, eds. R. Naroll and R. Cohen. Garden City, NY: Natural History Press.

Hill, Kim, and A. Magdalena Hurtado. 2004. The ethics of anthropological research with remote tribal populations. In *Lost paradises and the ethics of research and publication*, eds. F. M. Salzano and A. M. Hurtado, 193–210. Oxford, UK: Oxford University Press.

Explanation and Evidence

Lambert, Patricia M., Banks L. Leonard, Brian R. Billman, Richard A. Marlar, Margaret E. Newman, and Karl J. Reinhard. 2000. Response to critique of the claim of cannibalism at Cowboy Wash. *American Antiquity* 65(2):397–406.

Lawless, Robert, Vinson H. Sutlive, Jr., and Mario D. Zamora, eds. 1983. *Fieldwork: The human experience.* New York: Gordon and Breach.

McCain, Garvin, and Erwin M. Segal. 1988. *The game of science.* 5th ed. Monterey, CA: Brooks/Cole.

Murdock, George P., and Douglas R. White. 1969. Standard cross-cultural sample. *Ethnology* 8:329–69.

Nagel, Ernest. 1961. *The structure of science: Problems in the logic of scientific explanation.* New York: Harcourt, Brace & World.

Ogburn, William F. 1922. *Social change.* New York: Huebsch.

Peacock, James L. 1986. *The anthropological lens: Harsh light, soft focus.* Cambridge, UK: Cambridge University Press.

Romney, A. Kimball, Susan C. Weller, and William H. Batchelder. 1986. Culture as consensus: A theory of culture and informant accuracy. *American Anthropologist* 88:313–38.

Szklut, Jay, and Reed, Robert Roy. 1991. Community anonymity in anthropological research: A reassessment. In *Ethics and the profession of anthropology: Dialogue for a new era,* ed. Carolyn Fluehr-Lobban, 97–116. Philadelphia: University of Pennsylvania Press.

Thomas, David Hurst. 1986. *Refiguring anthropology: First principles of probability and statistics.* Prospect Heights, IL: Waveland.

Whiting, John W. M. 1964. Effects of climate on certain cultural practices. In *Explorations in cultural anthropology,* ed. W. Goodenough. New York: McGraw-Hill.

Willie L. McKether

INCREASING POWER IN A BLACK COMMUNITY: A NETWORKED APPROACH

Although social network analysis can contribute insight about social relationships embedded in ethnographic data, such as oral history interviews, seemingly few anthropologists use social network analysis as a method for examining ethnographic data. Expanding upon a study of an African American migration from southern regions of the United States to Saginaw, MI, this article uses network analysis to examine a 1967 dual mobilization network structure that emerged as two combative African American networks fought to increase black power in the small community. This research demonstrates that social network analysis can provide qualitative researchers insights not easily or even readily gained through simple narrative analysis. [network analysis, anthropological methods, social movement].

INTRODUCTION

Few anthropologists (e.g., Barnes 1954, White and Johansen 2005; Foster 1979) use social network analysis as a method for examining ethnographic data. Although ethnographic data collected by anthropologists provides data types ideally suited for networked approaches to data analysis (White and Johansen 2005), the vast majority of anthropologists seemingly rely on traditional methods and approaches, such as coding, linguistic, word, and theme analysis for their examination of collected data. While such traditional approaches continue to produce ethnographies that tell us much about social and cultural life across a range of settings, we potentially miss social interaction at a deeper level of continuity when we rely solely on such traditional methods. As White and Johansen (2005) observe:

> The benefits here derive from taking the same data as used by the ethnographer in analyzing observations to produce an ethnographic report but, through the avenue of network coding and analysis, to reach a set of results and explanations that may add entirely new dimensions and explanations to the ethnography. [6]

Consistent with White and Johansen's observation, the purpose of this article is to show how social network analysis was used to provide additional insight into an anthropological study of a social movement aimed at increasing black power in Saginaw, MI. Network analysis is particularly appropriate to examine this public effort to increase black power[1] because the important relationships that contributed to the success of the movement may have been missed if only the observable aspects of the movement were examined. As such, this article describes how social network analysis was used to examine ethnographic data and illustrates how taking a structured approach to data analysis reveals important relationships embedded in interview and other ethnographic data.

Based on an ethnohistorical study of a 1967 social movement in Saginaw,[2] MI that erupted into a community-wide riot/rebellion, this article specifically shows how economic and political power was increased in the black community as the direct outcome of competitive network structures. One of the networks was embedded in a grassroots organization known as United Power; the second network was led by the city's powerful black mayor. The combative mobilization structures emerged when the class-based networks framed their grievances differently as they each challenged the same political opportunity structures that constrained the black community's social, economic, and political development.

For qualitative researchers, interview or narrative data are an important and often used source of data. Through both manual techniques and computer software programs designed to store, analyze, and manipulate narrative data, qualitative researchers typically examine words and code data in order to make inferences and construct the social worlds of people based on lived experiences. While such traditional approaches to examining narrative data continue to be widely used by many anthropologists, investigators seldom take advantage of quantitative methods like network analysis to explore their data from a structured approach.

Transforming Anthropology, Vol. 19, Number 1, pp. 65–75, ISSN 1051-0559, electronic ISSN 1548-7466. © 2011 by the American Anthropological Association. All rights reserved.
DOI: 10.1111/j.1548-7466.2011.01120.x.

65

Social network analysis is a methodological approach that examines the relationships (referred to as links or ties) an individual actor or actors have with other individuals, groups, or organizations (referred to as alters) in an environment. Specifically, as articulated by Wasserman and Faust (1994): "The concept of a network emphasizes the fact that each individual has ties to other individuals, each of whom in turn is tied to a few, some, or many others, and so on" (9). A primary goal of social network analysis is to depict the structure of a group (Wasserman and Faust 1994) by examining important relationships reflected in the strength, direction, and complexity (or number) of ties embedded in a network. The strength of such an approach is that it enables an analysis of social phenomena beyond the abstract social structures traditionally studied by researchers in the social and behavioral sciences (Wellman 1999).

Depending on the goals and magnitude of the research project, social network analysis typically begins with the researcher identifying the appropriate study population and data collection methods. In social network analysis, data collection methods may include techniques that range from non-narrative survey instruments that ask informants exclusively about relationships to narrative-based interviews where relationship questions are embedded in the narrative interview (e.g., McKether 2005). Once collected, network data may be entered, stored, and manipulated through a variety of interactive software programs[3] designed specifically to examine and visualize individual or ego-centered networks (e.g., UCINET, EGONET) on the one hand or whole social networks on the other. The generated output provides visual and textual patterned network representation leading to new interpretations of qualitative data.

Ego-centered (or personal) networks make the individual the focus of attention where ego describes people (alters) close to him or her (Boissevain 1974; Wellman and Berkowitz 1988). According to Wellman (1999), such investigations: "Enable researchers to study community ties, whoever with, wherever located, and however structured . . . and avoid the trap of looking for community only in spatially defined ways" (19). Whole networks, which may include ego-centered networks, describe the structure of relationships of a population (Wellman 1999). In recent years, researchers across the social and behavioral sciences have used both personal networks (e.g., Bastani 2007; Granovetter 1973; Grossetti 2007; Lubbers et al. 2007), and whole networks (Stack 1974; Wellman and Berkowitz 1988) in empirical studies to describe social phenomena in a variety of contexts and cultural settings.

Social movement research focuses on social insurgency at the macro, meso, or micro levels of analysis. Although the various levels of social movement research are oftentimes examined separately and independently, they are interrelated and continuous (Staggenborg 2002), reflecting the researcher's interest in a particular unit of analysis. The macro level of social movement analysis examines large-scale demographic, ideological, social, economic, and political factors in an environment that predispose individuals and groups toward mobilization (Gerhards and Rucht 1992; Tilly 1978). A micro level of social movement analysis directs attention away from large scale features of society and focuses on individual motivation for participation in social movement activity. The meso or intermediate level of social movement analysis examines how individuals and groups mobilize for social insurgency and is viewed as the critical link that bridges the macro and micro levels. Social movement scholars McAdam et al. said:

> . . . we come away convinced that the real action in social movements takes place at some level intermediate between the macro and micro. It is there in the existing associational groups or networks of the aggrieved community that the first groping steps toward collective action are taken . . . it is this level that we know the least. [1988:729]

To provide a methodological process for examining the important role of the meso level of social movement mobilization, McAdam (1988) introduced the micro-mobilization context as the mechanism and process that links the meso level with the macro and micro levels of social insurgency. According to the concept, the meso level is the setting in which political (e.g., union) and non-political (e.g., church) groups as well as groups of informal networks amalgamate to mobilize others into collective action. Additionally, within the micro-mobilization context several processes important to mobilization occur, including frame alignment[4]; individuals make rational decisions about whether or not they will participate in the movement; and where resources, such as members, communication networks, and leaders are mobilized.

METHOD

The methodological approach I used in this study of African American social insurgency was based upon the application of traditional anthropological research methods of inductive, naturalistic inquiry. Data collection consisted primarily of ethnographic oral history interviewing combined with an examination of resources such as news articles, census data, photographs, church, and organizational records. In addition to these traditional qualitative research methods, I also used social network analysis to provide insights about the types and strength of ties movement participants had with one another and with others in the community.

STUDY POPULATION

The network data and maps generated for this article are drawn from a subset of 96 interviews used in a larger study of black migration (McKether 2005). The original study population was comprised of individuals who had migrated to Saginaw, MI as adults before 1967 or individuals who moved to Saginaw as children with their parents and came of age there before 1960. The subset for which this study is based is comprised of 27 men and women[5] who had direct or indirect ties with a social movement organization or with movement leaders. The interviews used in this study were selected specifically to illustrate the power of gathering information about social relationships and then using a structured process to convert oral history data into visual social network maps and data. In addition to the people interviewed for this study, the study population is also comprised of people interviewees said they had ties with during the time of the social movement.

DATA CONVERSION AND PROCESSING: CREATING SOCIAL NETWORK MAPS

Converting the interviews into social network data required the following five software programs: Microsoft Office Word, Excel 2003, Atlas.ti 5.0, SPSS Version 13, and MULTINET Version 4.44. The data conversion and processing involved five major steps: (1) transcribing and storing interviews, (2) data cleaning and preparation for importing into Atlas.ti, (3) importing and coding the interview-rich text files in Atlas.ti, (4) creating the Atlas.ti SPSS data extract, and (5) creating an Excel Multinet link file.

The conversion process required me to use the functional features of the multiple software programs. For example, I used the functionality of Microsoft Word to store and edit each of the interviews, and subsequently to save them as text documents. I used Microsoft Excel to create a simple Node file with a name and assigned ID. I then used Atlas.ti to code and create relationship links to export the data as an SPSS data file, and then exported the data from SPSS into an Excel Link file. Finally, I imported the Excel Node file and the Link file into Multinet for social network analysis. Although the data tables created in SPSS could have been exported to various networking software programs, I used Multinet because it was designed to manipulate nodes with multiple attributes, such as demographic data and links with multiple relations.

BACKGROUND INFORMATION: CASE STUDY

On July 27, 1967 a public display of discontentment erupted in Saginaw leaving United Power member Joe Cain and many others, including women and children, injured and traumatized. The riot/rebellion[6] occurred after a privately held meeting between leaders of United Power and Mayor Henry Marsh fell apart when Marsh said to members of United Power, "I wouldn't be here if I didn't want to listen to this garbage."[7] While the exact events leading up to the rebellion/riot are still debated 41 years later, there is agreement that the black protest led to positive social, economic, and political changes for African Americans in the growing black community.

THE POWERFUL BLACK MAYOR: HENRY G. MARSH

Attorney Henry G. Marsh migrated to Saginaw in 1954 after earning his law degree from Wayne State University and after practicing law in Detroit for several years. By the time of his arrival, as they had since at least the early 1940s, African Americans in the city were already engaged in individual and largely unorganized fights against their limited social, economic, and political opportunities. Although there had never been a publicly elected black leader in Saginaw, leadership within the African American community came primarily from labor leaders, business owners, and members of the black clergy.

Upon his arrival, Henry Marsh became active in several organizations, including the Saginaw Branch of the National Association for the Advancement of Colored People (NAACP) and the Frontiers Club of Saginaw, an African American men's service club that provided men in local communities throughout the United States a collective vehicle in which to improve their local communities. In the process of becoming acclimated to the city, Henry Marsh observed race-based discrimination and disparate treatment of African Americans. He observed, for example, that the vast majority of African Americans lived within a few wards on the city's east side, that almost all African American children attended the same East side school, that there were few African American teachers, and that few was mostly assigned to the same school in which African American children attended. Of the pre-existing conditions he found upon his arrival to Saginaw, Marsh said:

> There wasn't a single restaurant in Saginaw, white restaurant that blacks could go in, only one ... The Bancroft Hotel was a big hotel, but it did not accept Blacks in their restaurant, bar, or to live ... This would have been true for at least the first four or five years ... But there were no bars, none, that were integrated ... Housing was almost totally segregated, confined to what they call first ward. [Henry Marsh in discussion with the author, April 2002]

To address these and other issues, although he was a member of the NAACP and Frontiers group, Marsh personally organized a group he called the community council. Marsh recalled:

> I've always been mouthy, so I gradually got involved in community affairs. We organized a club called the Community Council ... it was a group of black activists, and we set about doing some things in the black community. Unlike now, we used our own money, and the news started getting around that we were doin' things ... I was sort of a rabble-rouser. We did a lot of things and we gained the respect of a good many people in the community. [Henry Marsh in discussion with the author, April 2002]

Based in large part on his activist work in the community and successful law practice with partner Carl Poston, in 1957 Henry Marsh was invited to join Saginaw's Junior Chamber of Commerce, which according to Marsh expanded his circle of friends. In 1959 Marsh was asked by fellow Junior Chamber member, then Saginaw Mayor James Harvey, if he would join the newly created Human Relations Commission. Marsh accepted and was elected chairman of the commission.

In late 1959 Henry Marsh decided to run for a position on the Saginaw city council. With endorsement of The Committee of 50, a group comprised mostly of white business owners and professionals, in the 1961 election Henry Marsh was elected to Saginaw city council, becoming the first elected African American official in the city's history. After his election to Saginaw city council Marsh continued his criticism of race relations in the city. He openly criticized white as well as African American residents. He continued his criticism of whites for their overt and covert race-based discrimination against African Americans, and he criticized African Americans

for not doing more to help themselves, and for, in general, blaming "the white man" for all of their problems.

During his term in office Henry Marsh was criticized by some segments of the African American community for being too closely aligned with powerful whites, for publicly criticizing African Americans, and for being too slow in responding to issues that directly affected the African American community. Despite such criticism, he continued to receive political support from African Americans in the city. For example, with help of black voters,[8] in 1965 Henry Marsh was re-elected to a second term on the Saginaw city council. In the second election, as in his first run, Henry Marsh received more votes than any other candidate, which contributed to his colleagues on city council electing him Mayor of the city. During his second term as a council member and first as Mayor, which coincided with the height of the civil rights movement taking place throughout the United States, Henry Marsh faced perhaps his biggest critics: a group of young impatient African Americans and sympathetic whites organized as the United Power.

THE EMERGENCE OF UNITED POWER

A year after Henry Marsh was unanimously selected by an all-white Saginaw city council to become the city's first African American Mayor, a group of African American and white residents started a reading and debating group where they discussed and focused on issues affecting the African American community. In 1966 as the group started to meet on a regular basis and became formalized, it incorporated under the name United Power. The United Power organization was led mostly by young adults whose parents had migrated to Saginaw between 1920 and 1940, and whose fathers worked for General Motors. One exception was then 48 years Jessie Daily. Other early leaders of United Power included Alfred Loveless and Omowale Art Smith.

The primary purpose of United Power was to seek positive changes in the African American community by uniting African Americans and giving them a collective voice. Omowale Smith said the specific purpose of United Power was, "To inform, involve and unite black people to act in their own self-interest, and to identify, articulate our collective self-interest and to act on it."[9] United Power's purpose and mission was further articulated and expanded in 1968 in a second year anniversary issue of the organization's newspaper, The Saginaw Afro Herald:

> Our main interest is black people—more specifically, grass-roots black people with no voice,

no freedom, no means, less money and very little hope. We shall give them a voice, teach them freedom, give them a means to obtain and use wisely that very powerful money, and we will keep alive their hope ... Our motto is simple; right down to earth, in language that everybody can easily understand. It is "To Inform, Involve, and Unite." [1968:4]

United Power became a vocal and public critic of Henry Marsh, accusing him of being too white and too slow in responding to the immediate and pressing needs of the African American community: better housing, more and better jobs, and an end to racial discrimination in public places. United Power's newspaper characterization of Marsh as an "Uncle Tom" who had sold out the African American community is an indication of how its members perceived the Mayor. Between 1966 and 1967 United Power grew stronger in both membership as well as its criticism of the city's first elected black mayor, ultimately erupting into a riot on July 27, 1967.

RESULTS
Network data generated through Negopy[10] show that the movement's mobilization structure at the meso level was comprised of two network structures or groups, and that bridge links existed between the two networks. Results also show that the two combative network structures exhibited different characteristics that, baring other explanations, helped contribute to the overall success of the black power movement. Differences between the two network structures include network type and maturity, node composition, tie structure, and network composition.

Figure 1 is a visual representation of the dual mobilization network that existed leading up to the 1967 riot. The network map shows that the two

network structures were comprised of the ego-centered Henry Marsh network and the whole United Power network. The longer dashed lines leading away from an individual indicate a tie (relationship) the person said they had with the person to whom the line extends. The shorter dashed lines leading to someone indicate that someone else in the network said they had a tie (relationship) with the person to whom the lines extend. A solid line extending between two people indicates a reciprocal relationship in that both people in the relationship mentioned each other in the interviews.

Based on information extracted from the interviews, Figure 1 reflects how people in the community mobilized in each of the groups.[11] Group One, the Marsh network, is comprised of people who said in their interviews that they had a friendship, economic, or political relationship with Henry Marsh.[12] Group Two, the United Power network, was comprised of a number of people who either said they were members of the grassroots organization or were identified by past leaders as being members of the organization.

THE MARSH NETWORK: GROUP ONE
Network data show that the Marsh network was comprised of at least 12 central nodes[13] with a standard deviation[14] of 0.238 (see Table 1).

The small standard deviation indicates that the Marsh network was comprised of a tightly connected group with everyone in the group having easy access to other group members. However, Henry Marsh's −2.61, Carl Poston's −1.08, and Harry Browne's −0.32 distance ratios indicate they were the most central people in the group and thus had easier access to other group members than members with lower distance ratio scores. Henry Marsh's larger distance ratio indicates that he was the most

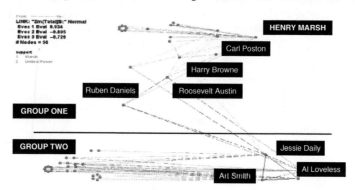

Figure 1. Marsh and United Power networks.
Note: **Network map generated using Multinet social network software program.**

Table 1. Marsh network.

Node	Network member	Distance ratio
5	Henry Marsh*	− 2.61
8	Carl Poston*	− 1.08
2	Harry Browne	− 0.32
1	Roosevelt Austin*	0.06
11	Ruben Daniels	0.83

*Person interviewed for study. Standard deviation: 0.238.

central person in his ego-centered network, and that most decisions made in the network were made by Marsh directly, or indirectly by someone who had strong ties with Marsh, such as Carl Poston or Harry Browne.

Network and interview data also show that the most central people in the Marsh network had multiple relationship ties with one another, and hence had multiplexed relationships that made group members either strong or weak tie members of the group. In general, the more ties group members have with one another the stronger the tie; members with fewer ties are considered to have weaker ties (Neogpy Manual 1995) (see Table 2).

The table shows that Carl Poston and Harry Browne had multiple personal, social, economic, and political links with Henry Marsh. This portion of Marsh's ego-centered network constituted the network's effective or strong tie segment (Granovetter 1973). Each of the men and their wives belonged to the Marsh Couple's Club, a social club comprised of other skilled professionals including teachers, physicians, and small business owners. In addition to the Marsh Couples Club, the men were all close personal friends, they supported one another's run for local government, they were all members of the local branch of the NAACP, they were all members of the local Frontiers International Association, and were all members of the Chamber of Commerce. Attorneys Henry Marsh and Carl Poston also shared a law practice together. Such a multiplexed relationship

meant that these leaders and central nodes not only spent considerable time together and shared a common social justice identity, but also, because of their overlapping membership in various groups and organizations, the network had increased visibility in the community. Although Roosevelt Austin and Ruben Daniels[15] were members of the Marsh network, and each of them powerful and influential men in the community, they had fewer ties to the Mayor and thus constituted the extended or weak tie segment of the network (Granovetter 1973).

The Marsh network was comprised of individuals that had ties to local organizations and churches, or in many cases, were leaders of the organizations and churches with whom they had ties. Such ties had the effect of extending Henry Marsh's power base and influence in the community. Figure 2 shows the composition of the Marsh network and how members of the Marsh network were connected to one another and to organizations.

The map reflects a Marsh network comprised of individuals who shared the Marsh social justice ideology, and thus a common identity. The map also indicates that members of the Marsh network were linked to organizations and churches that shared the network's social justice ideology, such as the NAACP, the Frontiers organization, the UAW, as well as several of the city's most powerful churches. The map provides a visual representation of Henry Marsh's far reaching influence throughout the community through group members who belonged to organizations and churches that Marsh himself did not have membership.

THE UNITED POWER NETWORK: GROUP TWO

Network data show that the United Power network was comprised of 22[16] central nodes with a standard deviation of 0.239 (see Table 3). The network's small standard deviation indicates that the group had little variability and was a tightly connected group of in-

Table 2. Marsh multiplex network.

Network member	Link/relationship types						
	Marsh Couples Club	Personal friends	Work colleagues	Political friends	Member NAACP	Member Frontiers	Chamber of Commerce
H. Marsh	X	X	X	X	X	X	X
C. Poston	X	X	X	X	X	X	X
H. Browne	X	X		X	X	X	X
R. Austin				X	X	X	
R. Daniels		X		X		X	

NAACP, National Association for the Advancement of Colored People.

LINK: "Total[B:Marsh Network<3]" Normal
Evec 1 Eval 0.915
Evec 2 Eval −0.776
Evec 3 Eval −0.706
Nodes = 42

Marsh Network
1   Individual
2   Organization

Figure 2. Marsh networkcComposition.
Note: **Network map generated using Multinet social network software program.**

dividuals, where in general, all group members had easy access to other group members. Data show that the United Power organization was the most central node with a distance ratio of − 3.28, and that the organization's President Al Loveless was the second most central node, followed by member and leader Jessie Daily's − 1.29, and Vice President Omowale Art Smith's − 0.89 distance ratios.

These data suggest that the social movement organization served as the foundation around which members clustered, and where the organization's social justice and anti-establishment identity permeated. However, although members clustered around the United Power organization and were tightly connected, further analysis shows members of the organization did not have significant social, economic, or political ties outside of the organization, making it a single-stranded network (see Table 4).

A listing of 11 of the 22 central nodes that comprised the United Power network and their ties reflect the organization's single-stranded tie composition. As a single-stranded network, the United Power organization was comprised primarily of individual members who had a tie to the organization and other members, but few or no ties to external organizations

or groups. However, several members of United Power interviewed for the study confided that several local black businesses and churches supported them financially but did not want the public to know of their support of the grass roots organization.

Figure 3 provides a visual representation of United Power's network composition and show that the network was comprised primarily of the organization, around which members clustered. The single-stranded United Power network suggests it was a weak tie network, in that, organizational members had few ties among themselves and even fewer with organizations and groups external to the network.

Consequently, as an inward-focused network the organization had to rely mostly on its membership for human and financial resources, and leadership. Additionally, because the organization lacked external ties with other local social justice

Table 3.   United Power network.

Node	Network member	Distance ratio
50	United Power	− 3.28
4	Al Loveless*	− 2.08
3	Jessie Daily*	− 1.29
7	Omowale Smith*	− 0.89

*Person interviewed for study. Standard deviation: 0.239.

Table 4.   United Power single-stranded network.

Network member	Link/relationship type	
	United Power	Personal friends
Al Loveless	X	X
Jessie Daily	X	X
Art Smith	X	X
L. Oats	X	X
C. Henderson	X	X
J. Cain	X	X
D. Beatty	X	X
C. Beatty	X	X
E. Beamon	X	X
D. Rowe	X	X
N. J. Brooks	X	X

Figure 3. United Power network composition.
Note: Network map generated using Multinet social
network software program.

organizations[17] such as the NAACP, the Frontiers,
and the UAW, it had to rely on its social injustice
framing of issues to appeal to segments of the community that both identified with its framing and were
marginalized due to their lower status in the community.

THE STRENGTH OF WEAK TIES: BRIDGE LINKS BETWEEN THE TWO NETWORKS[18]

Through liaisons and bridge links, network analysis
makes a distinction between node relationships that
connect two groups. Liaisons are nodes (people) that
do not belong to a particular group but have ties
with group members that belong to different groups.
Bridge links on the other hand are nodes (people)
who are members of one group but have a relationship or ties with a node or nodes from another
group, all the while maintaining allegiance with a
single group (Negopy Manual 1995).

Network and interview data show that bridge
links, comprised of weak tie members, connected the
Mayor's ego-centered network and United Power's
whole network. Table 5, the Negopy-generated
bridge link table, show that at least two members of
the Mayor's ego network, Roosevelt Austin and
Ruben Daniels, had ties or a relationship with Jessie
Daily and the United Power network. As members

Table 5. Bridge link table.*

From node	To node
Roosevelt Austin	United Power
Ruben Daniels	Jessie Daily
Ruben Daniels	United Power

*Actually Negopy generated two bridge link tables, one
for each group. The table shown is a combined table showing only bridge links that was common for both tables.

of the Mayor's weak tie network, both Austin and
Daniels served as bridge links between the two net-
works through their ties with Daily and United
Power.

Reverend Roosevelt Austin migrated to Saginaw in 1953, and in 1955 was appointed senior
pastor at Zion Baptist Church, one the city's largest
and oldest black Baptist churches. Ruben Daniels
was a life-long resident of the city and was one the
city's earliest black police officers. In 1965 Daniels
retired from the police department to become director of the First Ward Community Center, an urban-
based center that provided social activities for the
city's marginalized black youth. As director of the
center Ruben Daniels both supervised and became
personal friends with United Power member Jessie
Daily, who recalled Daniels with fond memories,
saying:

> Mr. Ruben Daniels was the best thing that ever
> happened to the First Ward Community Center
> . . . He was really sincere and he helped a whole
> lot of Black peoples get jobs that couldn't get
> jobs . . . everybody knew him, he was a good
> policeman, the white people said he was a like-
> able child, he was a likeable man. Everybody
> loved Ruben. [Jessie Daily in discussion with the
> author, September 2002]

In addition to being friends with Daily, Daniels
also became close friends with Henry Marsh, who
acknowledged, "I loved him like a brother . . . Ruben
got jobs for people" (Henry Marsh in discussion
with the author, April 2002). Although Daily and
Daniel's friendships had been established well before
the 1966/67 contentious period, his friendship with
Marsh and Daily played a significant linking role
during and before the July 27 riot/rebellion.

According to interviews with members from
both networks as well as news accounts, by late 1966
the relationship between Mayor Henry Marsh and
members of the United Power organization had deteriorated to a point where United Power was
showing public contempt for the Mayor, for example labeling Marsh an "Uncle Tom" in the
organization's newspaper. It was during this period
of mutual distrust and dislike that both Ruben
Daniels and Reverend Roosevelt Austin served as
critical bridge links between the two networks. Austin recalled the role that he and Daniels played:

> . . . there was Ruben Daniels and myself that
> were, what they called the Blacks that wanted to
> get things done . . . And of course Ruben and I
> were able to fit in both camps. We met with the

brothers who wanted to burn and talked 'em out of it. We met with the brothers who were mad, and we said, "If we use this energy together we can do much more." And Ruben and I were the guys, you know, that were able to do that. Because back then the Art Smiths and that group didn't see eye to eye with Marsh and his group. [Roosevelt Austin discussion with the author, August 2002]

Although Austin served as a bridge link, as he indicates in the above interview excerpt and as reflected in the Negopy bridge link data, according to Jessie Daily and Henry Marsh's interviews, Ruben Daniels likely served as the strongest weakest link between the two contentious networks.

In the months following the July 27 rebellion/ riot, Mayor Henry Marsh established a committee comprised of over two hundred members of the Saginaw community. The committee included residents from various socioeconomic backgrounds and gender, including members of United Power. The Committee of two hundred was assembled into subcommittees that focused on and made recommendations to the Mayor regarding ways to alleviate the city's deteriorating housing stock and shortage; employment; education; and public accommodations. The powerful employment subcommittee was chaired by Ruben Daniels.

Within two years of the committee's organization, the City of Saginaw received Federal grant money to establish a local Community Action Committee, a self-help, federally funded program designed to address problems in low income urban areas, such as unemployment, underemployment, and deteriorating housing conditions. Members of United Power demanded and were granted positions on governance boards that made key decisions about how the government funds were used and allocated in the black community.

In addition to the government grants that established self-help programs under the Marsh mayoral administration, Henry Marsh and Roosevelt Austin spearheaded a subcommittee that led to the establishment of a local Opportunities Industrialization Center, a center that provided job training and preparation for unskilled and underemployed residents; and, with full support of the United Power organization, Henry Marsh headed a campaign that led to the establishment of a multi-million dollar Career Opportunities Complex, a center that partnered with local businesses to provide hands-on and technical job training for high school students. In 1969 the City of Saginaw was awarded the All American City honor by the U.S. Department of Housing and Urban Development; a designation spearheaded by Marsh but protested by United Power.

Both former Mayor Henry Marsh and past leaders of United Power claim responsibility for the positive developments in Saginaw's African American community that occurred after the 1967 riot/ rebellion. Henry Marsh argues that the increase in black power occurred under his mayoral administration, and if not for his political and social connections, and hence network, the positive changes would not have occurred. Members of United Power alternatively argue that positive changes in the black community occurred as a direct result of their agitating and mobilizing people at the grassroots levels, and forcing members of "the establishment," including Mayor Henry Marsh, to take action to improve the social and economic conditions of people who could not speak for themselves.

DISCUSSION AND IMPLICATIONS

With an overall goal of showing how the anthropologist's methodological tool kit can be expanded by using network analysis, in this article I used features of network analysis to examine the dual mobilization network structure of a 1967 social movement. Through selected network data and simple network maps, I described and interpreted the data in a way unattainable through traditional anthropological methods. In the analysis, I showed not only that the movement was comprised of two competing groups, but also how the structure and function of the groups contributed to the overall success of the fight for black power.

In this article I also described how I converted ethnographic and qualitative data, particularly interview data, into social network data and maps. The interview method of data collection allowed data to be gathered from an insider's perspective and provided first-hand accounts about the social movement. The rich interview data allowed me to assess the social, economic, and political relations that produced the dual network structures.

Social network analysis enabled me to examine the people and organizations mentioned across each of the interviews. The analysis of social network data and maps facilitated my investigation of both the ego-centered networks embedded in each interview, as well as the whole social network that emerged in the analysis of all the interviews taken together. This multi-faceted approach was particularly useful because it provided not only an analysis of the specific links individuals had with one another, with places and with organizations, but also allowed for visualization, through the mapping function in Multinet, of the links and relationships across all of the interviews. Through such an analysis, I was able to uncover the effect of specific individuals on the social movement as well as on the interactions within each of the groups.

This ability to extract and examine ego and whole social networks embedded in interview data can be used by researchers across a wide range of disciplines and with a variety of purposes to supplement existing strategies and research methods. The network analysis methods are particularly useful for scholars who desire to explore specific kinds of links in and across interview datasets, no matter how the data are collected. While network analysis played an essential role in my anthropological study of a black social movement, the analysis processes described in this article can be replicated by researchers in other disciplines who want to combine the rich explanation of qualitative data with the analytical strength of quantitative analysis methods.

NOTES

1. For this study, black power refers to increased and equal access to skilled as well as unskilled jobs; equal access to good housing, public spaces, and political offices; and local black control of government funds.

2. The field site is located approximately one hundred miles north of Detroit, MI.

3. This is not intended to reflect the entire spectrum of social network programs, rather is intended to provide the reader with a sampling of programs used in analyzing social network data.

4. Frame alignment is the process where social insurgent members collectively articulate their grievances.

5. All interviewees signed a public disclosure form allowing their names and transcripts to be held in public domain. All interviews are part of a public library collection in Saginaw, MI.

6. Former Mayor Henry Marsh prefers to use riot while members of United Power prefer rebellion. This is an attempt to placate both sides.

7. Members of United Power and former Mayor Henry Marsh agree that either these exact words or something very close were said by the mayor.

8. Based on review of voting precinct and election results.

9. Omowale Art Smith in discussion with the author, December 2002.

10. Negopy is a network program designed to examine network structure among groups that comprise a dataset. A group is defined as a collection of individuals that have more interaction with members of their group than with non-members or members of other groups.

11. Specific names are highlighted to show particular kinds of relationships within and between the two network groups.

12. Because not all people mentioned in the interviews were interviewed, in some cases the author inferred a reciprocal relationship between the interviewee and the person they mentioned.

13. All network members are not shown here. As this is to only demonstrate the usefulness of network data, only nodes that influence an individual network and relations between the two networks in the dataset are used.

14. A group's standard deviation is a measure of variability within the group. An individual group member's distance ratio is a measure of the number of steps it takes for the group member to reach other members of the group; it is also a measure of how central the individual is to the group. Individuals that are most central within a group will have a higher distance ratio than other group members.

15. Ruben Daniels died in 1993 and was not interviewed for this project. All of his ties are based on information provided by people who were interviewed.

16. All members of each network are not shown here. As this is to only demonstrate the usefulness of network data, only nodes that influence an individual network and relations between the two networks in the dataset are used.

17. In their interviews, leaders of United Power said they sought financial support, leadership, and legal advice from groups and individuals outside of the Saginaw community, such as the Congress on Racial Equality, and attorneys from cities located up to one hundred miles from Saginaw.

18. This characterization of weak ties serving as bridge links in community organization reflects Granovetter's argument that in community organizing weak ties are more likely than strong ties to link members from different groups (see Granovetter's "The Strength of Weak Ties").

REFERENCES CITED
Barnes, John
1954 Class and Communities in a Norwegian Island Parish. Human Relations 7:39–58.

Bastani, Susan
  2007   Family Comes First: Men's and Women's Personal Networks in Tehran. Social Networks 29(3):357–374.
Boissevain, Jeremy
  1974   Friends of Friends: Networks, Manipulators and Coalitions. Oxford: Basil Blackwell.
Foster, Brian
  1979   Formal Studies and the Anthropological Perspective. Social Networks 1:241–255.
Gerhards, Jurgen, and Dieter Rucht
  1992   Mesomobilization: Organizing and Framing in Two Protest Campaigns in West Germany. American Journal of Sociology 3:555–595.
Granovetter, Mark
  1973   The Strength of Weak Ties. American Journal of Sociology 78:1360–1380.
Grossetti, Michel
  2007   Are French Workers Different? Social Networks 29(3):391–404.
Lubbers, Miranda, Jose Luis Molina, and Chris McCarty
  2007   A Typology of Personal Networks of Immigrants in Spain. Paper presented at the Meeting of the International Network of Social Network Analysis, Corfu, Greece, May 2.
McAdam, Doug
  1988   Micromobilization Contexts and Recruitment to Activism. In International Social Movement Research. Bert Klandermans, Hanspeter Kriesi and Sidney Tarrow, eds. Pp. 125–154. Connecticut: JAI Press.
McAdam, Doug, John McCarty, and Mayer Zald
  1988   Social Movements. In Handbook of Sociology. Neil J. Smelser, ed. Pp. 695–737. Newbury Part: Sage.

McKether, Willie
  2005   "Voices in Transition": African American migration to Saginaw, Michigan: 1920 to 1960. Ph.D. dissertation, Department of Anthropology, Wayne State University, Detroit.
Stack, Carol
  1974   All Our Kin. New York, NY: Basic Books.
Staggenborg, Suzanne
  2002   The Meso in Social Movement Research. In Social Movements: Identity, Culture and the State. David S. Meyer, Nancy Whittier and Belinda Robnett, eds. Pp. 124–139. Oxford: Oxford University Press.
Tilly, Charles
  1978   From Mobilization to Revolution. Reading: Addison-Wesley.
Wasserman, Stanley, and Katherine Faust
  1994   Social Network Analysis: Methods and Applications. Cambridge, UK: Cambridge University Press.
Wellman, Barry
  1999   Networks in the Global Village: Life in Contemporary Communities. Boulder, CO: Westview Press.
Wellman, Barry, and S. D. Berkowitz
  1988   Social Structures: A Network Approach. Cambridge, UK: Cambridge University Press.
White, Douglas R., and Ulla C. Johansen
  2005   Network Analysis and Ethnographic Problems. New York: Lexington Books.

The First Hominids and the Emergence of Homo

From Chapter 6 of *Human Evolution and Culture,* Seventh Edition. Carol R. Ember, Melvin Ember, Peter N. Peregrine. Copyright © 2012 by Pearson Education, Inc. All rights reserved.

The First Hominids and the Emergence of *Homo*

The First Hominids and the Emergence of *Homo*

((•—[Listen to the **Chapter Audio** on **myanthrolab.com**   [□•—[Read on **myanthrolab.com**

Bipedal locomotion is a defining feature of the hominids. Undisputed bipedal hominids lived in East Africa about 4 million years ago. These hominids, and some others who may have lived later in eastern and southern Africa, are generally classified in the genus *Australopithecus*. Here, we discuss what we know or suspect about the transition from hominoids to hominids, the emergence of australopithecines, and their relationship to later hominids, including ourselves. Then we turn to early hominid tools and lifestyles.

The Evolution of Bipedal Locomotion

Perhaps the most crucial change in early hominid evolution was the development of *bipedal locomotion*, or walking on two legs. We know from the fossil record that other important physical changes—including the expansion of the brain, modification of the female pelvis to allow bigger-brained babies to be born, and reduction of the face, teeth, and jaws—did not occur until about 2 million years after the emergence of bipedalism. Other human characteristics, such as an extended period of infant and child dependency and increased meat-eating, may also have developed after that time.

We do not know whether bipedalism developed quickly or gradually, because the fossil record for the period between 8 million and 4 million years ago is very skimpy. We do know, on the basis of their skeletal anatomy, that many of the Miocene anthropoids were capable of assuming an upright posture. For example, *brachiation,* swinging by the arms through the trees, puts an animal in an upright position; so does climbing up and down trees with the use of grasping hands and feet.[1] It is also likely that the protohominids were capable of occasional bipedalism, just as many modern monkeys and apes are.[2]

Definitely bipedal hominids emerged in Africa, judging by the available fossil record. The emergence of bipedal hominids coincides with a change about 16 million to 11 million years ago from extensive tropical forest cover to more discontinuous patches of forest and open country.[3] Gradually, the African rain forests, deprived of intense humidity and rainfall, dwindled in extent; areas of **savanna** (grasslands) and scattered deciduous woodlands became more common. The tree-dwelling primates did not completely lose their customary habitats because some tropical forests remained in wetter regions, and natural selection continued to favor the better-adapted tree dwellers in those forested areas. But the new, more open country probably favored characteristics adapted to ground living in some primates as well as other animals. In the evolutionary line leading to humans, these adaptations included bipedalism.

Theories for the Evolution of Bipedalism

What may have favored the emergence of bipedal hominids? One early idea is that bipedalism was adaptive for life amid the tall grasses of the savannas because an erect posture may have made it easier to spot ground predators as well as potential prey.[4] But baboons and some other Old World monkeys also live in savanna environments, yet, although they occasionally stand erect, they have not evolved fully bipedal locomotion. And recent evidence suggests that the area where early hominids lived in East Africa was not predominantly savanna; rather, it seems to have been a mix of woodland and open country.[5]

Other theories stress the importance of freeing the hands to perform other activities at the same time. Gordon Hewes emphasized the importance of carrying hunted or scavenged meat,[6] but many paleoanthropologists now question whether early hominids hunted or even scavenged.[7]

However, the ability to carry any food to a place safe from predators may have been one of the more important advantages of bipedalism. C. Owen Lovejoy has suggested that food carrying might have been important for another reason. If males provisioned females and their babies by carrying food back to a home base, the females would have been able to conserve energy by not traveling and therefore might have been able to produce and care for more babies.[8]

But carrying food or provisioning families might not have been the only benefit of freeing the hands; feeding itself may have been more efficient. Clifford Jolly has argued that bipedalism would have allowed early hominids to efficiently harvest small seeds and nuts because both hands could be used to pick up food and move it directly to the mouth.[9] In the changing environments of East Africa, where forests were giving way to more open woodlands and savannas, an advantage in foraging for small seeds and nuts might well have proven important for survival, and thus have been favored by natural selection.

Bipedalism might also have been favored by natural selection because the freeing of the hands would allow protohominids to use, and perhaps even make, tools that they could carry with them. Sherwood Washburn noted that some contemporary ground-living primates dig for roots to eat, "and if they could use a stone or a stick they might easily double their food supply."[10] David Pilbeam suggested that tool use by the more open-country primates may have appreciably increased the number and amount of plant foods they could eat: In order to be eaten, many of the plant foods in the grassy areas probably had to be chopped, crushed, or otherwise prepared with the aid of tools.[11] Tools may also have been used to kill and butcher animals for food. Without tools, primates in general are not well equipped physically for regular hunting or even scavenging.

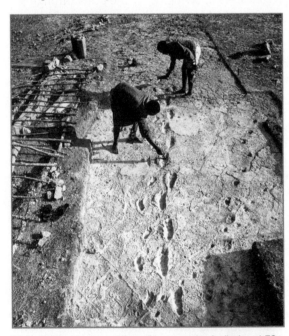

Mary Leakey's expedition discovered a trail about 70 yards long of 3.8-million-year-old fossilized footprints at Laetoli, Tanzania. Shown here is one part of the trail left by two adults who were clearly upright walkers. The footprints shows a well-developed arch and forward-facing big toe.

Their teeth and jaws are not sharp and strong enough, and their speed afoot is not fast enough. Finally, tools may have been used as weapons against predators, which would have been a great threat to the relatively defenseless ground-dwelling protohominids. In Milford Wolpoff's opinion, it was the advantage of carrying weapons *continuously* that was responsible for transforming occasional bipedalism to completely bipedal locomotion.[12] In particular, Sue Savage-Rumbaugh has suggested that the ability to abduct or snap the wrist would have permitted early humans "to perfect both throwing and rock-striking skills [for toolmaking] and consequently to develop throwing as a much more effective predator defense system than apes could ever manage."[13]

But some anthropologists question the idea that tool use and toolmaking favored bipedalism. They point out that the first clear evidence of stone tools appears more than 2 million years *after* the emergence of bipedalism. So how could toolmaking be responsible for bipedalism? Wolpoff suggests an answer. Even though bipedalism appears to be at least 2 million years older than stone tools, it is not unlikely that protohominids used tools made of wood and bone, neither of which would be as likely as stone to survive in the archaeological record. Moreover, unmodified stone tools present in the archaeological record might not be recognizable as tools.[14]

Some researchers have taken a closer look at the mechanics of bipedal locomotion to see if it might be a more efficient form of locomotion in the savanna-woodland environment, where resources are likely to be scattered. Compared with the quadrupedal locomotion of primates such as chimpanzees, bipedalism appears to be more efficient for long distances.[15] But why travel long distances? If the ancestors of humans had the manipulative ability and tool-using capability of modern chimpanzees (e.g., using stones to crack nuts), and those ancestors had to move around in a more open environment, then those individuals who could efficiently travel longer distances to exploit those resources might do better.[16]

Finally, bipedalism might have been favored by natural selection as a way of regulating body temperature, particularly in the increasingly hot and dry environments of East Africa at the end of the Miocene and the beginning of the Pliocene. Peter Wheeler has argued that a bipedal posture limits the area of the body directly exposed to the sun, especially when the sun is at its hottest, at midday.[17] Bipedal posture would also facilitate convective heat loss by allowing heat to rise up and away from the body rather than being trapped underneath it. Cooling through the evaporation of sweat would also be facilitated by a bipedal posture, as more skin area would be exposed to cooling winds. Thus, natural selection may have favored bipedalism because it reduced heat stress in the warming environments of East Africa.

All theories about the origin of bipedalism are speculative. We do not yet have direct evidence that any of the factors we have discussed were actually responsible for bipedalism. Any or all of the factors may explain the transformation of an occasionally bipedal protohominid to a completely bipedal hominid.

The "Costs" of Bipedalism

We must remember that there are also "costs" to bipedal walking. Bipedalism makes it harder to overcome gravity to supply the brain with sufficient blood,[18] and the weight of the body above the pelvis and lower limbs puts greater stress on the hips, lower back, knees, and feet. As Adrienne Zihlman points out, the stresses on the lower body are even greater for pregnant and nursing females who carry their infants.[19]

We must also remember that the evolution of bipedalism required some dramatic changes in the ancestral ape skeleton. Although apes today can and do walk bipedally, they cannot do so efficiently or for long periods of time. To be habitually bipedal, the ancestral ape skeleton had to be modified, and the major changes that allowed the early hominids to become fully bipedal occurred primarily in the skull, pelvis, knees, and feet.[20] Let's take a look at each of these changes.

In both ancient and modern apes, the spinal column enters the skull toward the back, which makes sense because apes generally walk on all fours, with the spine roughly parallel to the ground. In bipedal hominids, the spinal column enters the skull at the bottom, through a hole called the **foramen magnum**. Thus, when hominids became bipedal, the skull ended up on top of the spinal column.

The shape of ancient and modern ape pelvises is considerably different from that of a bipedal hominid. Ape pelvises are long and flat, forming a bony plate in the lower back to which the leg muscles attach. In bipedal hominids, the pelvis is bowl-shaped, which supports the internal organs and also lowers the body's center of gravity, allowing better balance on the legs. The hominid pelvis also provides a different set of muscle attachments and shifts the orientation of the femurs (the upper leg bones) from the side of the pelvis to the front. These changes allow hominids to move their legs forward in a bipedal stride (and do things like kick a soccer ball). Apes, in comparison, move their legs forward (when they walk bipedally) by shifting their pelvis from side to side, not by kicking each leg forward alternately as we do.[21]

Another change associated with the hominid ability to kick the leg forward is our "knock-kneed" posture. Ape legs hang straight down from the pelvis. Bipedal hominid legs, on the other hand, angle inward toward one another. This configuration not only helps us move our legs forward but also helps us maintain a center of gravity in the midline of our bodies, so that our center of gravity does not shift from side to side when we walk or run.

Finally, the feet of bipedal hominids have two major changes compared to those of apes. First, hominid feet have an enlarged group of ankle bones forming a robust heel that can withstand the substantial forces placed on them as a result of habitual bipedalism. Second, hominid feet have an arch, which also aids in absorbing the forces endured by the feet during bipedal locomotion. ("Flat-footed" people who lack it have chronic problems in their feet, ankles, knees, and back).[22]

We don't know for sure when these changes took place, but fossils from East Africa—Ethiopia, Tanzania, and Kenya—clearly show that bipedal hominids lived there between 4 million and 5 million years ago.

The Transition from Hominoids to Hominids

Western Chad, in north-central Africa, and its windswept deserts do not seem a likely place to find fossil apes or hominids, but paleoanthropologist Michel Brunet thinks it might be.[23] Western Chad was covered by an ancient lake, and for several million years was a location where forest-dwelling mammals, including primates, congregated. Around 7 million years ago, a primate called **Sahelanthropus tchadensis** lived on the shores of the lake, where Brunet and his colleagues recovered its fossilized bones in 2001. *Sahelanthropus,* represented by an almost complete skull, has a unique mix of hominid and hominoid traits. Although the skull itself is hominoid, with a small brain, large brow ridges, and wide face, the teeth seem more hominidlike, especially the canines, which do not project below the tooth row.[24] Unfortunately, there is no evidence that *Sahelanthropus* was bipedal. For now, we have to wait for additional evidence to know whether *Sahelanthropus* was the first bipedal ape.

There is, however, tantalizing evidence that another possible early hominid, **Orrorin tugenensis,** was bipedal. Discovered in western Kenya by Brigitte Senut and colleagues in 1998, *Orrorin tugenensis* consists of 19 specimens of jaw, teeth, finger, arm, and leg bones, including the top of a femur.[25] The femur in *Orrorin,* according to Brian Richmond and William Jungers, shows adaptations to bipedalism, including a long, angled "head" (or top).[26] *Orrorin* dates between 5.8 and 6 million years, so it may turn out to be the earliest hominid if further research supports *Orrorin* bipedalism.

In 1992, a team of researchers led by anthropologist Tim White began surveying a

Reconstructed skull of *Sahelanthropus tchadensis,* possibly the earliest hominid, dating to almost 7 million years ago.

4.4-million-year-old fossil deposit at Aramis, in the Middle Awash region of Ethiopia. There, they discovered 17 fossils of what may be the earliest hominid (more have been found since, including some fragments dating perhaps as early as 5.8 million years ago): *Ardipithecus ramidus.*[27]

What makes **Ardipithecus ramidus** unique is the combination of apelike dentition along with evidence of bipedal locomotion and an overall hominidlike skeleton. Like apes, *Ardipithecus* has relatively small cheek teeth with thin enamel and relatively large canines. However, its arm bones seem hominidlike, and the base of its skull shows the foramen magnum positioned underneath the skull, just as in definitely bipedal hominids.[28] The feet of *Ardipithecus* also seem adapted to bipedalism.[29] Although more evidence is needed to be sure, *Ardipithecus* may be the earliest hominid yet found.

Australopithecus: The First Definite Hominid

Although some doubt remains about the status of *Ardipithecus* as a hominid genus, there is no doubt that the australopithecines (members of the genus **Australopithecus**) dating from about 4 million years ago in eastern Africa were hominids. Their teeth share the basic hominid characteristics of small canines, flat and thickly enameled molars, and a parabolic dental arch, and there is unambiguous evidence that even the earliest australopithecines were fully bipedal. Not only do their skeletons reflect bipedal locomotion, but at Laetoli, Tanzania, more than 50 hardened humanlike footprints about 3.6 million years old give striking confirmation that the hominids there were fully bipedal. However, all of the australopithecines, including the later ones, seem also to have been capable of climbing and moving in trees, judging by arm versus leg length and other skeletal features.[30]

Most scholars divide the various australopithecine species into two groups, the "gracile" australopithecines and the "robust" australopithecines.[31]

Gracile Australopithecines

The **gracile australopithecines** include *A. anamensis, A. afarensis,* and *A. africanus.* All of them have smaller dentition and lighter facial and dental musculature than the robust australopithecines.

Australopithecus anamensis The earliest australopithecine species, dating between 3.9 million and 4.2 million years ago, is **Australopithecus anamensis,** found in several locations in northern Kenya.[32] It was a small bipedal hominid with teeth similar to those of the later *A. afarensis.*[33] The more controversial specimens have long bones, suggesting well-developed bipedalism, but their elbow and knee joints look more like those of the later *Homo* genus than like those of any other species of *Australopithecus.* It has been said that *A. anamensis* is "*afarensis*-like from the neck up and *Homo*-like from the neck down."[34]

Australopithecus afarensis *Australopithecus afarensis* dates from about 4 to 3 million years ago. Remains from at least two dozen individuals were unearthed at Laetoli, Tanzania.[35] There is no question that the Laetoli hominids were bipedal, because the now-famous trail of footprints was found at the Laetoli site. Two hominids walking erect and side by side left their tracks in the ground 3.6 million years ago. The remains of at least 35 individuals have been found at another site, Hadar, in Ethiopia. The Hadar finds are remarkable for their completeness. Whereas paleoanthropologists often find just parts of the cranium and jaws, many parts of the skeleton were also found at Hadar. For example, paleoanthropologist Donald Johanson found 40 percent of the skeleton of a female hominid he named Lucy, after the Beatles' song "Lucy in the Sky with Diamonds."[36]

A reconstruction of a female *Australopithecus afarensis* skeleton. Note how long the arms are relative to the legs, and the long fingers. Both suggest *A. afarensis* was at least partially arboreal.

Dating of the hominid remains at Laetoli suggests that the hominids there lived between 3.8 million and 3.6 million years ago.[37] Recent dating of the Hadar remains suggests that they are somewhat younger—less than 3.2 million years old. Lucy probably lived 2.9 million years ago.[38] The environment Lucy lived in was semiarid, upland savanna with rainy and dry seasons.[39]

A. afarensis was a small hominid, but, like most of the living great apes, was sexually dimorphic. Females weighed perhaps 65 pounds and stood a little more than 3 feet tall; males weighed more than 90 pounds and stood about 5 feet tall.[40] *A. afarensis* teeth were large compared to their body size, and they had thick molar enamel. They also had large, apelike canines, which, on some specimens, projected beyond the adjacent teeth. However, even the longer canines did not rub against the lower teeth or fit into a diastema (a space between the teeth), and thus did not prevent side-to-side movement of the lower jaw.[41] This is important, because side-to-side movement of the lower jaw allowed *A. afarensis* to efficiently chew small seeds and nuts. The thick enamel on the molars and wear patterns on the molar crowns suggest that such small, hard materials made up a significant part of the diet of *A. afarensis*.[42] The cranium of *A. afarensis* reflects its dentition. The face juts forward because of the large teeth and jaws, and the base of the skull flares out to provide attachment areas for large neck muscles to support the heavy face. The brain is small, about 400 cubic centimeters (cc), but relatively large for an animal this size.[43]

The arms and legs of *A. afarensis* were about the same length, and the fingers and toe bones are curved, suggesting they were heavily muscled. Most scholars believe these limb proportions and strong hands and feet point to spending a lot of time in the trees, probably feeding, sleeping, and avoiding terrestrial predators.[44] The pelvis and leg bones of *A. afarensis*, however, demonstrate that it moved bipedally when on the ground. The pelvis is wide and flaring, but has the bowl-like shape of all later hominids. The legs angle inward, and the feet have an arch and an ankle much like later hominids.[45] Detailed analyses of the Laetoli footprints suggest that *A. afarensis* may have had a shorter and less efficient stride than modern humans.[46]

Although *A. afarensis* is the most well-represented australopithecine species, it was not the first one discovered. That distinction rests with *Australopithecus africanus.*

Australopithecus africanus In 1925, Raymond Dart, professor of anatomy at the University of Witwatersrand in Johannesburg, South Africa, presented the first evidence that an erect bipedal hominid existed in the Pliocene epoch—the skull of an infant bipedal hominid, which has come to be known as the Taung Child. Since the Taung child's discovery 80 years ago, the remains of hundreds of other similar australopithecines have been unearthed from caves at Sterkfontein and Makapansgat in South Africa. Dating of the australopithecine finds from the South African limestone caves is difficult because absolute dating techniques cannot be applied. Relative dating suggests that the South African **Australopithecus africanus** lived between 3 million and 2 million years ago. The climate was probably semiarid, not too different from the climate of today.[47] *A. africanus* had a rounded braincase, a fairly well-developed forehead, moderate brow ridges, and a projecting face.[48] The estimated cranial capacity for the various finds from Taung and Sterkfontein is between 428 and 485 cc.[49]

Like *A. afarensis, A. africanus* was very small; the adults were 3½–4½ feet tall, weighed 60–90 pounds, and were sexually dimorphic.[50] The large, chinless jaw of *A. africanus* resembles that of *A. afarensis,* but some of the dental features of *A. africanus* are similar to those of modern humans—broad incisors and small, short canines. And, although the premolars and molars were larger than in modern humans, their form was very similar. Presumably, function and use were also similar.

Fossil skull of an *Australopithecus africanus* (STS 5) nicknamed "Mrs. Ples" found by Robert Broom at Sterkfontein cave in 1947.

Other Gracile Australopithecines New fossils from eastern Africa found in the last two decades suggest some other species of gracile australopithecine. Two groups of fossils are considered by most scholars to represent new australopithecine species, named ***Australopithecus bahrelghazali*** and ***Australopithecus garhi.*** *A. bahrelghazali* is currently represented by a single, fragmentary jaw, and only a handful of skull and limb fragments represent *A. garhi.*

Australopithecus garhi, found in rock dating to approximately 2.5 million years ago, is particularly interesting. *A. garhi* has larger molars than *A. afarensis,* yet does not have the huge face and jaws of the robust australopithecines. It also lacks the enlarged brain of early *Homo.* Several limb bones were found in the same rock layers, and these do resemble *A. afarensis. A. garhi,* then, looks like *afarensis* but with greatly enlarged molars.[51] It may represent one end of the range of variation in *afarensis,* or it may represent an adaptation to eating tough foods, similar to that made by the robust australopithecines, discussed shortly.

It is interesting that the remains of butchered animals were found in the same rock layer as the *A. garhi* remains. Several bones found near the *A. garhi* fossils show unambiguous cut marks and signs of having been broken with a stone tool. Unfortunately, no stone tools have been found, but the evidence for butchery suggests they must have been used. And since no other species of hominid have been found in the area, it is reasonable to think that *A. garhi* was the toolmaker and butcher. The fossil's discoverer, Berhane Asfaw, suggests that *A. garhi* is in the right place, at the right time, and has the right physical and behavioral traits to be the direct ancestor of early *Homo.*[52]

Equally intriguing is *Australopithecus bahrelghazali,* not so much because of its physical features, but because it was found further west, in what is now central Chad. Most scholars assume the early hominids represent a specific adaptation to the Rift Valley (a long valley in East Africa where the earth is pulling apart, exposing fossils from millions of years ago). The discovery of an early australopithecine some 2,500 kilometers (1,550 or so miles) west of the Rift Valley calls this assumption into question.[53] *A. bahrelghazali* dates to about 3 million years ago, and is very similar to contemporary *A. afarensis* fossils from the Rift Valley. It differs from *A. afarensis* in some distinct ways (its premolars, for example, have thinner enamel and more well-defined roots).

A related hominid genus, ***Kenyanthropus platyops,*** is thought by some scholars to be yet another australopithecine (and hence should not be regarded as a separate genus). The nearly

Fossil skull of *Australopithecus boisei* found by Louis and Mary Leakey in 1959. Note its huge face and teeth and its sagittal crest.

complete 3.5-million-year-old skull of *Kenyanthropus platyops* from western Kenya shows traits that Meave Leakey and her colleagues suggest separate it from the australopithecines that lived at the same time. Its face is smaller and flatter, and its molars are smaller than those of the australopithecines. Leakey believes *Kenyanthropus* may be a direct link to *Homo,* but others are not so sure. The skull is distorted, and scholars are not convinced that its features lie outside the range of the australopithecines.[54]

Robust Australopithecines

The **robust australopithecines** lived in eastern Africa and in southern Africa from about 2.7 million to 1 million years ago, and are quite distinct from the gracile australopithecines. Indeed, some paleoanthropologists think these fossils are so different that they deserve to be classified in a different genus, which they call *Paranthropus,* literally, "beside humans." The three main robust australopithecines, from oldest to youngest, are: *Australopithecus aethiopicus, Australopithecus robustus,* and *Australopithecus boisei.*

In contrast to the gracile australopithecines, the robust australopithecines had thicker jaws, with larger molars and premolars but smaller incisors, more massive muscle attachments for chewing, and well-developed sagittal crests and ridges to support heavy chewing.[55] In addition, *A. robustus* and *A. boisei* have somewhat larger cranial capacities (about 490–530 cc) than the gracile species.

It used to be thought that the robust australopithecines were substantially bigger than the other australopithecines, but recent calculations suggest that these australopithecines were not substantially different in body weight or height. The robustness is primarily in the skull and jaw, most strikingly in the teeth. The body of the robust forms is similar to that of *A. africanus,* so the brain of the robust australopithecines was relatively larger than the brain of *A. africanus.*[56]

Australopithecus aethiopicus *Australopithecus aethiopicus* is the earliest and least known of the robust australopithecines. *A. aethiopicus* fossils were found in northern Kenya and southern Ethiopia and date between 2.3 million and 2.7 million years ago. *A. aethiopicus* differed from *A. afarensis* specimens from roughly the same region and perhaps even the same time period by having much larger dentition, particularly molars; huge cheekbones; projecting and dish-shaped (round and flat) faces; and large sagittal crests. But they are similar to *A. afarensis* in most other ways. Overall, *A. aethiopicus* resembles *A. afarensis,* but with a massively "scaled-up" dental apparatus.[57]

Australopithecus robustus In 1936, Robert Broom, then curator of vertebrate paleontology at the Transvaal Museum in South Africa, began seeking fossils for the museum, particularly hominids that might support Raymond Dart's earlier discovery of the Taung Child. In 1938, a quarry manager gave Broom a hominid jaw that had been found in a nearby cave called Kromdraai. Broom immediately began excavating in the cave, and within days was able to piece together the skull of what would prove to be a new australopithecine species—***Australopithecus robustus.***[58]

Although Broom had expected another example of *A. africanus,* this one was different. It had larger teeth, a massive jaw, and a flatter face than *A. africanus.*[59] Because of these differences,

Broom and many scholars today believe the robust australopithecines are unique enough to warrant classification in a separate *Paranthropus* genus.

How did two strikingly different hominid species evolve in the same environment? In 1954, John T. Robinson proposed that *A. africanus* and *A. robustus* had different dietary adaptations— *A. africanus* being an omnivore (dependent on meat and plants) and *A. robustus* a vegetarian, with a need for heavy chewing. Robinson's view was hotly debated for many years. Evidence from electron microscopy supports Robinson's view that *A. robustus* ate mostly small, hard objects such as seeds, nuts, and tubers. But how different was *A. africanus* in this respect? Recent analyses suggest that *A. africanus* also practiced fairly heavy chewing.[60]

The idea that *A. robustus* was just a vegetarian is also questioned by a relatively new chemical technique that analyzes strontium–calcium ratios in teeth and bones to estimate the proportion of plant versus animal food in the diet. This new kind of analysis suggests that *A. robustus* was an omnivore.[61] Thus *A. robustus* may have needed large teeth and jaws to chew seeds, nuts, and tubers, but that doesn't mean that it didn't eat other things too. Most paleoanthropologists think that *A. robustus* died out shortly after 1 million years ago[62] and is not ancestral to our own genus, *Homo*.[63]

Australopithecus boisei Legendary paleoanthropologist Louis Leakey began his search for a human ancestor in 1931, at Olduvai Gorge in western Tanzania. It was not until 1959 that his efforts paid off with the discovery of *A. boisei* (named after a benefactor, Charles Boise). **Australopithecus boisei** lived between about 2.3 million and 1.3 million years ago.[64] Like *A. robustus,* it seems to have lived in a dry, open environment and ate a lot of coarse seeds, nuts, and roots. And, like *A. robustus,* most paleoanthropologists think *A. boisei* is not ancestral to our genus, *Homo*.[65] What did *A. boisei* look like? Compared with *A. robustus, A. boisei* had even more extreme features that reflected a huge chewing apparatus—enormous molar teeth and expanded premolars that look like molars; a massive, thick and deep jaw; thick cheekbones; and a more pronounced sagittal crest.[66] Indeed, *A. boisei* has been called a "hyper-robust" australopithecine—a name that definitely captures the species.

The picture that emerges from this brief overview of the australopithecines is one of diversity. There seem to have been many different species of australopithecine, and even within species there seems to be a relatively high level of variation.[67] All shared similar environments in eastern and southern Africa, but those environments were diverse and changing. Forests were giving way to open woodlands and grasslands. Large lakes were formed and then broken apart through uplifting and volcanic activity in the Rift Valley of eastern Africa. And the climate continued to warm until the end of the **Pliocene,** some 1.6 million years ago.

At this point, you may well be wondering how all these species fit together. Figure 1 shows one model about how the known fossils may be related. The main disagreement among paleontologists concerns which species of *Australopithecus* were ancestral to the line leading to modern humans. For example, the model shown in Figure 1 suggests that *A. africanus* is not ancestral to *Homo,* only to one line of robust australopithecines. *Australopithecus afarensis* is viewed as ancestral to both lines of robust australopithecines and to the line leading to modern humans. Those who think that *A. afarensis* was the last common ancestor of all the hominid lines shown in Figure 1 think the split to *Homo* occurred over 3 million years ago.[68]

Despite the uncertainty and disagreements about what species was ancestral to the *Homo* line, paleoanthropologists widely agree about other aspects of early hominid evolution: (1) There were at least two separate hominid lines between 3 million and 1 million years ago; (2) the robust australopithecines were not ancestral to modern humans but became extinct about 1 million

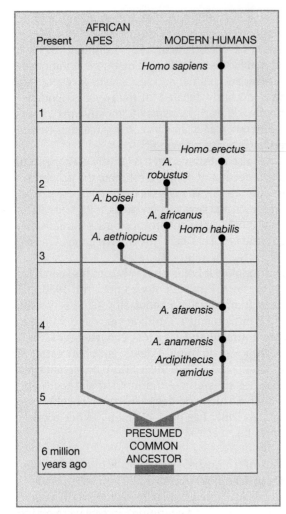

Figure 1 Phylogenetic Time Lines

Source: Adapted from *The New York Times*, September 5, 1995, p. C9. Dates changed slightly to reflect recent redating.

years ago; and (3) *Homo habilis* (and successive *Homo* species) were in the direct ancestral line to modern humans. Now we turn to our direct ancestors, the first members of the *Homo* genus.

Early *Homo* Species

Early hominids classified in our own genus, *Homo,* are generally divided into two species: **Homo habilis** and **Homo rudolfensis.** Both are known primarily from the western parts of Kenya and Tanzania, but remains have been found elsewhere in eastern and southern Africa, including the Omo Basin of Ethiopia and Sterkfontein cave in South Africa. Both lived in the same place and time as the robust australopithecine, *Australopithecus boisei,* and may later have lived at the same time as *Homo erectus.*

Homo habilis appears to be the earlier of these two species, appearing around 2.3 million years ago. Compared with the australopithecines, *H. habilis* had a significantly larger brain, averaging 630–640 cc,[69] and reduced molars and premolars.[70] The rest of the skeleton is reminiscent of the australopithecines, including the presence of powerful hands and relatively long arms, suggesting that *H. habilis* was at least partially arboreal. *H. habilis* may also have been sexually dimorphic like the australopithecines, as individuals seem to have greatly differed in size.

Homo rudolfensis is roughly contemporary with *Homo habilis,* and shares many of its features. Indeed, many paleoanthropologists make no distinction between the two species, putting *H. rudolfensis* into *H. habilis.* Those who do see them as distinct species point to the larger and more thickly enameled cheek teeth of *H. rudolfensis,* its flatter and broader face, and its more modernlike limb proportions. Even with its larger teeth and broader face, the dentition of *H. rudolfensis* is considerably reduced over the australopithecines and, as in *H. habilis,* its brain is at least a third larger. We have little postcranial skeletal material for either early *Homo* species, so it is impossible to tell whether the female pelvis had changed. However, with brains averaging a third larger than that of the australopithecines, it seems likely that some modifications must have developed to allow bigger-brained babies to be born.

The expansion of the brain is only one of a number of trends in hominid evolution. Another is the routine use of patterned or nearly standardized stone tools, which is considered one sign of the emergence of culture. It is assumed, but not known for sure, that patterned stone tools were made by the first members of our own genus, *Homo,* for we first see a number of trends in the genus *Homo* that probably started because of habitual stone toolmaking and use—expansion of the brain, modification of the female pelvis to accommodate bigger-brained babies, and reduction in the teeth, face, and jaws.

Even though stone tools are found at various sites in East Africa before the time early *Homo* appeared, most anthropologists surmise that members of early *Homo* species, rather than the australopithecines, made those tools. But the fact is that none of the earliest stone tools is clearly associated with early *Homo,* so it is impossible as yet to know who made them.[71]

The earliest identifiable stone tools found so far come from various sites in East Africa and date from about 2.5 million years ago,[72] and maybe earlier. They range from very small flakes (thumb-size) to cobble or core tools that are fist-size.[73] These early tools were apparently made by striking a stone with another stone, a technique called **percussion flaking.** Both the sharp-edged flakes and the sharp-edged cores (the pieces of stone left after flakes are removed) were probably used as tools. Unfortunately, little can be inferred about lifestyles from the earliest tool sites because little else was found with the tools. In contrast, finds of later tool assemblages at Olduvai Gorge in Tanzania have yielded a rich harvest of cultural information. Of the Olduvai site, Louis Leakey wrote,

> [It] is a fossil hunter's dream, for it shears 300 feet through stratum after stratum of earth's history as through a gigantic layer cake. Here, within reach, lie countless fossils and artifacts which but for the faulting and erosion would have remained sealed under thick layers of consolidated rock.[74]

The oldest cultural materials from Olduvai (Bed I) date from Lower Pleistocene times (about 1.6 million years ago). The stone artifacts include core tools and sharp-edged flakes. Flake tools predominate. Among the core tools, so-called choppers are common. Choppers are cores that have been partially flaked and have a side that might have been used for chopping. Other core tools, with flaking along one side and a flat edge, are called scrapers. Whenever a stone has facets removed from only one side of the cutting edge, we call it a **unifacial tool.** If the stone has facets removed from both sides, we call it a **bifacial tool.** Although there are some bifacial tools in the early stone tool assemblages, they are not as plentiful or as elaborated as in later tool traditions. The kind of tool assemblage found in Bed I and to some extent in later (higher) layers is referred to as **Oldowan** (see Figure 2).[75]

Archaeologists have experimented with what can be done with Oldowan tools. The flakes appear to be very versatile; they can be used for slitting the hides of animals, dismembering animals, and whittling wood into sharp-pointed sticks (wooden spears or digging sticks). The larger stone tools (choppers and scrapers) can be used to hack off branches or cut and chop tough animal joints.[76] Those who have made and tried to use stone tools for various purposes are so impressed by the sharpness and versatility of flakes that they wonder whether most of the core tools were really used as tools. The cores could mainly be what remained after wanted flakes were struck off.[77] Archaeologists surmise that many early tools were also made of wood and bone, but these do not survive in the archaeological record. Present-day populations use sharp-pointed digging sticks for extracting roots and tubers from the ground; stone flakes are very effective for sharpening wood to a very fine point.[78] None of the early flaked stone tools can plausibly be thought of as weapons. So, if the toolmaking hominids were hunting or defending themselves with weapons, they had to have used wooden spears, clubs, or unmodified stones as missiles. Later, Oldowan tool assemblages also include stones that were flaked and battered into

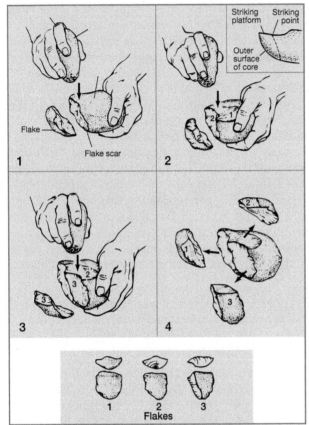

Figure 2 **The Production of a Simple Oldowan Chopper Core and the Resultant Flakes**

Source: Freyman 1987. Reprinted by permission of the artist, Ed Hanson.

a rounded shape. The unmodified stones and the shaped stones might have been lethal projectiles.[79]

Experiments may indicate what can be done with tools, but they cannot tell us what was *actually* done with them. Other techniques, such as microscopic analysis of the wear on tools, are more informative. Lawrence Keeley used high-powered microscopes in his experimental investigations of tools and found that different kinds of "polish" develop on tools when they are used on different materials. The polish on tools used for cutting meat is different from the polish on tools used for woodworking. On the basis of microscopic investigation of the 1.5-million-year-old tools from the eastern side of Lake Turkana, Keeley and his colleagues concluded that at least some of the early tools were probably used for cutting meat, others for cutting or whittling wood, and still others for cutting plant stems.[80]

For many years, it seemed plausible to assume that hominids were the hunters and the animals their prey. However, archaeologists had to reexamine this assumption with the emergence of the field of *taphonomy,* which studies the processes that can alter and distort an assemblage of bones. So, for example, flowing water can bring bones and artifacts together, which may have happened at Olduvai Gorge about 1.8 million years ago. (The area of what is now the gorge bordered the shores of a shallow lake at that time.) Other animals such as hyenas could have also brought carcasses to some of the same places that hominids spent time.[81]

But there is little doubt that hominids were cutting up animal carcasses for meat shortly after 2 million years ago. Pat Shipman suggested that scavenging, not hunting, was the major meat-getting activity of the hominids living there between 2 million and 1.7 million years ago. For example, the cut marks made by the stone tools usually (but not always) overlie teeth marks made by carnivores. This suggests that the hominids were often scavenging the meat of animals killed and partially eaten by nonhominid predators. The fact that the cut marks were sometimes made first, however, suggested to Shipman that the hominids were also sometimes the hunters.[82] There is also no consensus about how to characterize the Olduvai sites that contain concentrations of stone tools and animal bones. In the 1970s, there was a tendency to think of them as home bases to which hominids (presumably male) brought meat to share with others (presumably nursing mothers and young children). Indeed, Mary Leakey identified two locations where she thought early hominids had built simple structures. One was a stone circle that she suggested formed the base of a small brush windbreak. The other was a circular area of dense debris surrounded by an area virtually without debris. Leakey suggested that the area lacking debris may represent the location of a ring of thorny brush with which early hominids surrounded their campsite in order to keep out predators—much like pastoralists living in the region do today.[83] But archaeologists today are not so sure that these sites were home bases. For one thing,

A replica of an Oldowan stone tool is used to chop into a large bone to extract the nutrient-rich marrow. Few animals have jaws powerful enough to break open the bones of large mammals, but stone tools would have allowed early humans to do so.

carnivores also frequented the sites. Places with meaty bones lying around may not have been so safe for hominids to use as home bases. Second, the animal remains at the sites had not been completely dismembered and butchered. If the sites had been hominid home bases, we would expect more complete processing of carcasses.[84] Third, natural processes as simple as trees growing through a site can create circular areas of debris such as the ones Leakey identified as structures, and without better evidence that early hominids made them, one cannot be sure that the circles of debris were indeed structures.[85]

Alternatively, some archaeologists are beginning to think that these early sites with many animal bones and tools may just have been places where hominids processed food but did not live. Why would the hominids return repeatedly to a particular site? Richard Potts suggests one possible reason—that hominids left caches of stone tools and stones for toolmaking at various locations to facilitate recurrent food-collecting and -processing activities.[86]

Stone Tools and Culture

The presence of patterned stone tools means that these early hominids had probably developed *culture.* Archaeologists consider a pattern of behavior, such as a particular way to make a tool that is shared and learned by a group of individuals, to be a sign of cultural behavior. To be sure, toolmaking does not imply that early humans had anything like the complex cultures of humans today. Chimpanzees have patterns of tool use and toolmaking that appear to be shared and learned, but they do not have that much in the way of cultural behavior.

It seems clear from the archaeological record that early hominids were making and using stone tools on a regular basis. Tools are frequently found in discrete concentrations, and often in association with animal bones and other debris from human activity suggesting, as we have already noted, campsites or even small shelters used by groups of individuals over periods of time. In such a situation, sharing of food at least amongst closely related individuals is very likely. Even when food-sharing takes place among chimpanzees, it is usually among closely related individuals.[87] Thus, the ancient locations of early hominid social activity may be evidence of family groups. How would such a system of social behavior—the creation of a common meeting, resting, and living place for a group of related individuals to share food—have evolved? Let's consider one model.

One Model for the Evolution of Culture

Early *Homo* had a brain almost one-third larger than that of the australopithecines. As we discuss later in the section on trends in hominid evolution, one of the possible consequences of brain expansion was the lessening of maturity at birth. Compared with other animals, we spend not only a longer proportion of our life span, but also the longest absolute period in a dependent state. Prolonged infant dependency has probably been of great significance in human cultural evolution. According to Theodosius Dobzhansky,

> it is this helplessness and prolonged dependence on the ministrations of the parents and other persons that favors . . . the socialization and learning process on which the transmission of culture wholly depends. This may have been an overwhelming advantage of the human growth pattern in the process of evolution.[88]

It used to be thought that the australopithecines had a long period of infant dependency, just as modern humans do, but the way their teeth apparently developed suggests that the early australopithecines followed an apelike pattern of development. Thus, prolonged maturation may be relatively recent, but just how recent is not yet known.[89]

Although some use of tools for digging, defense, or scavenging may have influenced the development of bipedalism, full bipedalism may have made possible more efficient toolmaking and consequently more efficient foraging and scavenging. Indeed, we have fairly good evidence that early hominids were butchering and presumably eating big game some 2 million years ago.

Whenever it was that hominids began to scavenge for game and perhaps hunt regularly, the development of scavenging would have required individuals to travel long distances frequently in search of suitable carcasses. Among groups of early *Homo*, longer infant and child dependency may have fostered the creation of home bases or at least established meeting places. The demands of childbirth and caring for a newborn might have made it difficult for early *Homo* mothers to travel for some time after the birth. Certainly, it would have been awkward for a mother carrying a nursing child to travel long distances to hunt. Although carrying an infant might be possible with a sling, successful hunting might not be so likely with a needy and potentially noisy child along. Because early *Homo* males (and perhaps females without young children) would have been freer to roam farther from home, they probably became the scavengers or hunters. Women with young children may have gathered wild plants within a small area that could be covered without traveling far from the home base or meeting place.

The creation of home bases or meeting places among early *Homo* groups may itself have increased the likelihood of wider food-sharing. If mothers with young children were limited to gathering plant foods in a relatively small area, the only way to ensure that they and their children could obtain a complete diet would have been to share the other foods obtained elsewhere. Sharing would have made it more likely that their offspring would survive to have offspring. Thus, if early *Homo* had home bases and families, those characteristics could have encouraged the development of the learned and shared behaviors we call culture.[90] Obviously this is a "just-so" story—a tale that we may never be able to prove really happened. However, it is a tale that is consistent with the archaeological record.[91] Patterned stone tools do not appear until early *Homo* comes on the scene. With early *Homo,* we see the start of several trends in hominid evolution that appear to reflect the manufacture and use of patterned stone tools—the expansion of the brain, the modification of the female pelvis to accommodate bigger-brained babies, and a general reduction in the size of teeth, face, and jaws.

Trends in Hominid Evolution
Expansion of the Brain

The australopithecines had relatively small cranial capacities, about 380–530 cubic centimeters (cc)—not much larger than that of chimpanzees. But around 2.3 million years ago, close to the time that patterned stone tools first appeared, some hominids show evidence of enlarged brain capacity. These hominids, early *Homo,* had cranial capacities averaging about 630–640 cc, which is about 50 percent of the brain capacity of modern humans (which averages slightly more than 1,300 cc). (See Figure 3.) The australopithecines were small, and the earliest *Homo* finds were hardly bigger, so much of the increase in brain size over time might have been a result of later hominids' bigger bodies. When we correct for body size, however, it turns out that brain size increased not only absolutely but also relatively after 2 million years ago. Between about 4 million and 2 million years ago, relative brain size remained just about the same. Only in the last 2 million years has the hominid brain doubled in relative size and tripled in absolute size.[92] Many anthropologists think that the increase is linked to the emergence of stone toolmaking about 2.5 million years ago. The reasoning is that stone toolmaking was important for the survival of our ancestors, and therefore natural selection would have favored bigger-brained individuals because they had motor and conceptual skills that enabled them to be better toolmakers. According to this view, the expansion of the brain and more sophisticated toolmaking would have developed together. Other anthropologists think that the expansion of the brain may have been favored by other factors, such as warfare, hunting, longer life, and language.[93] One intriguing theory is that life in complex social groups requires increased intelligence and memory, and that the creation of home bases and family groups may have fostered the expansion of the hominid brain.[94] Whatever the factors favoring bigger brains, they also provided

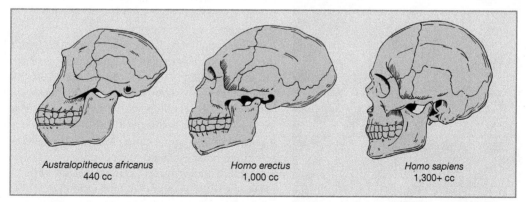

Australopithecus africanus
440 cc

Homo erectus
1,000 cc

Homo sapiens
1,300+ cc

Figure 3 **Comparison of the estimated cranial capacities of** *Australopithecus africanus,* ***Homo erectus,*** **and** *Homo sapiens,* **demonstrating the expansion of the brain in hominid evolution**

Source: Estimated cranial capacities from Tattersall, Delson, and Van Couvering 2000. Reproduced by permission of Routledge, Inc., part of The Taylor & Francis Group.

humans with an expanded capacity for culture. Thus, along with bipedalism, the expansion of the brain marks a watershed in human evolution.

As the hominid brain expanded, natural selection also favored the widening of the female pelvis to allow larger-brained babies to be born.[95] But there was probably a limit to how far the pelvis could widen and still be adapted to bipedalism. Something had to give, and that something was the degree of physical development of the human infant at birth—for instance, the human infant is born with cranial bones so plastic that they can overlap. Because birth takes place before the cranial bones have hardened, the human infant with its relatively large brain can pass through the opening in the mother's pelvis. Human infants are born at a relatively early stage of development, and are wholly dependent on their parents for many years. As we have noted, this lengthy period of infant dependency may have been an important factor in the evolution of culture.

Reduction of the Face, Teeth, and Jaws

As in the case of the brain, substantial changes in the face, teeth, and jaws do not appear in hominid evolution until after about 2 million years ago. The australopithecines all have cheek teeth that are very large relative to their estimated body weight, perhaps because the diet of the australopithecines was especially high in plant foods,[96] including small, tough objects such as seeds, nuts, and tubers. The australopithecines have thick jawbones, probably also related to their chewing needs. The australopithecines have relatively large faces that project forward below the eyes. But when we get to the *Homo* forms, we see reduction in the size of the face, cheek teeth, and jaws (see Figure 4). It would seem that natural selection in favor of a bigger and stronger chewing apparatus was relaxed. One reason might be that members of the *Homo* genus started to eat foods that were easier to chew. Such foods might have included roots, fruits, and meat. As we discuss later, it may have been the development of habitual tool use and the control of fire that allowed members of the *Homo* genus to change their diet to include foods that are easier to chew, including meat. If food is cooked and easy to chew, individual humans with smaller jaws and teeth would not be disadvantaged, and therefore the face, cheek teeth, and jaw would get smaller on average over time.[97]

The expansion of the brain and reduction of the face occurred at about the same time, and were probably related. A recent discovery in human genetics appears to provide direct evidence of a connection. Researchers studying muscle diseases in modern humans discovered that humans have a unique myosin gene called MYH16 (myosin is a protein in muscle tissue) that is only present in jaw muscles. Comparing MYH16 to related genes in primates, the researchers determined that MYH16 evolved about 2.4 million years ago—around the time the brain began to enlarge and the face and jaw began to shrink. So, the expansion of the brain appears to have been aided by a mutation in myosin that caused jaw muscles to shrink.[98]

The skull of a *Homo habilis/rudolfensis* (ER-1470) found by Richard Leakey in 1972. Note its high forehead and large braincase.

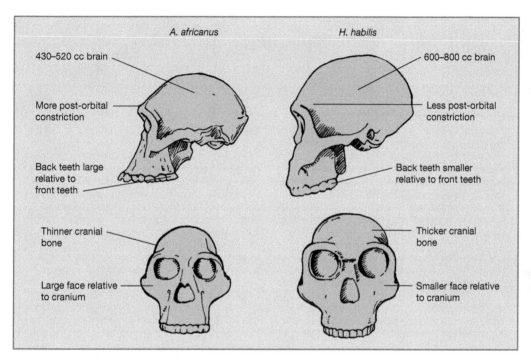

Figure 4 **Comparison of *A. africanus* and *H. habilis***

Homo erectus

Homo erectus was the first hominid species to be widely distributed in the Old World (see the box "The First Migrants"). Until recently, it was assumed that it was *H. erectus* who moved out of Africa because *H. erectus* lived in East Africa about 1.6 million years ago but not until after about 1 million years ago in Asia.[99] However, recent redating suggests that *H. erectus* in Java is somewhat older, dating to perhaps 1.8 million years ago.[100] And newer *H. erectus* fossils from Dmanisi, in the southeastern European nation of Georgia, have recently been dated to at least 1.7 million years ago.[101] If these dates are accurate, earlier hominids, possibly *H. habilis*, probably moved out of Africa earlier. Indeed, one well-preserved skull found at Dmanisi in 2001 has some features that are reminiscent of *H. habilis*—a brain only about 600 cc, relatively large canines, and a relatively thin browridge.[102]

Some scholars see enough differences between Asian and African populations of *H. erectus* to argue that they should be separated into two distinct species, *Homo erectus* for the Asian populations and ***Homo ergaster*** for the African ones. Furthermore, *Homo erectus* (or *Homo ergaster*) fossils are also found in Europe. But some paleoanthropologists think that the finds in Europe typically classified as *H. erectus* are actually early examples of *H. sapiens*.[103] Others think that the European fossils and similar ones found in southern Africa and the Near East should be grouped into a distinct species, *Homo heidelbergensis*. There is also *Homo floresiensis*, a diminutive hominid that appears to be a miniature form of *Homo erectus* that evolved only on the isolated island of Flores, Indonesia. It is all a bit confusing; later we will try to sort it all out.

MIGRANTS AND IMMIGRANTS

The First Migrants

Hominids evolved in Africa, yet today hominids are found on every continent. Who were the first hominids to leave Africa, and when did they first leave? For many years, the clear answer was that *Homo erectus* were the first to leave Africa, and they did so perhaps 700,000 to 1 million years ago. In recent years, new findings and sources of evidence have led scholars to question this established answer.

The first new information came from geochemist Carl Swisher, who in the mid-1990s redated the Java sites where *Homo erectus* fossils had been found and determined they dated to perhaps 1.8 million years ago. Because the earliest *H. erectus* fossils in Africa share a similar date, this created a problem—how did *H. erectus* appear in Java at about the same time they appeared in Africa? As this question was being pondered, a remarkable set of new *H. erectus* fossils were being uncovered in Dmanisi, Georgia. Dated at 1.7 million years ago, these fossils made it clear that *H. erectus* left Africa almost as soon as they had evolved. The discovery of a *Homo habilis*–like fossil at Dmanisi, and of Oldowan-like tools at Riwat, Pakistan, and Longgupo, China, suggested that *H. habilis* may have been the first to leave Africa, and *H. erectus* followed a path their predecessors blazed. If they were following an earlier migration, it could explain how *H. erectus* were able to move so quickly across Asia.

A more unusual source of information on when hominids first left Africa comes from the parasites that accompanied them. All hominoids are plagued by lice, but humans host a distinct species, *Pediculus humanus*. Geneticist David Reed and his colleagues found that *P. humanus* diverged from other lice about 5.6 million years ago—about the time the first hominids appeared. More interesting, however, Reed and colleagues discovered that there are two subspecies of *P. humanus* that appear to have diverged about 1.2 million years ago. One subspecies is found worldwide today; the other is restricted to the New World. Reed and colleagues suggest this is evidence that at least some hominid migrants (probably *H. erectus*) became isolated in Asia by at least 1.2 million years ago, where their lice diverged from that of other hominid populations, only to be picked up much later by modern human migrants who ended up colonizing the New World.

So, who were the first hominid migrants? They may have been *H. habilis*, or they may have been very early *H. erectus*. When did the first hominid migrations out of Africa take place? Probably slightly less than 2 million years ago, but once these hominids left, they moved quickly, and they moved long distances. By 1.6 million years ago, *H. erectus* was in both western and southern Asia, and by 1.2 million years ago, their populations had moved far enough to have become isolated from one another. Whether or not they were the first migrants out of Africa, *H. erectus* migrated fast and far.

Sources: Reed et al. 2004; Tattersall 1997.

Physical Characteristics of *Homo erectus*

The *Homo erectus* skull generally was long, low, and thickly walled, with a flat frontal area and prominent browridges. It had a unique pentagonal shape when looked at from the back, formed in part by a rounded ridge, called a **sagittal keel,** running along the crest of the skull. There was also a ridge of bone running horizontally along the back of the skull, called an **occipital torus,** which added to the skull's overall long shape (see Figure 5).[104]

Compared with early *Homo, H. erectus* had relatively small teeth. *H. erectus* was the first hominid to have third molars that were smaller than the second or first molars, as in modern humans. The molars also had an enlarged pulp cavity, called **taurodontism,** which may have allowed the teeth to withstand harder use and wear than the teeth of modern humans. But the *H. erectus* jaw was lighter and thinner than in either early *Homo* or the australopithecines, and the face was less **prognathic,** or forward thrusting, in the upper and lower jaw. The brain, averaging 895–1,040 cc, was larger than that found in any of the australopithecines or early *Homo* species, but smaller than the average brain of a modern human.[105] Endocasts, which provide a picture of the surface of the brain, suggest that it was organized more like the brain of modern humans than like that of australopithecines.

Homo erectus had a prominent, projecting nose, in contrast to the australopithecines' flat, nonprojecting nose.[106] From the neck down, *H. erectus* was practically indistinguishable from *H. sapiens.* In contrast to the smaller australopithecines and early *Homo* species living in East Africa

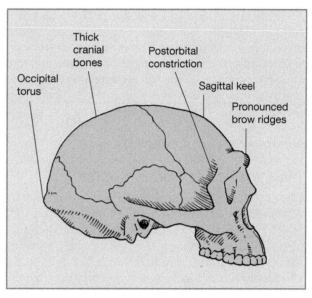

Figure 5 *Homo erectus* **Features**

around the same time, *H. erectus* was comparable to modern humans in size. The almost complete skeleton of the boy at Nariokotome, Kenya, suggests that he was about 5½ feet tall and about 8 years of age when he died; researchers estimate that he would have been over 6 feet tall had he lived to maturity. About 1.6 million years ago, the Nariokotome region was probably open grassland, with trees mostly along rivers.[107] *Homo erectus* in East Africa was similar in size to Africans today who live in a similarly open, dry environment.[108] *H. erectus* was also less sexually dimorphic than either the australopithecines or early *Homo,* comparable to modern humans.

Homo floresiensis

Whether or not there are distinct African and Asian species of *Homo erectus,* most scholars agree that **Homo floresiensis** is a distinct species that is closely related to *Homo erectus. H. floresiensis* has only been found on the Indonesian island of Flores, and only a handful of individuals have been located to date. All are tiny (they stood perhaps 3 feet tall), and have very small brains, on the order of 380 cc.[109] The structure of the brain, however, seems closely related to that of *H. erectus,* as do the structures of the skull.[110] In other words, *H. floresiensis* appears to be a tiny version of *H. erectus. H. floresiensis* even made tools that look similar to those made by *H. erectus,* and in some cases the tools look even more sophisticated.

The skull of the dwarf species *Homo floresiensis* next to that of a modern human. Note how small it is in comparison.

How might a miniature version of *H. erectus* have evolved? The answer is that both dwarfism and gigantism are common phenomena in isolated populations. Dwarfism appears to be an adaptation that occurs when there are few predators—a species in isolation can become smaller, and have a large population, if there are no predators threatening them. This may be what happened on Flores.[111] It is interesting that the island also hosted a number of dwarf species in addition to *H. floresiensis,* including a dwarf elephant that appears to have been one of the favorite foods of *H. floresiensis.* Perhaps even more interesting is the fact that *H. floresiensis* may have survived until as recently as 12,000 years ago—well into the time period when modern humans were living in Indonesia.

The Evolution of *Homo erectus*

The evolution of *Homo erectus* reflects a continuation of the general evolutionary trends we discussed previously. The brain continued to expand, increasing more than a third over early *Homo* (just as early *Homo* had increased more than a third over the australopithecines). The face, teeth, and jaws continued to shrink, taking on an almost modern form. An increasing use and variety of tools may have led to a further development of the brain. *Homo erectus* was eating and probably cooking meat, and this may have led to further reduction in the teeth and jaws.

As noted above, *Homo erectus* does not appear to be as sexually dimorphic as earlier hominids. What might have caused this change? In other primates, sexual dimorphism appears to be linked to social systems in which males are at the top of dominance hierarchies due to physical size and prowess and such males control sexual access to multiple females in the group. In contrast, lack of sexual dimorphism seems most pronounced in the animals where *pair bonding* exists—that is, where a male and a female form a breeding pair that lasts for a long period of time (there are several distinct variations of male–female bonding in modern human cultures).[112] Could male–female bonding have developed in *Homo erectus?* It seems possible.

In animal species where females can feed themselves and their babies after birth, pair bonding is rare. But in species where females cannot feed both themselves and their babies, pair bonding is common. Why? We think it is because a strong male–female bond provides a good solution to the problem of incompatibility between a mother's feeding requirements and tending a newborn baby. A male partner can bring food and/or watch the newborn while the mother gets food.[113] But most primates lack pair bonding. This may be because primate infants are able to cling to their mother's fur soon after birth, so that the mother's hands are free to forage. Human infants demonstrate a residual form of this innate ability to cling during their first few weeks of life. This is called the *Moro reflex.*[114]

We have no way of knowing if *Homo erectus* had fur like other primates, but we think probably not, because we think they may have worn clothing, as we discuss later. The brain in *Homo erectus* may also have already expanded enough that *Homo erectus* infants, like modern human infants, could not adequately support their heads even if they could hold onto their mother's fur. In any case, when early hominids began to depend on scavenging and hunting for food (and for skins to be used in clothing), it would have been difficult and hazardous for a parent with a newborn baby to engage in these activities with a baby along. Marriage would have been an effective solution to this problem because each parent could help protect the baby while the other was away getting food. (Further discussion of this theory might be warranted.)

Another important aspect of the evolution of *Homo erectus* was the movement of populations out of eastern and southern Africa. It seems likely that cultural innovations were the key to allowing *Homo erectus* to move into new environments. Why? Because upon entering new environments, *Homo erectus* would have been faced with new (and generally colder) climatic conditions, new and different sources of raw material for tools, and new plants and animals to rely on for food. All animals adapt to such changes through natural selection, but natural selection typically takes a relatively long time and requires physical changes in the adapting organisms. *Homo erectus* was able to adapt to new environments very quickly and without apparent physical changes. This suggests that the primary mechanisms of adaptation for *Homo erectus* were cultural rather than biological.

What cultural adaptations might *Homo erectus* have made? Fire usage might have been the crucial cultural adaptation to colder climates. As we discuss below, there is tantalizing evidence that *Homo erectus* used fire. But fire can only warm people when they are stationary; it doesn't help when people are out collecting food. To be mobile in colder climates, *Homo erectus* may have begun to wear animal furs for warmth. Some *Homo erectus* tools look like the hide-processing tools used by more recent human groups,[115] and it seems unlikely that *Homo erectus* could have survived in the colder locations where they have been found, in eastern Europe and Asia, without some form of clothing. And if *Homo erectus* was wearing furs for warmth, they must have been hunting. *Homo erectus* could not have depended on scavenging to acquire skins—the skin is the first thing predators destroy when they dismember a carcass.

Lower Paleolithic Cultures

The stone tool traditions of *Homo erectus* are traditionally called **Lower Paleolithic.** These stone tool traditions involve "core" tool techniques, in which a core of stone, rather than a flake, is used as the basic raw material for finished tools (we will talk more about Lower Paleolithic stone tool technology shortly). Because stone tools are the most common cultural material in the archaeological record of these ancient peoples, the entire culture of *Homo erectus* is often termed *Lower Paleolithic,* a practice we follow here.

The archaeological finds of tools and other cultural artifacts dating from 1.5 million years to about 200,000 years ago are assumed to have been produced by *Homo erectus.* But hominid fossils are not usually associated with these materials. Therefore some of the tools during this period were possibly produced by hominids other than *H. erectus,* such as australopithecines earlier and *H. sapiens* later. But the so-called *Acheulian* tool assemblages dating from 1.5 million years ago to more than a million years later are very similar to each other, and *H. erectus* is the only hominid that spans the entire period. Thus, it is conventionally assumed that *H. erectus* was responsible for most if not all of the Acheulian tool assemblages.[116]

The Acheulian Tool Tradition

The stone toolmaking tradition known as the **Acheulian** was named after the site at St. Acheul, France, where the first examples were found. But the oldest Acheulian tools recovered are from East Africa, on the Peninj River in Tanzania, dating back about 1.5 million years.[117] In contrast to Oldowan, Acheulian assemblages have more large tools created according to standardized designs or shapes. Oldowan tools have sharp edges made by a few blows. Acheulian toolmakers shaped the stone by knocking more flakes off most of the edges. Many of these tools were made from very large flakes that had first been struck from very large cores or boulders.

One of the most characteristic and common tools in the Acheulian tool kit is the so-called **hand axe,** which is a teardrop-shaped, bifacially flaked tool with a thinned sharp tip. Other large tools resemble cleavers and picks. There were also many kinds of flake tools, such as scrapers with a wide edge.

Figure 6 In later Acheulian technology, the characteristic hand axes were made by the soft-hammer method

Early Acheulian tools appeared to have been made by blows with a hard stone, but later tools are wider and flatter and may have been made with a **soft hammer** of bone or antler.[118] Tools made by a **hard hammer** technique, rock against rock, have limits in terms of their sharpness and form because only large and thick flakes can be made with a hard hammer technique. Flakes created by soft hammer flaking are much thinner and longer than hard hammer flakes, and the flintknapper generally has better control over their size and shape. This means that thinner and sharper tools can be made, as well as tools with complex shapes.

Were hand axes made for chopping trees, as their name suggests? Experiments suggest that they are not good for cutting trees; they seem more suited for butchering large animals.[119] Lawrence Keeley microscopically examined some Acheulian hand axes, and the wear on them is more consistent with animal butchery. They may also have been used for woodworking, particularly hollowing and shaping wood, and they are also good for digging.[120] William Calvin has even suggested that a hand axe could be used as a projectile thrown like a discus into a herd of animals in the hope of injuring or killing an animal.[121]

Acheulian tools are found widely in Africa, Europe, and western Asia, but bifacial hand axes, cleavers, and picks are not found as commonly in eastern and southeastern Asia.[122] Because *H. erectus* has been found in all areas of the Old World, it is puzzling that the tool traditions seem to differ from west to east. Some archaeologists have suggested that large bifacial tools may be lacking in eastern and southeastern Asia because *H. erectus* in Asia had a better material to make tools out of—bamboo. Bamboo has been used recently in Southeast Asia for many purposes, including incredibly sharp arrows and sticks for digging and cutting. Geoffrey Pope has shown that bamboo is found precisely in those areas of Asia where hand axes and other large bifacial tools are largely missing.[123]

Big Game Eating

Some of the Acheulian sites have produced evidence of big game eating. F. Clark Howell, who excavated sites at Torralba and Ambrona, Spain, found a substantial number of elephant remains and unmistakable evidence of human presence in the form of tools. Howell suggests that the humans at those sites used fire to frighten elephants into muddy bogs from which they would be unable to escape.[124] To hunt elephants in this way, the humans would have had to plan and work cooperatively in fairly large groups.

But do these finds of bones of large- and medium-sized animals, in association with tools, tell us that the humans definitely were big game hunters? Some archaeologists who have reanalyzed the evidence from Torralba think that the big game may have been scavenged. Because the Torralba and Ambrona sites are near ancient streams, many of the elephants could have died naturally, their bones accumulating in certain spots because of the flow of water.[125] What seems fairly clear is that the humans did deliberately butcher different kinds of game—different types of tools are found with different types of animals.[126] Thus, whether the humans hunted

Homo erectus ate—and probably hunted—large game animals, and they probably also learned to control fire.

big game at Torralba and Ambrona is debatable; all we can be sure of, as of now, is that they consumed big game and probably hunted smaller game.

Control of Fire

One way in which *H. erectus* is thought to have hunted is by using *fire drives*—a technique still used by hunting and gathering peoples in recent times. It is highly effective: Animals are driven out of their hiding places and homes by fire and dispatched by hunters positioned downwind of the oncoming flames. Most peoples who use this technique today set fires deliberately, but fires caused by lightning strikes may have also been utilized. Did *H. erectus* set these fires? Because *H. erectus* was the first hominid to be found throughout the Old World and in areas with freezing winters, most anthropologists presume that *H. erectus* had learned to control fire, at least for warmth. There is archaeological evidence of fire in some early sites, but fires can be natural events.[127]

Suggestive but not conclusive evidence of the deliberate use of fire comes from Kenya in East Africa and is over 1.4 million years old.[128] More persuasive evidence of human control of fire, dating from nearly 800,000 years ago, comes from the site of Gesher Benot Ya'aqov in Israel. Here, researchers found evidence of burned seeds, wood, and stone, as well as concentrations of burned items suggestive of hearths.[129] Evidence of the deliberate use of fire comes from Europe somewhat later. Unfortunately, the evidence of control of fire at Gesher Benot Ya'aqov and European sites is not associated with *H. erectus* fossils, so the link between deliberate use of fire and *H. erectus* cannot definitely be established yet.[130] The control of fire was a major step in increasing the energy under human control. Cooking would have made all kinds of food (not just meat) more safely digestible and therefore more usable.[131] Fires would also have kept predators away, a not inconsiderable advantage given that there were many.

Campsites

Acheulian sites were usually located close to water sources, lush vegetation, and large stocks of herbivorous animals. Some camps have been found in caves, but most were in open areas surrounded by rudimentary fortifications or windbreaks. Several African sites are marked by stony rubble brought there by *H. erectus,* possibly for the dual purpose of securing the windbreaks and providing ammunition in case of a sudden attack.[132]

The presumed base campsites display a wide variety of tools, indicating that the camp was the center of many group functions. More specialized sites away from camp have also been found. These are marked by the predominance of a particular type of tool. For example, a butchering site in Tanzania contained dismembered hippopotamus carcasses and rare heavy-duty smashing and cutting tools. Workshops are another kind of specialized site encountered with some regularity. They are characterized by tool debris and are located close to a source of natural stone suitable for toolmaking.[133]

A camp has been excavated at the Terra Amata site near Nice, on the French Riviera. The camp appears to have been occupied in the late spring or early summer, judging by the pollen found in fossilized human feces. The excavator describes stake holes driven into the sand, paralleled by lines of stones, presumably marking the spots where the people constructed huts of roughly 30 × 15 feet (see Figure 7). A basic feature of each hut was a central hearth that seems to have been protected from drafts by a small wall built just outside the northeast corner of the hearth. The evidence suggests that the Terra Amata occupants gathered seafood such as oysters and mussels, did some fishing, and hunted in the surrounding area. The animal remains suggest that they obtained both small and large animals but mostly got the young of larger animals such as stags, elephants, boars, rhinoceroses, and wild oxen. Some of the huts contain recognizable toolmakers' areas, scattered with tool debris; occasionally, the impression of an animal skin shows where the toolmaker actually sat.[134]

Figure 7 A Reconstruction of the Oval Huts Built at Terra Amata. These huts were approximately 30 × 15 feet.

Source: Copyright © 1969 by Eric Mose.

The First Hominids and the Emergence of *Homo*

Summary ─────────────────────────────────────

1. The drying trend in climate that began about 16 million to 11 million years ago diminished the extent of African rain forests and gave rise to areas of savanna and scattered deciduous woodlands. The new, more open country probably favored characteristics adapted to ground living in some primates. In the evolutionary line leading to humans, these adaptations included bipedalism, a crucial change in early hominid evolution.

2. There are several theories for the development of bipedalism: It may have increased the emerging hominid's ability to see predators and potential prey while moving through the tall grasses of the savanna; by freeing the hands for carrying, it may have facilitated transferring food from one place to another, for tool use for subsistence activities or weapons, for more efficient traveling over long distances, or for cooling the body.

3. *Sahelanthropus, Orrorin,* and *Ardipithecus* are likely candidates for the first hominid. They date as early as 6 million years ago, and may have walked bipedally. Undisputed hominids dating before 4 million years ago have been found in East Africa. These definitely bipedal hominids are now generally classified in the genus *Australopithecus.*

4. At least six species of australopithecine have been identified, and these are generally divided into two types: gracile and robust. The gracile australopithecines have relatively smaller teeth and jaws, and include *A. anamensis, A. afarensis,* and *A. africanus.* The robust australopithecines have relatively larger teeth and jaws, and are more muscular than the gracile australopithecines. They include *A. aethiopicus, A. robustus,* and *A. boisei.*

5. The earliest identifiable stone tools found so far come from various sites in East Africa and date from about 2.5 million years ago. Flake tools predominate, but choppers are also common. These early stone tools are referred to as Oldowan.

6. The presence of stone tools and perhaps home bases suggests that early hominids had culture.

7. Important physical changes in early hominids that led to the evolution of our genus, *Homo,* include the expansion of the brain, the modification of the female pelvis to allow bigger-brained babies to be born, and the reduction of the face, teeth, and jaws. These physical changes are seen in the species *Homo habilis* and *Homo rudolfensis,* both of which date to around 2.3 million years ago. Early *Homo* appears to have used tools and scavenged or possibly hunted meat, so culture, or the evolution of cultural behavior, seems to have played a role in these physical changes as well.

8. *Homo erectus* emerged about 1.8 million to 1.6 million years ago and was the first hominid species to be widely distributed in the Old World. It had a larger brain capacity than *Homo habilis* and an essentially modern postcranial skeleton. What differentiates *Homo erectus* most from modern humans is the shape of the skull, which is long, low, and has prominent browridges.

9. Some of the locations where *Homo erectus* lived in eastern Europe and Asia were quite cold, and *Homo erectus* was probably able to adapt to these new and often colder environments through cultural adaptations, such as use of fire for warmth and cooking, furs for clothing, and hunting.

10. Lower Paleolithic tools and other cultural artifacts from about 1.6 million to about 200,000 years ago were probably produced by *H. erectus.* Acheulian is the name given to the most well-known tool tradition of this period. Acheulian tools include both small flake tools and large tools, but hand axes and other large bifacial tools are characteristic.

The First Hominids and the Emergence of *Homo*

Critical Questions

1. How could there have been more than one species of hominid living in East Africa at the same time?

2. Why might early hominids have begun to make stone tools? How would stone tools have been more useful than wood or bone tools?

3. When compared to earlier hominids, *Homo erectus* is larger and has a larger brain and smaller teeth. How might these physical changes correlate with apparent behavioral changes in *Homo erectus?*

4. *Homo erectus* lived in many places in the Old World. What may have enabled them to spread so widely?

Read the Original Source on myanthrolab.com

Read the chapter by Scott Simpson titled "*Australopithecus afarensis* and Human Evolution" on MyAnthroLab. Answer the following questions.

1. Why is the Afar region of Ethiopia such a rich and important area for finding early hominid fossils?

2. How does Simpson come to the conclusion that only one species, *A. afarensis,* is represented in the collections from Hadar and Laetoli?

Photo Credits

Glossary

Acheulian A stone toolmaking tradition dating from 1.5 million years ago. Compared with the Oldowan tradition, Acheulian assemblages have more large tools created according to standardized designs or shapes. One of the most characteristic and prevalent tools in the Acheulian tool kit is the so-called hand axe, which is a teardrop-shaped bifacially flaked tool with a thinned sharp tip. Other large tools might have been cleavers and picks.

Ardipithecus ramidus Perhaps the first hominid, dating to about 4.5 million years ago. Its dentition combines apelike and australopithecine-like features, and its skeleton suggests it was bipedal.

Australopithecus Genus of Pliocene and Pleistocene hominids.

Australopithecus aethiopicus An early robust australopithecine.

Australopithecus afarensis A species of *Australopithecus* that lived 4 million to 3 million years ago in East Africa and was definitely bipedal.

Australopithecus africanus A species of *Australopithecus* that lived between about 3 million and 2 million years ago.

Australopithecus anamensis A species of *Australopithecus* that lived perhaps 4.2 million years ago.

Australopithecus bahrelghazali An early gracile australopithecine, dating to about 3 million years ago, and currently represented by only a single jaw. It is an interesting species because it is found in western Chad, distant from the East African Rift Valley where all other early australopithecines have been found.

Australopithecus boisei An East African robust australopithecine species dating from 2.2 million to 1.3 million years ago with somewhat larger cranial capacity than *A. africanus*. No longer thought to be larger than other australopithecines, it is robust primarily in the skull and jaw, most strikingly in the teeth. Compared with *A. robustus*, *A. boisei* has even more features that reflect a huge chewing apparatus.

Australopithecus garhi A gracile australopithecine, dating to about 2.5 million years ago.

Australopithecus robustus A robust australopithecine species found in South African caves dating from about 1.8 million to 1 million years ago. Not as large in the teeth and jaws as *A. boisei*.

Bifacial tool A tool worked or flaked on two sides.

The First Hominids and the Emergence of *Homo*

Foramen magnum Opening in the base of the skull through which the spinal cord passes en route to the brain.

Gracile australopithecines The earliest group of australopithecines, usually differentiated from the robust australopithecines by their lighter dentition and smaller faces.

Handaxe A teardrop-shaped stone tool characteristic of Acheulian assemblages.

Hard hammer A technique of stone tool manufacture where one stone is used to knock flakes from another stone. Flakes produced through hard hammer percussion are usually large and crude.

Homo erectus The first hominid species to be widely distributed in the Old World. The earliest finds are possibly 1.8 million years old. The brain (averaging 895–1,040 cc) was larger than that found in any of the australopithecines or *H. habilis* but smaller than the average brain of a modern human.

Homo ergaster The African form of *Homo erectus*. Many paleoanthropologists do not make a formal distinction between *Homo ergaster* and *Homo erectus*.

Homo floresiensis A dwarf species of hominid that lived on the Indonesian island of Flores until about 12,000 years ago and probably descended from an isolated *Homo erectus* population.

Homo habilis Dating from about 2 million years ago, an early species belonging to our genus, *Homo*, with cranial capacities averaging about 630–640 cc, about 50 percent of the brain capacity of modern humans.

Homo rudolfensis Early species belonging to our genus, *Homo*. Similar enough to *Homo habilis* that some paleoanthropologists make no distinction between the two.

Kenyanthropus platyops A nearly complete 3.5-million-year-old skull found in western Kenya. It is thought by some scholars to be a species of gracile australopithecine (and hence should not be regarded as a separate genus).

Lower Paleolithic The period of the Oldowan and Acheulian stone tool traditions.

Occipital torus A ridge of bone running horizontally across the back of the skull in apes and some hominids.

Oldowan The earliest stone toolmaking tradition, named after the tools found in Bed I at Olduvai Gorge, Tanzania, from about 2.5 million years ago. The stone artifacts include core tools and sharp-edged flakes made by striking one stone against another. Flake tools predominate. Among the core tools, so-called choppers are common.

Orrorin tugenensis An apparently bipedal primate dating to between 5.8 and 6 million years, making it possibly the earliest known hominid.

Percussion flaking A toolmaking technique in which one stone is struck with another to remove a flake.

Pliocene The geological epoch 5.2 million to 1.6 million years ago during which the earliest definite hominids appeared.

Prognathic A physical feature that is sticking out or pushed forward, such as the faces in apes and some hominid species.

Robust australopithecines A later group of australopithecines usually differentiated from the gracile australopithecines by their heavier dentition and larger faces.

Sagittal keel An inverted V-shaped ridge running along the top of the skull in *Homo erectus*.

Sahelanthropus tchadensis A hominoid found in Chad dating to around 7 million years ago.

Savanna Tropical grassland.

Soft hammer A technique of stone tool manufacture in which a bone or wood hammer is used to strike flakes from a stone.

Taurodontism Having teeth with an enlarged pulp cavity.

Unifacial tool A tool worked or flaked on one side only.

Notes

1. Thorpe, Holder, and Crompton 2007.
2. Rose 1984.
3. Bilsborough 1992, 64–65.
4. Oakley 1964.
5. Kingston, Marino, and Hill 1994.
6. Hewes 1961.
7. Shipman 1986; Trinkaus 1987.
8. Lovejoy 1981.
9. C. Jolly 1970.
10. Washburn 1960.
11. Pilbeam 1972, 153.
12. Wolpoff 1971.
13. Savage-Rumbaugh 1994.
14. Wolpoff 1983.
15. Zimmer 2004.
16. Zihlman 1992.
17. Wheeler 1984; 1991.
18. Falk 1988.
19. Zihlman 1992, 414.
20. Lovejoy 1988.
21. Aiello and Dean 1990, 268–74.
22. Aiello and Dean 1990, 507–08.
23. Gibbons 2002.
24. Brunet et al. 2002; Wong 2003.
25. Aiello and Collard 2001; Pickford et al. 2002; Wong 2003.
26. Richmond and Jungers 2008.
27. T. D. White, Suwa, and Asfaw 1995.
28. T. D. White, Suwa, and Asfaw 1994.
29. Hailie-Selassie 2001.
30. Rose 1984; Susman et al. 1985.
31. Conroy 1990, 274; Culotta 1995; Wilford 1995.
32. Culotta 1995.
33. Leakey et al. 1995.
34. Tattersall and Schwartz 2000, 93.
35. Johanson and White 1979; Simpson 2009; T. D. White et al. 1981.
36. Johanson and Edey 1981, 17–18.
37. Johanson and White 1979.
38. Lewin 1983.
39. Conroy 1990, 291–92; Simpson 2009.
40. Fleagle 1999, 515–18.
41. Fleagle 1999, 515, 520.
42. Grine 1988a.
43. Kimbel et al. 1984.
44. Clarke and Tobias 1995; Jungers 1988b.
45. Lovejoy 1988.
46. Clarke and Tobias 1995; Tattersall and Schwartz 2000, 88–89.
47. Conroy 1990, 280–82.
48. Pilbeam 1972, 107.
49. Holloway 1974.
50. Szalay and Delson 1979, 504.
51. Asfaw et al. 1999.
52. Brunet et al. 1995.

53. Ibid.
54. Leakey et al. 2001.
55. Szalay and Delson 1979, 504; B. Wood 1992.
56. Jungers 1988a; McHenry 1988.
57. Grine 1993; Walker and Leakey 1988.
58. Broom 1950.
59. Fleagle 1999, 522.
60. McHenry 2009.
61. Ibid.
62. Grine 1988b.
63. Stringer 1985.
64. McHenry 2009.
65. Fleagle 1999, 529.
66. McHenry 2009.
67. Fleagle 1999, 511–15.
68. B. Wood 1992.
69. McHenry 2009; Tobias 1994.
70. Simpson 2009.
71. Susman 1994.
72. Ibid.
73. Holden 1997.
74. Leakey 1960.
75. Clark 1970, 68; Schick and Toth 1993, 97–99.
76. Schick and Toth 1993, 153–70.
77. Ibid., 129.
78. Ibid., 157–59.
79. Isaac 1984.
80. Schick and Toth 1993, 175–76.
81. Speth 2009.
82. Shipman 1986. For the idea that scavenging may have been an important food-getting strategy even for protohominids, see Szalay 1975.
83. M. Leakey 1971.
84. Potts 1988, 253–58.
85. Potts 1984.
86. Potts 1988, 278–81.
87. Boyd and Silk 2000, 249–50.
88. Dobzhansky 1962, 196.
89. Bromage and Dean 1985; Gibbons 2008; B. H. Smith 1986.
90. Chapais 2008.
91. Gowlett 2008.
92. McHenry 1982.
93. McHenry 1982.
94. Dunbar and Shultz 2007; Herrmann et al. 2007; Silk 2007.
95. Simpson et al. 2008.
96. Pilbeam and Gould 1974.
97. Leonard 2002.
98. Stedman et al. 2004.
99. Rightmire 2000.
100. Swisher et al. 1994.
101. Balter and Gibbons 2000; Gabunia et al. 2000.
102. Vekua et al. 2002; Gore 2002.
103. Wolpoff and Nkini 1985; see also Balter 2001; Rightmire 2000.
104. Day 1986, 409–12; Fleagle 1999, 534–35; Kramer 2009.
105. Rightmire 2000; Tobias 1994.
106. Franciscus and Trinkaus 1988.
107. Feibel and Brown 1993.
108. Ruff and Walker 1993.
109. Brown et al. 2004; Morwood et al. 2004.
110. Falk et al. 2005.
111. Weston and Lister 2009; Wong 2005.
112. Fleagle 1999, 306.
113. M. Ember and C. R. Ember 1979; cf. Lovejoy 1981.
114. Clayman 1989, 857–58.

115. Bordes 1968, 51–97.
116. Phillipson 1993, 57.
117. Schick and Toth 1993, 227, 233.
118. Ibid., 231–33; Whittaker 1994, 27.
119. Schick and Toth 1993, 258–60; Whittaker 1994, 27.
120. Lawrence Keeley's analysis reported in Schick and Toth 1993, 260; see that page for their analysis of tool use.
121. Calvin 1983.
122. Yamei, Potts, and Baoyin 2000.
123. Ciochon, Olson, and James 1990, 178–83; Pope 1989.
124. Howell 1966.
125. Binford 1987; Klein 1987.
126. L. G. Freeman 1994.
127. A good example of this problem is the ongoing debate about fire use at Zhoukoudian cave, as reported by Weiner et al. 1998.
128. Isaac 1984, 35–36. Other evidence for deliberate use of fire comes from the Swartkrans cave in South Africa and is dated 1 million to 1.5 million years ago; see Brain and Sillen 1988.
129. Goren-Inbar et al. 2004.
130. Binford and Ho 1985.
131. Leonard 2002.
132. Clark 1970, 94–95.
133. Ibid., 96–97.
134. de Lumley 1969.

Bibliography

Aiello, Leslie C., and Mark Collard, 2001. Our newest oldest ancestor? *Nature* 410 (November 29):526–27.
Aiello, Leslie C., and Christopher Dean. 1990. *An introduction to human evolutionary anatomy.* London: Academic Press.
Asfaw, Berhane, Tim White, Owen Lovejoy, Bruce Latimer, Scott Simpson, and Glen Suwa. 1999. *Australopithecus garhi:* A new species of early hominid from Ethiopia. *Science* 284 (April 23):629–36.
Balter, Michael. 2001. In search of the first Europeans. *Science* 291 (March 2):1722–25.
Balter, Michael, and Ann Gibbons. 2000. A glimpse of humans' first journey out of Africa. *Science* 288 (May 12):948–50.
Bilsborough, Alan. 1992. *Human evolution.* New York: Blackie Academic & Professional.
Binford, Lewis R. 1987. Were there elephant hunters at Torralba? In *The evolution of human hunting,* eds. M. Nitecki and D. Nitecki. New York: Plenum Press.
Binford, Lewis R., and Chuan Kun Ho. 1985. Taphonomy at a distance: Zhoukoudian, "The cave home of Beijing Man"? *Current Anthropology* 26:413–42.
Bordes, François. 1968. *The old stone age.* New York: McGraw-Hill.
Boyd, Robert, and Joan Silk. 2000. *How humans evolved.* 2nd ed. New York: Norton.
Brain, C. K., and A. Sillen. 1988. Evidence from the Swartkrans Cave for the earliest use of fire. *Nature,* 336 (December 1):464–66.
Bromage, Timothy G., and M. Christopher Dean. 1985. Reevaluation of the age at death of immature fossil hominids. *Nature* 317 (October 10):525–27.
Broom, Robert. 1950. *Finding the missing link.* London: Watts.
Brown, Peter J., T. Sutikna, M. J. Morwood, R. P. Soejono, Jatmiko, E. Wayhu Saptomo, and Rokus Awe Due. 2004. A new small-bodied hominin from the Late Pleistocene of Flores, Indonesia. *Nature* 431 (October 28):1055–061.
Brunet, Michel, Alain Beauvilain, Yves Coppens, Elile Heintz, Aladji H. E. Moutaye, and David Pilbeam. 1995. The first australopithecine 2,500 kilometers west of the Rift Valley (Chad). *Nature* 378:273–75.
Brunet, Michel, Franck Guy, David Pilbeam, Hassane Taisso Mackaye, Andossa Likius, Djimdoumalbaye Ahounta, Alain Beauvilain, Cécile Blondel, Hervé Bocherens, Jean-Renaud Boisserie, Louis De Bonis, Yves Coppens, Jean Dejax, Christiane Denys, Philippe Duringer, Véra Eisenmann, Gongdibé Fanone, Pierre Fronty, Denis Geraads, Thomas Lehmann, Fabrice Lihoreau, Antoine Louchart, Adoum Mahamat, Gildas Merceron, Guy Mouchelin, Olga Otero, Pablo Pelaez Campomanes, Marcia Ponce De Leon, Jean-Claude Rage, Michel Sapanet, Mathieu Schuster, Jean Sudre, Pascal Tassy, Xavier Valentin, Patrick Vignaud, Laurent Viriot, Antoine Zazzo, and Christoph Zollikofer. 2002. A new hominid from the upper Miocene of Chad, Central Africa. *Nature* 418 (July 11):145–51.
Calvin, William H. 1983. *The throwing Madonna: Essays on the brain.* New York: McGraw-Hill.
Chapais, Bernard. 2008. *Primeval kinship: How pair-bonding gave birth to human society.* Cambridge, MA: Harvard University Press.
Ciochon, Russell, John Olsen, and Jamie James. 1990. *Other origins: The search for the giant ape in human prehistory.* New York: Bantam.
Clark, J. Desmond. 1970. *The prehistory of Africa.* New York: Praeger.
Clarke, Ronald J., and P. V. Tobias. 1995. Sterkfontein member 2 foot bones of the oldest South African hominid. *Science* 269 (July 28):521–24.
Clayman, Charles B., ed. 1989. *American Medical Association encyclopedia of medicine.* New York: Random House.
Conroy, Glenn C. 1990. *Primate evolution.* New York: Norton.
Culotta, Elizabeth. 1995. New hominid crowds the field. *Science* 269 (August 18):918.
Day, Michael. 1986. *Guide to fossil man.* 4th ed. Chicago: University of Chicago Press.
de Lumley, Henry. 1969. A Paleolithic camp at Nice. *Scientific American* (May):42–50.
Dobzhansky, Theodosius. 1962. *Mankind evolving: The evolution of the human species.* New Haven, CT: Yale University Press.

The First Hominids and the Emergence of *Homo*

Dunbar, Robin, and Susanne Shultz. 2007. Evolution of the social brain. *Science* 317 (September 7):1344–47.

Ember, Melvin, and Carol R. Ember. 1979. Male-Female bonding: A cross-species study of mammals and birds. *Behavior Science Research* 14:37–56.

Falk, Dean. 1988. Enlarged occipital/marginal sinuses and emissary foramina: Their significance in hominid evolution. In *Evolutionary history of the "robust" australopithecines,* ed. F. E. Grine. New York: Aldine.

Falk, Dean, C. Hildebolt, K. Smith, M. J. Morwood, T. Sutikna, P. Brown, Jatmiko, E. W. Saptomo, B. Brunsden, F. Prior. 2005. The brain of LBI, *Homo floresiensis. Science* 308 (April 8):242–45.

Feibel, Craig S., and Francis H. Brown. 1993. Microstratigraphy and paleoenvironments. In *The Nariokotome* Homo erectus *Skeleton,* eds. A. Walker and R. Leakey. Cambridge, MA: Harvard University Press.

Fleagle, John G. 1999. *Primate adaptation and evolution.* 2nd ed. San Diego, CA: Academic Press.

Franciscus, Robert G., and Erik Trinkaus. 1988. Nasal morphology and the emergence of *Homo erectus. American Journal of Physical Anthropology* 75:517–27.

Freeman, Leslie G. 1994. Torralba and Ambrona: A review of discoveries. In *Integrative paths to the past,* eds. R. Corruccini and R. Ciochon. Upper Saddle River, NJ: Prentice Hall.

Gabunia, Leo, A. Vekua, D. Lordkipanidze, et al. 2000. Earliest Pleistocene hominid cranial remains from Dmanisi, Republic of Georgia: Taxonomy, geological setting, and age. *Science* 288 (May 12):1019–25.

Gibbons, Ann. 2002. One scientist's quest for the origin of our species. *Science* 298 (November 29):1708–11.

Gibbons, Ann. 2008. The birth of childhood. *Science* 322 (November 14):1040–43.

Gore, Rick. 2002. The first pioneer? *National Geographic* (August).

Goren-Inbar, Naama, N. Alperson, M. Kislev, O. Simchoni, Y. Melamed, A. Ben-Nun, and E. Werker. 2004. Evidence of hominid control of fire at Gesher Benot Ya'aqov, Israel. *Science* 304 (April 30):725–27.

Gowlett, John A. J. 2008. Deep roots of kin: Developing the evolutionary perspective from prehistory. In *Early human kinship: From sex to social reproduction,* eds. Nicholas Allen, Hilary Callan, Robin Dunbar, and Wendy James, 41–57. Oxford, UK: Blackwell.

Grine, Frederick E. 1988a. Evolutionary history of the 'robust' australopithecines: A summary and historical perspective. In *Evolutionary history of the "robust" australopithecines,* ed. F. E. Grine. New York: Aldine.

Grine, Frederick E., ed. 1988b. *Evolutionary history of the "robust" australopithecines.* New York: Aldine.

Grine, Frederick E. 1993. Australopithecine taxonomy and phylogeny: Historical background and recent interpretation. In *The Human evolution source book,* eds. R. Ciochon and J. Fleagle. Upper Saddle River, NJ: Prentice Hall.

Hailie-Selassie, Yohannes. 2001. Late Miocene hominids from the Middle Awash, Ethiopia. *Nature* 412 (July 12):178–81.

Herrmann, Esther, Joseph Call, Maria Victoria Herandez-Lloreda, Brain Hare, and Michael Tomasello. 2007. Humans have evolved specialized skills in social cognition: The cultural intelligence hypothesis. *Science* 317 (September 7):1360–65.

Hewes, Gordon W. 1961. Food transport and the origin of hominid bipedalism. *American Anthropologist* 63:687–710.

Holden, Constance. 1997. Tooling around—Dates show early Siberian settlement. *Science* 275 (February 28):1268.

Holloway, Ralph L. 1974. The casts of fossil hominid brains. *Scientific American* (July):106–15.

Howell, F. Clark. 1966. Observations on the earlier phases of the European Lower Paleolithic. In *Recent studies in paleoanthropology. American anthropologist.* Special publication, April, 88–200.

Isaac, Glynn. 1984. The archaeology of human origins: Studies of the Lower Pleistocene in East Africa, 1971–1981. In *Advances in world archaeology,* eds. F. Wendorf and A. Close. Orlando, FL: Academic Press.

Johanson, Donald C., and Maitland Edey. 1981. *Lucy: The beginnings of humankind.* New York: Simon & Schuster.

Johanson, Donald C., and Tim D. White. 1979. A systematic assessment of early African hominids. *Science* 203 (January 26):321–30.

Jolly, Clifford. 1970. The seed-eaters: A new model of hominid differentiation based on a baboon analogy. *Man* 5:5–28.

Jungers, William L. 1988a. New estimates of body size in australopithecines. In *Evolutionary history of the "robust" australopithecines,* ed. F. Grine. New York: Aldine.

Jungers, William L. 1988b. Relative joint size and hominoid locomotor adaptations with implications for the evolution of hominid bipedalism. *Journal of Human Evolution* 17:247–65.

Kimbel, William H., T. D. White, and D. C. Johansen. 1984. Cranial morphology of *Australopithecus afarensis:* A comparative study based on composite reconstruction of the adult skull. *American Journal of Physical Anthropology* 64:337–88.

Kingston, John D., Bruno D. Marino, and Andrew Hill. 1994. Isotopic evidence for Neogene hominid paleoenvironments in the Kenya Rift Valley. *Science* 264 (May 13):955–59.

Klein, Richard G. 1987. Reconstructing how early people exploited animals: Problems and prospects. In *The evolution of human hunting,* eds. M. Nitecki and D. Nitecki. New York: Plenum Press.

Kramer, Andrew. 2009. The natural history and evolutionary fate of *Homo erectus.* In MyAnthroLibrary, eds. C. R. Ember, M. Ember, and P. N. Peregrine. MyAnthroLibrary.com. Pearson.

Leakey, Louis S. B. 1960. Finding the world's earliest man. *National Geographic* (September):420–35.

Leakey, Meave, C. S. Feibel, I. McDougall, and A. Walker. 1995. New four-million-year-old hominid species from Kanapoi and Allia Bay, Kenya. *Nature* 376 (August 17):565–71.

Leakey, Meave, Fred Spoor, Frank Brown, Patrick Gathogo, Christopher Kiarie, Louise Leakey, Ian McDougall. 2001. New Hominin genus from Eastern Africa shows diverse middle Pliocene lineages. *Nature* 410 (March 22):433–51.

Leakey, Mary. 1971. *Olduvai Gorge: Excavations in Beds I and II.* Cambridge, UK: Cambridge University Press.

Leonard, William M. 2002. Food for thought: Dietary change was a driving force in human evolution. *Scientific American* (December):108–15.

Lewin, Roger. 1983. Fossil Lucy grows younger, again. *Science* 219 (January 7):43–44.

Lovejoy, C. Owen. 1981. The origin of man. *Science* 211 (January 23):341–50.

Lovejoy, C. Owen. 1988. Evolution of human walking. *Scientific American* (November):118–25.

McHenry, Henry M. 1982. The pattern of human evolution: Studies on bipedalism, mastication, and encephalization. *Annual Review of Anthropology* 11:151–73.

McHenry, Henry M. 1988. New estimates of body weight in early hominids and their significance to encephalization and megadontia in "robust" australopithecines. In *Evolutionary history of the "robust" australopithecines,* ed. F. E. Grine. New York: Aldine.

McHenry, Henry M. 2009. Robust australopithecines. Our family tree, and homoplasy. In MyAnthroLibrary, eds. C. R. Ember, M. Ember, and P. N. Peregrine. MyAnthroLibrary.com. Pearson.

The First Hominids and the Emergence of *Homo*

Morwood, Michael J., R. Soejono, R. Roberts, T. Sutikna, C. Turney, K. Westaway, W. Rink, J. Zhao, G. van den Bergh, R. Due, D. Hobbs, M. Moore, M. Bird, and L. Fiffeld. 2004. Archaeology and age of a new hominin from Flores in Eastern Indonesia. *Nature* 431 (October 28):1087–91.

Oakley, Kenneth. 1964. On man's use of fire, with comments on tool-making and hunting. In *Social life of early man,* ed. S. L. Washburn. Chicago: Aldine.

Phillipson, David W. 1993. *African archaeology.* 2nd ed. New York: Cambridge University Press.

Pickford, Martin, Brigette Senut, Dominique Gommercy, and Jacques Treil. 2002. Bipedalism in *Orrorin tugenensis* revealed by its femora. *Comptes Rendu de l'Académie des Science des Paris,* Palevol 1, 1–13.

Pilbeam, David. 1972. *The ascent of man.* New York: Macmillan.

Pilbeam, David, and Stephen Jay Gould. 1974. Size and Scaling in Human Evolution. *Science* 186 (December 6):892–900.

Pope, Geoffrey G. 1989. Bamboo and human evolution. *Natural History* (October):49–57.

Potts, Richard. 1984. Home bases and early hominids. *American Scientist* 72:338–47.

Potts, Richard. 1988. *Early hominid activities at Olduvai.* New York: Aldine.

Richmond, Brian G., and William L. Jungers. *Orrorin tugenensis* femoral morphology and the evolution of human bipedalism. *Science* 319 (21, March 2008):1662–65.

Rightmire, G. Philip. 2000. *Homo erectus.* In *Encyclopedia of human evolution and prehistory,* eds. I. Tattersall, E. Delson, and J. van Couvering. New York: Garland.

Rose, M. D. 1984. Food acquisition and the evolution of positional behaviour: The case of bipedalism. In *Food acquisition and processing in primates,* eds. D. Chivers, B. Wood, and A. Bilsborough. New York: Plenum Press.

Ruff, Christopher B., and Alan Walker. 1993. Body size and body shape. In *The Nariokotome* Homo erectus *skeleton,* eds. A. Walker and R. Leakey. Cambridge, MA: Harvard University Press.

Savage-Rumbaugh, E. Sue. 1994. Hominid evolution: Looking to modern apes for clues. In *Hominid culture in primate perspective,* eds. D. Quiatt and J. Itani. Niwot: University Press of Colorado.

Schick, Kathy D., and Nicholas Toth. 1993. *Making silent stones speak.* New York: Simon & Schuster.

Shipman, Pat. 1986. Scavenging or hunting in early hominids: Theoretical framework and tests. *American Anthropologist* 88:27–43.

Silk, Joan. 2007. Social components of fitness in primate groups. *Science* 317 (September 7):1347–51.

Simpson, Scott W. 2009. *Australopithecus afarensis* and human evolution. In MyAnthroLibrary, eds. C. R. Ember, M. Ember, and P. N. Peregrine. MyAnthroLibrary.com. Pearson.

Simpson, Scott W., Jay Quade, Naomi Levin, Robert Butler, Guillaume Dupont-Nivet, Melanie Everett, and Sileshi Semaw. 2008. A female *Homo erectus* pelvis from Gona, Ethiopia. *Science* 322 (November 14):1089–91.

Smith, B. Holly. 1986. Dental development in *Australopithecus* and early *Homo. Nature* 323 (September 25):327–30.

Speth, John D. 2009. Were our ancestors hunters or scavengers? In MyAnthroLibrary, eds. C. R. Ember, M. Ember, and P. N. Peregrine. MyAnthroLibrary.com. Pearson.

Stedman, Hansell, B. Kozyak, A. Nelson, D. Thesier, L. Su, D. Low, C. Bridges, J. Shrager, N. Minugh-Purvis, and M. Mitchell. 2004. Myosin gene mutation correlates with anatomical changes in the human lineage. *Nature* 428 (March 25):415–18.

Stringer, Christopher B. 1985. Evolution of a species. *Geographical Magazine* 57:601–07.

Susman, Randall L. 1994. Fossil evidence for early hominid tool use. *Science* 265 (September 9):1570–73.

Susman, Randall L., Jack T. Stern, Jr., and William L. Jungers. 1985. Locomotor adaptations in the Hadar hominids. In *Ancestors: The hard evidence,* ed. E. Delson, 184–92. New York: Alan R. Liss.

Swisher, Carl C., III, G. H. Curtis, T. Jacob, A. G. Getty, A. Suprijo, and Widiasmoro. 1994. Age of the earliest known hominids in Java, Indonesia. *Science* 263 (February 25):1118–21.

Szalay, Frederick S. 1975. Hunting-scavenging protohominids: A model for hominid origins. *Man* 10:420–29.

Szalay, Frederick S., and Eric Delson. 1979. *Evolutionary history of the primates.* New York: Academic Press.

Tattersall, Ian, and Jeffrey Schwartz. 2000. *Extinct humans.* Boulder, CO: Westview Press.

Thorpe, Susannah K. S, R. L. Holder, and R. H. Compton. 2007. Origin of human bipedalism as an adaptation for locomotion on flexible branches. *Science* 316 (June 2007):1328–31.

Tobias, Philip V. 1994. The craniocerebral interface in early hominids: Cerebral impressions, cranial thickening, paleoneurobiology, and a new hypothesis on encephalization. In *Integrative paths to the past,* eds. R. Corruccini and R. Ciochon. Upper Saddle River, NJ: Prentice Hall.

Trinkaus, Erik. 1987. Bodies, brawn, brains and noses: Human ancestors and human predation. In *The evolution of human hunting,* eds. M. Nitecki and D. Nitecki. New York: Plenum Press.

Vekua, Abesalom, David Lordkipanidze, G. Philip Rightmire, Jordi Agusti, Reid Ferring, Givi Maisuradze, Alexander Mouskhelishvili, Medea Nioradze, Marcia Ponce de Leon, Martha Tappen, Merab Tvalchrelidze, and Christoph Zollikofer. 2002. A new skull of early *Homo* from Dmanisi, Georgia. *Science* 297 (July 5):85–89.

Walker, Alan, and R. Leakey. 1988. The evolution of *Australopithecus boisei.* In *Evolutionary history of the "robust" australopithecines,* ed. F. Grine, 247–58. New York: Aldine.

Washburn, Sherwood. 1960. Tools and human evolution. *Scientific American* (September):62–75.

Weiner, Steve, Q. Xi, P. Goldberg, J. Liu, and O. Bar-Yousef. 1998. Evidence for the use of fire at Zhoukoudian, China. *Science,* 281 (July 10):251–53.

Weston, Eleanor, and Adrian Lister. 2009. Insular dwarfism in hippos and a model for brain size reduction in *Homo floresiensis. Nature* 459 (May 7):85–88.

Wheeler, Peter. 1984. The evolution of bipedality and loss of func-tional body hair in hominids. *Journal of Human Evolution* 13:91–98.

Wheeler, Peter. 1991. The influence of bipedalism in the energy and water budgets of early hominids. *Journal of Human Evolution* 23:379–88.

White, Timothy D., Donald C. Johanson, and William H. Kimbel. 1981. *Australopithecus africanus:* Its phyletic position reconsidered. *South African Journal of Science* 77:445–70.

White, Timothy D., G. Suwa, and B. Asfaw. 1994. *Australopithecus ramidus,* a new species of early hominid from Aramis, Ethiopia. *Nature* 371 (September 22):306–33.

White, Timothy D., G. Suwa, and B. Asfaw. 1995. Corrigendum: *Australopithecus ramidus,* a new species of early hominid from Aramis, Ethiopia. *Nature* 375 (May 4):88

Whittaker, John C. 1994. *Flintknapping: Making and understanding stone tools.* Austin: University of Texas Press.

The First Hominids and the Emergence of *Homo*

Wilford, John Noble. 1995. The transforming leap, from 4 legs to 2. *New York Times,* September 5, p. C1ff.

Wolpoff, Milford H. 1971. Competitive exclusion among lower Pleistocene hominids: The single species hypothesis. *Man* 6:601–13.

Wolpoff, Milford H. 1983. *Ramapithecus* and human origins: An anthropologist's perspective of changing interpretations. In *New interpretations of ape and human ancestry,* eds. R. Ciochon and R. Corruccini. New York: Plenum Press.

Wolpoff, Milford H., and Abel Nkini. 1985. Early and Early Middle Pleistocene hominids from Asia and Africa. In *Ancestors,* ed. E. Delson. New York: Alan R. Liss.

Wong, Kate. 2003. An ancestor to call our own. *Scientific American* (January):54–63.

Wong, Kate. 2005. The littlest human. *Scientific American* (February):56–65.

Wood, Bernard A. 1992. Evolution of australopithecines. In *The Cambridge encyclopedia of human evolution,* eds. S. Jones, R. Martin, and D. Pilbeam. New York: Cambridge University Press.

Yamei, Hou, R. Potts, Y. Baoyin, et al. 2000. Mid-Pleistocene Acheulean-like stone technology of the Bose Basin, South China. *Science* 287 (March 3):1622–26.

Zihlman, Adrienne L. 1992. The emergence of human locomotion: The evolutionary background and environmental context. In *Topics in primatology,* vol. 1, eds. T. Nishida, et al. Tokyo: University of Tokyo Press.

Zimmer, Carl. 2004. Faster than a hyena? Running may make humans special. *Science* 306 (November 19):1283.

The Emergence of
Homo sapiens

From Chapter 7 of *Human Evolution and Culture,* Seventh Edition. Carol R. Ember, Melvin Ember, Peter
N. Peregrine. Copyright © 2012 by Pearson Education, Inc. All rights reserved.

Recent finds in Africa indicate the presence of *Homo sapiens* perhaps 160,000 years ago. Completely modern-looking humans, ***Homo sapiens sapiens***, appeared by 50,000 years ago. One paleoanthropologist, Christopher Stringer, characterizes the modern human, *Homo sapiens sapiens*, as having "a domed skull, a chin, small eyebrows, browridges, and a rather puny skeleton."[1] Some of us might not like to be called puny, but except for our larger brain, most modern humans definitely are puny compared with *Homo erectus* and even with earlier forms of our own species, *H. sapiens*. We are relatively puny in several respects, including our thinner and lighter bones, as well as our smaller teeth and jaws.

Here, we discuss the fossil evidence, as well as the controversies, about the transition from *H. erectus* to modern humans, which may have begun 500,000 years ago. We also overview what we know archaeologically about the Middle Paleolithic (about 300,000 to 40,000 year ago) and Upper Paleolithic (40,000 to 10,000) years ago.

The Transition from *Homo erectus* to *Homo sapiens*

Most paleoanthropologists agree that *H. erectus* evolved into *H. sapiens*, but they disagree about how and where the transition occurred. There is also disagreement about how to classify some fossils from about 500,000 years to 200,000 years ago that have a mix of *H. erectus* and *H. sapiens* traits.[2] A particular fossil might be called *H. erectus* by some anthropologists and "archaic" *Homo sapiens* by others. And, as we shall see, still other anthropologists see so much continuity between *H. erectus* and *H. sapiens* that they think it is completely arbitrary to call them different species. According to these anthropologists, *H. erectus* and *H. sapiens* may just be earlier and later varieties of the same species and therefore all should be called *H. sapiens*. (*H. erectus* would then be *H. sapiens erectus*.)

Homo heidelbergensis

Some scholars have suggested that the "transitional" fossils share common traits and may actually represent a separate species—***Homo heidelbergensis***, named after a jaw found in 1907, near Heidelberg, Germany.[3] Other specimens that have been suggested as members of this species have been found in many parts of the Old World.[4] Although the classification of these "transitional" specimens is somewhat controversial, to simplify things, we will call all these "transitional" specimens *H. heidelbergensis*.

Homo heidelbergensis differs from *Homo erectus* in having smaller teeth and jaws, a much larger brain (on the order of 1,300 cc), a skull that lacks a sagittal keel and occipital torus, a browridge that divides into separate arches above each eye, and a more robust skeleton (see Figure 1). *Homo heidelbergensis* differs from *Homo sapiens* in retaining a large and prognathic face with relatively large teeth and jaws, a browridge, a long, low cranial vault with a sloping forehead, and in its more robust skeleton.[5]

Neandertals: *Homo sapiens* or *Homo neandertalensis*?

There may be disagreement about how to classify the mixed-trait fossils from 500,000 to 200,000 years ago, but recently an outright battle has emerged about many of the fossils that are less than 200,000 years old. Some anthropologists argue that they were definitely *Homo sapiens* and classify them as *Homo sapiens neandertalensis*. Other anthropologists argue that they were part of a distinct species, ***Homo neandertalensis,*** more commonly referred to as the **Neandertals.**

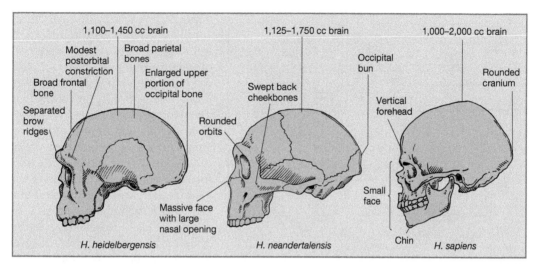

Figure 1 Comparison of the crania of *Homo heidelbergensis, Homo neandertalensis,* and *Homo sapiens,* showing important differences.

The Neandertals have been a confusing hominid fossil group since the first specimen was found in 1856. Somehow through the years, the Neandertals have become the victims of their cartoon image, which usually misrepresents them as burly and more ape than human. Actually, they might go unnoticed in a cross-section of the world's population today. Were they part of our species? For a while, the answer seemed to be yes. But recent archaeological and genetic evidence has led most to question the relationship between Neandertals and modern humans, and today the tide seems to have turned against those who would group them together. Let's take a look at some of the history of research on the Neandertals.

In 1856, three years before Darwin's publication of *Origin of Species,* a skullcap and other fossilized bones were discovered in a cave in the Neander Valley (*tal* is the German word for "valley"), near Düsseldorf, Germany. The fossils in the Neander Valley were the first that scholars could tentatively consider as an early hominid. (The fossils classified as *Homo erectus* were not found until later in the nineteenth century, and the fossils belonging to the genus *Australopithecus* were not found until the twentieth century.) After Darwin's revolutionary work was published, the Neandertal find aroused considerable controversy. A few evolutionist scholars, such as Thomas Huxley, thought that the Neandertal was not that different from modern humans. Others dismissed the Neandertal as irrelevant to human evolution; they saw it as a pathological freak, a peculiar, disease-ridden individual. However, similar fossils turned up later in Belgium, Yugoslavia, France, and elsewhere in Europe, which meant that the original Neandertal find could not be dismissed as an oddity.[6]

The view that the Neandertals were too "brutish" and "primitive" to have been ancestral to modern humans prevailed in the scholarly community until well into the 1950s. Now scholars agree that the skeletal traits of the Neandertals are completely consistent with bipedalism. Perhaps more important, when the australopithecine and *H. erectus* fossils were accepted as hominids in the 1940s and 1950s, anthropologists realized that the Neandertals did not look that different from modern humans—despite their sloping foreheads, large browridges, flattened braincases, large jaws, and nearly absent chins (see Figure 1).[7] And they had larger brains on the average than modern humans (about 150 cc larger).[8] Some scholars believe that the

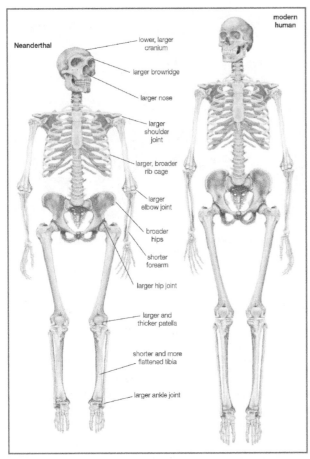

Neanderthal

modern human

lower, larger cranium

larger browridge

larger nose

larger shoulder joint

larger, broader rib cage

larger elbow joint

broader hips

shorter forearm

larger hip joint

larger and thicker patella

shorter and more flattened tibia

larger ankle joint

A comparison of a Neandertal (left) and a modern human skeleton. Note how similar they are, yet the Neandertal appears more stocky and robust.

large brain capacity of Neandertals suggests that they were capable of the full range of behaviors characteristic of modern humans. Their skeletons did, however, attest to one behavioral trait markedly different from behaviors of most modern humans: Neandertals apparently made very strenuous use of their bodies.[9]

While it took almost 100 years for scholars to accept the idea that Neandertals were not that different from modern humans and perhaps should be classified as *Homo sapiens neandertalensis,* recently there has been a growing debate over whether the Neandertals in western Europe interbred with modern-looking people who lived later in western Europe, after about 40,000 years ago. In 1997, a group of researchers from the United States and Germany published findings that forced a reconsideration of the Neandertals' relationship to modern humans. These scholars extracted mitochondrial DNA (mtDNA) from the original Neandertal specimen found in 1856.[10] Among individual modern humans, there are usually five to ten differences in the sequence of mtDNA examined by the U.S. and German researchers. Between modern humans and the Neandertal specimen, there tend to be about 25 differences—more than three times that among modern humans (see Figure 2). This suggested to the researchers that the ancestors of modern humans and the Neandertal must have diverged about 600,000 years ago.[11] If the last common ancestor of ours and the Neandertal lived that long ago, the Neandertal would be a much more distant relative than previously thought. This research has since been replicated with mtDNA from other Neandertal fossils.[12]

But mtDNA is only part of the story. Subsequently, nuclear DNA has been recovered and sequenced from Neandertals. Researchers have found that Neandertals and modern humans have identical versions of the FOXP2 gene, suggesting to some that they may have had language abilities similar to modern humans.[13] Neandertals also had fair skin, and at least some had red hair.[14] While these nuclear DNA findings suggest more similarity, some significant differences between Neandertal and modern human nuclear DNA have also been identified. For example, Neandertals apparently lack the modern human version of *microcephalin,* a gene that is associated with brain development.[15] And initial analyses of the nuclear DNA suggest that the ancestral modern human and Neandertal populations split more than a half million years ago, with only modest admixture after that time.[16]

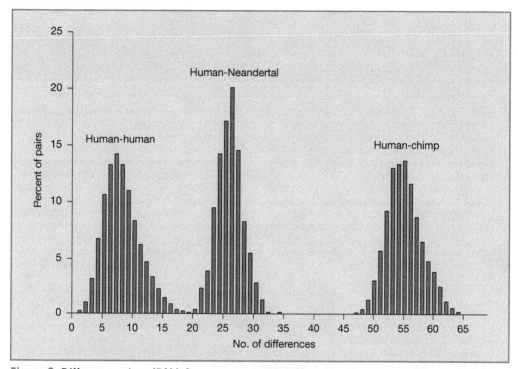

Figure 2 **Differences in mtDNA Sequences among Humans, Humans and Neandertals, and Humans and Chimpanzees**
The x-axis shows the number of sequence differences; the y-axis shows the percent of individuals that share that number of sequence differences.

Source: Krings 1997, 25.

Archaeological findings from Europe and the Near East also seem to indicate that Neandertals and modern humans were different species. It has been known for decades that both modern human and Neandertal fossils are found in the same locations in parts of the Levant, but recent improvements in dating technology and newly discovered fossils have even more clearly demonstrated that the two kinds of hominid coexisted. In fact, several caves in the Mount Carmel region of Israel contain both modern human and Neandertal occupations. The fact that these two groups of hominids coinhabited the Near East for perhaps as much as 30,000 years and did not interbreed much or share much in the way of tool technology strongly suggests that the two are different species.[17] Finds in Europe seem to corroborate that assessment. As early modern humans began moving into Europe, they appear to have displaced populations of Neandertals already living there. Sites with tools thought to be associated with Neandertals disappear throughout Europe as sites with tools thought to be associated with modern humans expand their range.[18] Significantly, the area of Europe last colonized by modern humans (Iberia) contains the very latest Neandertal fossils yet found, dating to some 30,000 years ago.[19]

With all this evidence pointing to Neandertals not being part of the modern human species, why is there an ongoing debate? In part, this is because none of the evidence is conclusive, and much of it can be interpreted in alternate ways. Perhaps more important, however, Neandertal culture, typically referred to as Middle Paleolithic after the predominant tool technology, has some features that make it seem similar to the culture of early modern humans.

Facial Reconstruction

Have you ever wondered how we know what early humans looked like? There are many pictures available, but how did the artists determine what to sculpt or draw? The answer lies in the field of forensic anthropology and more particularly in the field of facial reconstruction.

Facial reconstruction is based on knowledge of skull musculature and the thickness of soft tissue, determined over many years (the first such analysis was done in 1895) from cadavers and, more recently, magnetic resonance images of living people. From these measurements, forensic anthropologists have established a standard set of 21–34 locations on the skull where the average soft tissue thicknesses are known. The first step in facial reconstruction is to mark these locations on a cast of the skull to be reconstructed, using pegs that are the same length as the thickness of muscle and soft tissue at that location. Clay is then used to cover the skull cast to the depth of these pegs (the musculature of the face is first modeled in more sophisticated reconstructions, then clay is used to represent the soft tissues, up to the depth of the pegs).

The size and shape of the nose are reconstructed based on the size and shape of the nasal opening. The size and shape of lips and ears are more difficult to determine, and the skull itself can tell the forensic anthropologist almost nothing about hair or eye color, whether the person had facial hair, or how the person's hair was cut. Those aspects of facial reconstruction require some artistic intuition, and it is helpful to know something about the person, such as sex, age, and ethnicity.

But what about ancient humans? The standard measurements used to reconstruct faces

Boule's reconstruction of a Neandertal, as displayed at Chicago's Field Museum in 1929, illustrates how subjective fossil reconstructions can be. It falsely implies that Neandertals could not stand upright or straighten their knees, and that they were more primitive than we know today that they actually were.

from modern human skulls cannot be assumed to work for ancient skulls. For those, the forensic anthropologists have to go back to the basis of facial reconstruction—muscle and soft tissue. When reconstructing the faces of ancient humans, forensic anthropologists begin with a careful reconstruction of skull musculature, often aided by the comparative anatomy of modern great apes. Once the muscles are in place, glands, fatty tissue, and skin are added, and the face begins to take shape. The size and shape of the nose are determined much like that for modern humans, from the size and shape of the nasal opening. Lips, ears, eyes, and hair are, however, subject to almost pure guesswork—we really have no way of knowing how hairy our ancestors were, whether they had full lips like ours or thin lips like other great apes, or whether their ears were large or small.

Though based on study of the likely muscular anatomy in fossils and the comparative anatomy of modern humans and great apes, it is important to realize that the reconstruction of ancient faces is in part an artistic exercise. We can never know for sure what, for example, *Homo erectus* really looked like. We do not know how hairy they were or how they "styled" their hair. We do not know if their ears were like ours. We do not know the color of their eyes or skin. This is why reconstructions vary in the ways they depict ancient humans. We need to keep in mind when we look at reconstructions that they are educated, perhaps biased, guesses, and not necessarily true depictions of ancient people.

Sources: Moser 1998; Prag and Neave 1997.

Middle Paleolithic Cultures

The period of cultural history associated with the Neandertals is traditionally called the **Middle Paleolithic** in Europe and the Near East and dates from about 300,000 years to about 40,000 years ago.[20] For Africa, the term *Middle Stone Age* is used instead of Middle Paleolithic. The tool assemblages from this period are generally referred to as Mousterian in Europe and the Near East and as *post-Acheulian* in Africa.

Tool Assemblages

The Mousterian The Mousterian type of tool complex is named after the tool assemblage found in a rock shelter at Le Moustier in the Dordogne region of southwestern France. Compared with an Acheulian assemblage, a **Mousterian tool assemblage** has a smaller proportion of large core tools such as hand axes and cleavers and a bigger proportion of small flake tools such as scrapers.[21] Although many flakes struck off from a core were used "as is," the Mousterian is also characterized by flakes that were often altered or "retouched" by striking small flakes or chips from one or more edges (see Figure 3).[22] Studies of the wear on scrapers suggest that many were used for scraping hides or working wood. The fact that some of the tools, particularly points, were thinned or shaped on one side suggests that they were hafted or attached to a shaft or handle.[23]

Toward the end of the Acheulian period, a technique developed that enabled toolmakers to produce flake tools of a predetermined size instead of simply chipping flakes away from the core at random. In this **Levalloisian method,** toolmakers first shaped the core and prepared a

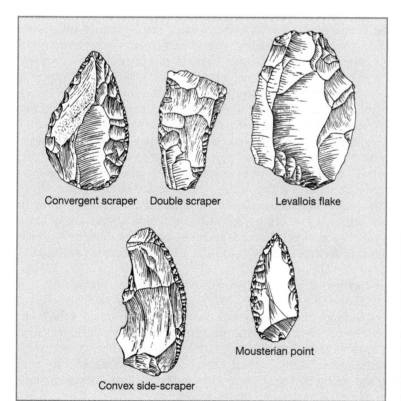

Convergent scraper   Double scraper   Levallois flake

Convex side-scraper   Mousterian point

Figure 3 Stone Tools of the Typical Mousterian Industry
Flakes were carefully retouched, usually on two sides. Mousterian tools, associated with Neandertals, are part of what archaeologists call the Middle Paleolithic, about 200,000 to 35,000 years before the present. Source: Klein 1974.

"striking platform" at one end. Flakes of predetermined and standard sizes could then be knocked off. Although some Levallois flakes date as far back as 400,000 years ago, they are found more frequently in Mousterian tool kits.[24]

The tool assemblages in particular sites may be characterized as Mousterian, but one site may have more or fewer scrapers, points, and so forth, than another site. A number of archaeologists have suggested possible reasons for this variation. For example, Sally Binford and Lewis Binford suggested that different activities may have occurred in different sites. Some sites may have been used for butchering and other sites may have been base camps; hence, the kinds of tools found in different sites should vary.[25] And Paul Fish has suggested that some sites may have more tools produced by the Levalloisian technique because larger pieces of flint were available.[26]

The Post-Acheulian in Africa Like Mousterian tools, many of the post-Acheulian tools in Africa during the Middle Stone Age were struck off prepared cores in the Levalloisian way. The assemblages consist mostly of various types of flake tools. A well-described sequence of such tools comes from the area around the mouth of the Klasies River on the southern coast of South Africa. This area contains rock shelters and small caves in which early and later *Homo sapiens* lived. The oldest cultural remains in one of the caves may date back 120,000 years.[27] These earliest tools include parallel-sided flake blades (probably used as knives), pointed flakes (possibly spearpoints), burins or gravers (chisel-like tools), and scrapers. Similar tools discovered at Border cave, South Africa, may have been used almost 200,000 years ago.[28]

Homesites

Most of the excavated Middle Paleolithic homesites in Europe and the Near East are located in caves and rock shelters. The same is true for the excavated Middle Stone Age homesites in sub-Saharan Africa. We might conclude, therefore, that Neandertals (as well as many early modern humans) lived mostly in caves or rock shelters. But that conclusion could be incorrect. Caves and rock shelters may be overrepresented in the archaeological record because they are more likely to be found than are sites that originally were in the open but now are hidden by thousands of years, and many feet, of sediment. Sediment is the dust, debris, and decay that accumulate over time; when we dust the furniture and vacuum the floor, we are removing sediment.

Still, we know that many Neandertals lived at least part of the year in caves. This was true, for example, along the Dordogne River in France. The river gouged deep valleys in the limestone of that area. Below the cliffs are rock shelters with overhanging roofs and deep caves, many of which were occupied during the Middle Paleolithic. Even if the inhabitants did not stay all year, the sites do seem to have been occupied year after year.[29] Although there is evidence of some use of fire in earlier cultures, Middle Paleolithic humans seem to have relied more on it. There are thick layers of ash in many rock shelters and caves and evidence that hearths were used to increase the efficiency of the fires.[30]

Quite a few Neandertal homesites were in the open. In Africa, open-air sites were located on floodplains, at the edges of lakes, and near springs.[31] Many open-air sites have been found in Europe, particularly eastern Europe. The occupants of the well-known site at Moldova in western Russia lived in river-valley houses framed with wood and covered with animal skins. Bones of mammoths, huge elephants now extinct, surround the remains of hearths and were apparently used to help hold the animal skins in place. Even though the winter climate near the edge of the glacier nearby was cold at that time, there still would have been animals to hunt because the plant food for the game was not buried under deep snow.

The hunters probably moved away in the summer to higher land between the river valleys. In all likelihood, the higher ground was grazing land for the large herds of animals the Moldova hunters depended on for meat. In the winter river valley sites, archaeologists have found skeletons of wolf, arctic fox, and hare with their paws missing. These animals probably were skinned for pelts that were made into clothing.[32]

Getting Food

How Neandertals and early modern humans got their food probably varied with their environment. In Africa, they lived in savanna and semiarid desert. In western and eastern Europe, they had to adapt to cold; during periods of increased glaciation, much of the environment was steppe grassland and tundra.

The European environment during this time was much richer in animal resources than the tundra of northern countries today. Indeed, the European environment inhabited by Neandertals abounded in big and small game, such as reindeer, bison, wild oxen, horses, mammoths, rhinoceroses, and deer, as well as bears, wolves, and foxes.[33] Some European sites have also yielded bird and fish remains. For example, people in a summer camp in northern Germany apparently hunted swans and ducks and fished for perch and pike.[34] Little, however, is known about the particular plant foods the European Neandertals may have consumed; the remains of plants are unlikely to survive thousands of years in a nonarid environment.

In Africa, too, early *Homo sapiens* varied in how they got food. For example, we know that the people living at the mouth of the Klasies River in South Africa ate shellfish as well as meat from small grazers such as antelopes and large grazers such as eland and buffalo.[35] But archaeologists disagree about how the Klasies River people got their meat when they began to occupy the caves in the area. Richard Klein thinks they hunted both large and small game. Klein speculates that, because the remains of eland of all ages have been found in Cave 1 at the Klasies River site, the people there probably hunted the eland by driving them into corrals or other traps, where animals of all ages could be killed. Klein thinks that buffalo were hunted differently. Buffalo tend to charge attackers, which would make it difficult to drive them into

Neandertals appear to have hunted a wide variety of game. In this reconstruction, two Neandertals are shown attacking a mastodon they have trapped in a pit.

traps. Klein believes that, because bones from mostly very young and very old buffalo are found in the cave, the hunters were able to stalk and kill only the most vulnerable animals.[36]

Lewis Binford thinks the Klasies River people hunted only small grazers and scavenged the eland and buffalo meat from the kills of large carnivores. He argues that sites should contain all or almost all of the bones from animals that were hunted. According to Binford, because more or less complete skeletons are found only from small animals, the Klasies River people were not, at first, hunting all the animals they used for food.[37]

However, evidence suggests that people were hunting big game as much as 400,000 years ago. Wooden spears that old were found in Germany in association with stone tools and the butchered remains of more than 10 wild horses. The heavy spears resemble modern aerodynamic javelins, which suggests they would have been thrown at large animals such as horses, not at small animals. This new evidence strongly suggests that hunting, not just scavenging, may be older than archaeologists once thought.[38]

Rituals

At Drachenloch cave in the Swiss Alps, a stone-lined pit holding the stacked skulls of seven cave bears was found in association with a Neandertal habitation. Why preserve these skulls? One reason might be for rituals intended to placate or control bears. Cave bears were enormous—some nearly 9 feet tall—and competed with Neandertals for prime cave living sites. Perhaps the Neandertals preserved the skulls of bears they killed in the cave as a way of honoring or appeasing either the bears or their spirits. But the evidence is not completely persuasive. In our own society, some may hang a deer or moose head on the wall without any associated ritual. At this point, we cannot say for certain whether or not Neandertals engaged in ritual behavior.[39]

The Emergence of Modern Humans

Cro-Magnon humans, who appear in western Europe about 35,000 years ago, were once thought to be the earliest specimens of modern humans, or *Homo sapiens sapiens*. (The Cro-Magnons are named after the rock shelter in France where they were first found in 1868.[40]) But we now

This *Homo sapiens* skull from Ethiopia is the oldest member of our species yet found, dating to 160,000 years ago.

know that modern-looking humans appeared earlier outside of Europe. As of now, the oldest unambiguous fossils classified as *H. sapiens* come from Ethiopia and date to perhaps 160,000 years ago.[41] Additional fossils, discovered in one of the Klasies River mouth caves in South Africa, are possibly as old as 100,000 years.[42] Other *Homo sapiens* fossils of about the same age have been found in Border cave in South Africa.[43] Remains of anatomically modern humans (*Homo sapiens sapiens*) found at two sites in Israel, at Skhul and Qafzeh, which used to be thought to date back 40,000 years to 50,000 years, may be 90,000 years old.[44] There are also anatomically modern human finds in Borneo, at Niah, from about 40,000 years ago and in Australia, at Lake Mungo, from about 30,000 years ago.[45]

These modern-looking humans differed from the Neandertals and other early *H. sapiens* in that they had higher, more bulging foreheads, thinner and lighter bones, smaller faces and jaws, chins (the bony protuberances that remain after projecting faces recede), and only slight browridges (or no ridges at all; see Figure 1).

Theories about the Origins of Modern Humans

Two theories about the origins of modern humans continue to be debated among anthropologists. One, which can be called the *single-origin theory,* suggests that modern humans emerged in Africa and then spread to other parts, replacing Neandertals. The second theory, which has been called the multiregional theory, suggests that modern humans evolved in various parts of the Old World after *Homo erectus* spread out of Africa.[46]

Single-Origin Theory According to the single-origin theory, the Neandertals did not evolve into modern humans. Rather, Neandertals were replaced by modern humans around 30,000 years ago. Single-origin theorists think that the originally small population of *H. sapiens sapiens* had some biological or cultural advantage, or both, that allowed them to spread and replace Neandertals.

The main evidence for the single-origin theory comes from the genes of living peoples. In 1987, Rebecca Cann and colleagues used genetic differences between living peoples to determine how long ago modern humans separated from our closest ancestors. Cann relied on the genes within a tiny structure found in all of our eukaryotic cells called *mitochondria.* Mitochondria produce enzymes needed for energy production, and they have their own DNA, which replicates when a cell replicates but is not thought to be under any pressure from natural selection.[47]

The only source of change in mitochondrial DNA (usually referred to as *mt*DNA) is random mutation. Mitochondrial DNA is inherited only from mothers in animals; it is not carried into an egg cell by sperm, but is left with the sperm's tail on the outside of the egg. These unique characteristics make it possible to use mtDNA to measure the degree of relatedness between two species, and even to say how long ago those species diverged.[48] The longer two species have been separated, the more differences there will be in their mtDNA, which is thought to mutate at a fairly constant rate of about 2 percent per million years. Thus, the number of differences between the mtDNA of two organisms can be converted into an estimated date in the past when those organisms stopped being part of the same breeding population. Although controversy remains over many of the details of how and why mtDNA mutates and about its accuracy for determining absolute dates of divergence, most scholars agree that it is a powerful tool for examining relative degrees of relatedness between species.[49]

Rebecca Cann and her colleagues presented evidence that the mtDNA from people in the United States, New Guinea, Africa, and East Asia showed differences suggesting that their common ancestor lived only 200,000 years ago. Cann and colleagues further claimed that, because the amount of variation among individuals was greatest in African populations, the common ancestor of all lived in Africa.[50] (It is generally the case that people living in a homeland exhibit more variation than any emigrant descendant population.)

There were many problems with early mtDNA studies, but those problems have been addressed over the years and new and better mtDNA analyses have been performed. Most scholars now agree that the mtDNA of modern humans shows a remarkably small degree of variation (in fact, less than half the variation found in most chimpanzee populations), which strongly suggests that we all share a very recent, common ancestry.[51] More detailed analyses of mtDNA diversity in modern humans have allowed scholars to identify the ancestral roots of contemporary populations around the world, and these analyses also point to modern human origins in East Africa and a subsequent spread out of that region.[52]

Evidence for an East African origin of modern humans and the subsequent expansion also comes from research on variation in the Y chromosome. The Y chromosome is the chromosome that determines whether a person is male. A male inherits an X chromosome from his mother and a Y chromosome from his father. Only men have a Y chromosome, and because there is only one copy in any given man, the Y chromosome is the only nuclear chromosome that, like mtDNA, does not undergo recombination. Although the Y chromosome can be affected by selection, it is thought that most variation in the Y chromosome, like variation in mtDNA, is caused by random mutations. Variation in the Y chromosome can therefore be analyzed in much the same way as variation in mtDNA.[53]

The results of research on variation in the Y chromosome mirror those on variation in mtDNA to a remarkable extent. Analysis of Y chromosome variation points to Africa as the source of modern humans, and suggests an exodus from Africa of modern humans. One of the major differences between mtDNA studies and those employing the Y chromosome is in the dating of the most recent common ancestor. As noted previously, studies of mtDNA suggest the most recent common ancestor lived about 200,000 years ago, whereas studies of the Y chromosome suggest the most recent ancestor lived only about 100,000 years ago.[54] Additional research, including new research on variation in nuclear DNA, may help to resolve these differences. For now, however, it seems clear that the modern human gene pool has a single, and fairly recent, origin in Africa.[55]

The mtDNA analyses of Neandertals, and the archaeological evidence suggesting that Neandertals and modern humans lived without much interaction or interbreeding in Europe and the Near East, also tend to support the single-origin theory. The *Homo sapiens* skeletal material from Ethiopia, Africa, in the 150,000–200,000-year-ago time range, further supports the single-origin theory.[56] However, such evidence does not necessarily contradict the validity of the multiregional theory of human origins.

Multiregional Theory According to the multiregional theory, *Homo erectus* populations in various parts of the Old World gradually evolved into anatomically modern-looking humans. The few scholars who continue to support this view believe that the "transitional" or "archaic" *H. sapiens* and the Neandertals represent phases in the gradual development of more "modern" anatomical features. Indeed, as we have noted, some of these scholars see so much continuity between *Homo erectus* and modern humans that they classify *Homo erectus* as *Homo sapiens erectus.*

Continuity is the main evidence multiregional theorists use to support their position. In several parts of the world, there seem to be clear continuities in distinct skeletal features between *Homo erectus* and *Homo sapiens.* For example, *Homo erectus* fossils from China tend to have broader faces with more horizontal cheekbones than specimens from elsewhere in the world, traits that also appear in modern Chinese populations.[57] Southeast Asia provides more compelling evidence, according to multiregional theorists. There, a number of traits—relatively thick cranial bones, a receding forehead, an unbroken browridge, facial prognathism, relatively large cheekbones, and relatively large molars—appear to persist from *Homo erectus* through modern populations (see Figure 4).[58] But others suggest that these traits cannot be used to establish a unique continuation from *Homo erectus* in Southeast Asia because these traits are found in modern humans all over the world. And still others argue that the traits are not as similar as the multiregional theorists claim.[59]

In support of their position, multiregional theorists argue that the mtDNA and Y chromosome evidence supports multiregional evolution rather than a single-origin theory of modern humans, that genetic variation in modern humans may reflect the emigration of *Homo erectus* out of Africa rather than the emigration of *Homo sapiens sapiens*. This interpretation would mean that the accepted rates of mutation in both mtDNA and the Y chromosome are wrong, that both actually mutate much more slowly than currently thought.[60] However, this interpretation is contradicted by established correlations between differences in mtDNA among human groups known to have colonized New Guinea and Australia at particular points in time, which seem to fit the accepted rate of mutation, and with the divergence between humans and apes, the date of which also seems to accord with the accepted faster rate of mtDNA mutation.

To explain why human evolution would proceed gradually and in the same direction in various parts of the Old World, multiregional theorists point to cultural improvements in cutting-tool and cooking technology that occurred all over the Old World. These cultural improvements may have relaxed the prior natural selection for heavy bones and musculature in the skull. The argument is that, unless many plant and animal foods were cut into small pieces and

Figure 4 Fossil Evidence for Regional Continuity
Continuity in Southeast Asian and Australian populations: Skulls of (a) *Homo erectus*, (b) early *Homo sapiens*, and (d) modern *Homo sapiens*, all from Southeast Asia and Australia, have similar foreheads, browridges, and occipital and facial shapes, whereas skulls from Africa, represented here by (c), an early *Homo sapiens*, have different forms. The similarity in Southeast Asian and Australian populations over more than 500,000 years argues for regional continuity rather than replacement.

thoroughly cooked in hearths or pits that were efficient thermally, they would be hard to chew and digest. Thus, people would have needed robust jaws and thick skull bones to support the large muscles that enabled them to cut and chew their food. But robust bone and muscle would no longer be needed after people began to cut and cook more effectively.[61]

Intermediate Theories There is also the intermediate interpretation that there may have been some replacement of one population by another, some local continuous evolution, and some interbreeding between early modern humans who spread out of Africa, and populations encountered in North Africa, Europe, and Asia.[62] As biologist Alan Templeton has noted, the debates over a single-origin versus multiregional evolution

> are based on the myth that replacement of one physical feature in a fossil series with another feature can only be created by one population replacing another (by exterminating them, for example), but such fossil patterns could be a reflection of one genotype replacing another

through gene flow and natural selection. Morphological replacement should not be equated with population replacement when one is dealing with populations that can interbreed.[63]

Interestingly, data on the genetic diversity of human body lice seems to support an intermediate theory of human origins. Humans are plagued by a single species of hair lice, *Pediculus humanus*, which happens to have two distinct genetic lineages. One is found worldwide, the other only in the Americas. These two genetic lineages of lice appear to have diverged over 1 million years ago. If modern humans evolved less than 200,000 years ago (and the worldwide louse lineage suggests it experienced some dramatic changes about 100,000 years ago, which may relate to modern humans leaving Africa), then how did the other lineage continue? One answer is that they were transferred to modern humans from a previously isolated population of *Homo erectus* in Asia.[64] But if that were the case, then very close contact—either body to body or sharing clothing—would had to have taken place between modern and archaic humans.

What Happened to the Neandertals?

Regardless of which theory (single-origin, multiregional, or intermediate) is correct, it seems clear that Neandertals and modern humans (*H. sapiens sapiens*) coexisted in Europe and the Near East for at least 20,000 years, and maybe as long as 60,000 years. What happened to the Neandertals? Three answers have generally been considered. First, they interbred with modern humans and the unique Neandertal characteristics slowly disappeared from the interbreeding population. Second, they were killed off by modern humans. Third, they were driven to extinction due to competition with modern humans. Let's take a look at each of these scenarios.

Interbreeding

The interbreeding scenario seems the most probable, yet evidence supporting it is weak. If modern humans and Neandertals interbred, we should be able to find "hybrid" individuals in the fossil record. In fact, a group of scholars has argued that an Upper Paleolithic skeleton from Portugal demonstrates a combination of modern human and Neandertal features.[65] The finding remains controversial, however, because it is a child's skeleton (approximately 4 years old) and its Neandertal-like features have not been corroborated by other scholars. More significantly, if the interbreeding hypothesis is correct, then the mtDNA analysis we have discussed several times here must be wrong. On the other hand, recent research on Neandertal tools suggests that some Neandertal groups adopted new techniques of tool manufacture that are thought to be uniquely associated with modern humans.[66] If Neandertals were learning from modern humans, then the idea that they could have interbred and perhaps been absorbed within the modern human population gains credibility.

Genocide

The genocide scenario, that modern humans killed off Neandertals, has appeal as a sensational story, but little evidence. Not a single "murdered" Neandertal has ever been found, and one might wonder, in a fight between the powerful Neandertals and the more gracile modern humans, who might get the better of whom.

Extinction

Finally, the extinction scenario, that Neandertals simply could not compete with modern humans, seems to have the best archaeological support. As we discussed earlier, there appear to be "refugee" populations of Neandertals in Iberia as recently as perhaps 30,000 years ago.

The "retreat" of Neandertals from the Near East, eastern Europe, and finally western Europe following the movement of modern humans into the region seems to support the "refugee" interpretation.[67] More importantly, physical anthropologist Erik Trinkaus has argued, based on both physical characteristics of the Neandertal skeleton and their apparent patterns of behavior, that Neandertals were less efficient hunters and gatherers than modern humans.[68] And they may have needed more food. Steve Churchill has suggested that Neandertals' stocky bodies and great muscle mass might have required 25 percent more calories than modern humans.[69] If this is true, a modern human group would have been able to live and reproduce more easily than a Neandertal group in the same territory, and this would likely drive the Neandertals away. When there were no new territories to run to, the Neandertals would go extinct—precisely what the archaeological record seems to suggest.[70]

But were modern humans and their cultures really that much more efficient than Middle Paleolithic cultures? As we will see, the Upper Paleolithic does seem to mark a watershed in the evolution of human culture, allowing humans to expand their physical horizons throughout the world and their intellectual horizons into the realms of art and ritual.

The Upper Paleolithic World

The period of cultural history in Europe, the Near East, and Asia known as the **Upper Paleolithic** dates from about 40,000 years ago to the period known as the *Neolithic* (beginning about 10,000 years ago, depending on the area). In Africa, the cultural period comparable to the Upper Paleolithic is known as the *Later Stone Age* and may have begun much earlier. In North and South America, the period begins when humans first entered the New World, some time before 12,000 years ago (these colonizers are typically called *Paleo-Indians*) and continues until what are called *Archaic traditions* emerged some 10,000 years ago. To simplify terminology, we use the term *Upper Paleolithic* to refer to cultural developments in all areas of the Old World during this period.

In many respects, lifestyles during the Upper Paleolithic were similar to lifestyles before. People were still mainly hunters, gatherers, and fishers who probably lived in small mobile bands. They made their camps out in the open in skin-covered huts and in caves and rock shelters. And they continued to produce smaller and smaller stone tools.

But the Upper Paleolithic is also characterized by a variety of new developments. One of the most striking is the emergence of art—painting on cave walls and stone slabs, and carving tools, decorative objects, and personal ornaments out of bone, antler, shell, and stone. Because more archaeological sites date from the Upper Paleolithic than from any previous period and some Upper Paleolithic sites seem larger than any before, many archaeologists think that the human population increased considerably during the

Upper Paleolithic bone needle and spear or harpoon points. Upper Paleolithic peoples made a much wider variety of tools than their predecessors.

125

Upper Paleolithic.[71] In addition, new inventions, such as the bow and arrow, the spear thrower, and tiny replaceable blades that could be fitted into handles, appear for the first time.[72]

The Last Ice Age

The Upper Paleolithic world had an environment very different from today's. The earth was gripped by the last ice age, with glaciers covering Europe as far south as Berlin and Warsaw, and North America as far south as Chicago. To the south of these glacial fronts was a tundra zone extending in Europe to the Alps and in North America to the Ozarks, Appalachians, and well out onto the Great Plains. Environmentally, both Europe and North America probably resembled contemporary Siberia and northern Canada. Elsewhere in the world conditions were not as extreme, but were still different from conditions today.[73] Annual temperatures were as much as 50 degrees Fahrenheit (10 degrees Celsius) below today's, and changes in ocean currents would have made temperature contrasts (i.e., the differences between summer and winter months) more extreme as well. Europe experienced heavy annual snowfall. The presence of huge ice sheets in the north changed the climate throughout the world. North Africa, for example, appears to have been much wetter than today, and South Asia was apparently drier. And everywhere the climate seems to have been highly variable.[74]

The plants and animals of the Upper Paleolithic world were adapted to these extreme conditions. Among the most important, and dramatic, were the large game animals collectively known as *Pleistocene megafauna*.[75] These animals, as their name suggests, were huge compared to their contemporary descendants. For example, in North America, giant ground sloths stood some 8–10 feet tall and weighed several thousand pounds. Siberian mammoths were the largest elephants ever to live—some standing more than 14 feet tall.

Upper Paleolithic Europe

With the vast supplies of meat available from megafauna, it is not surprising that many Upper Paleolithic cultures relied on hunting, and this was particularly true of the Upper Paleolithic peoples of Europe, on whom we focus here. Their way of life represents a common pattern throughout the Old World. But as people began to use more diverse resources in their environments, the use of local resources allowed Upper Paleolithic groups in much of the Old World to become more sedentary than their predecessors. They also began to trade with neighboring groups to obtain resources not available in their local territories.[76]

As was the case in the known Middle Paleolithic sites, most of the Upper Paleolithic remains that have been excavated were situated in caves and rock shelters. In southwestern France, some groups seem to have paved parts of the shelter floors with stones. Tentlike structures were built in some caves, apparently to keep out the cold.[77] Some open-air sites have also been excavated.

The site at Dolni Vestonice in what is now the Czech Republic, dated to around 25,000 years ago, is one of the first for which there is an entire settlement plan.[78] The settlement seems to have consisted of four tentlike huts, probably made from animal skins, with a great open hearth in the center. Around the outside were mammoth bones, some rammed into the ground, which suggests that the huts were surrounded by a wall. All in all, there were bone heaps from about 100 mammoths. Each hut probably housed a group of related families— about 20–25 people. (One hut was approximately 27 by 45 feet and had five hearths distributed inside it, presumably one for each family.) With 20–25 people per hut, and assuming that all four huts were occupied at the same time, the population of the settlement would have been 100–125 people.

Up a hill from the settlement was a fifth and different kind of hut. It was dug into the ground and contained a bake oven and more than 2,300 small, fired fragments of animal figurines. There were also some hollow bones that may have been musical instruments. Another interesting feature of the settlement was a burial find of a woman with a disfigured face. She may have been a particularly important personage; her face was found engraved on an ivory plaque near the central hearth of the settlement.

Upper Paleolithic Tools

Upper Paleolithic toolmaking appears to have had its roots in the Mousterian and post-Acheulian traditions because flake tools are found in many Upper Paleolithic sites. But the Upper Paleolithic is characterized by a preponderance of blades; there were also burins, bone and antler tools, and microliths. In addition, two new techniques of toolmaking appeared: *indirect percussion* and *pressure flaking*. Blades were found in Middle Paleolithic assemblages, but they were not widely used until the Upper Paleolithic. Although blades can be made in a variety of ways, **indirect percussion** using a hammer-struck punch was common in the Upper Paleolithic. After shaping a core into a pyramidal or cylindrical form, toolmakers put a punch of antler, wood, or other hard material into position and struck it with a hammer. Because the force is readily directed, toolmakers were able to strike off consistently shaped **blades,** which are more than twice as long as they are wide.[79]

The Upper Paleolithic is also noted for the production of large numbers of bone, antler, and ivory tools; needles, awls, and harpoons made of bone appear for the first time.[80] The manufacture of these implements may have been made easier by the development of many varieties of burins. **Burins** are chisel-like stone tools used for carving; bone and antler needles, awls, and projectile points could be produced with them.[81] Burins have been found in Middle and Lower Paleolithic sites but are present in great number and variety only in the Upper Paleolithic.

Pressure flaking also appeared during the Upper Paleolithic. Rather than using percussion to strike off flakes as in previous technologies, pressure flaking works by employing pressure with a bone, wood, or antler tool at the edge of the tool to remove small flakes. Pressure flaking would usually be used in the final stages of retouching a tool.[82]

As time went on, all over the Old World, smaller and smaller blade tools were produced. The very tiny ones, called **microliths,** were often hafted or fitted into handles, one blade at a time or several blades together, to serve as spears, adzes, knives, and sickles. The hafting required inventing a way to trim the blade's back edge so that it would be blunt rather than sharp. In this way, the blades would not split the handles into which they might be inserted; the blunting would also prevent the users of an unhafted blade from cutting themselves.[83]

Some archaeologists think that the blade technique was adopted because it made for more economical use of flint. André Leroi-Gourhan calculated that, with the old Acheulian technique, a 2-pound lump of flint yielded 16 inches of working edge and produced only two hand axes. If the more advanced Mousterian technique were used, a lump of equal size would yield 2 yards of working edge. The indirect percussion method of the Upper Paleolithic would yield as much as 25 yards of working edge.[84] Getting the most out of a valuable resource may have been particularly important in areas lacking large flint deposits.

Jacques Bordaz suggested that the evolution of toolmaking techniques, which continually increased the amount of usable edge that could be gotten out of a lump of flint, was significant because people could then spend more time in regions where flint was unavailable.[85] Another reason for adopting the blade toolmaking technique may have been that it made for easy repair of tools. For example, the cutting edge of a tool might consist of a line of razorlike microliths set into a piece of wood. The tool would not be usable if just one of the cutting edge's microliths broke off or was chipped. But if the user carried a small prepared core of flint from which an identical-sized microlith could be struck off, the tool could be repaired easily by replacing the lost or broken microlith. A spear whose point was lost could be repaired similarly. Thus, the main purpose of the blade toolmaking technique may not have been to make more economical use of flint but rather to allow easy replacement of damaged blades.[86]

How Were the Tools Used? One way of suggesting what a particular tool was used for in the past is to observe the manner in which similar tools are used by members of recent or contemporary societies, preferably societies with subsistence activities and environments similar to those of the ancient toolmakers. This method of study is called reasoning from **ethnographic analogy.** The problem with such reasoning, however, is obvious: We cannot be sure that the original use of a tool was the same as the present use. When selecting recent or contemporary cultures that may provide the most informative and accurate comparisons, we should try to choose those that derive from the ancient culture in which we are interested. If the cultures being compared are historically related, there is a greater likelihood that the two groups used a particular kind of tool in similar ways and for similar purposes.[87]

Another way of suggesting what a particular kind of tool was used for is to compare the visible and microscopic wear marks on the prehistoric tools with the wear marks on similar tools made and experimentally used by researchers. The idea behind this approach is that different uses leave different wear marks. A pioneer in this research was S. A. Semenov. For example, by cutting into meat with his re-created stone knives, he produced a polish on the edges that was like the polish found on blades from a prehistoric site in Siberia. This finding led Semenov to infer that the Siberian blades were probably also used to cut meat.[88]

The tools made by Upper Paleolithic peoples suggest that they were much more effective hunters and fishers than their predecessors.[89] During the Upper Paleolithic, and probably for the first time, spears were shot from a spear thrower rather than thrown with the arm. We know this because bone and antler **atlatls** (the Aztec word for "spear thrower") have been found in some sites. A spear propelled off a grooved board could be sent through the air with increased force, causing it to travel farther and hit harder, and with less effort by the thrower. The bow and arrow was also used in various places during the Upper Paleolithic; and harpoons, used for fishing and perhaps for hunting reindeer, were invented at this time.

These new tools and weapons for more effective hunting and fishing do not rule out the possibility that Upper Paleolithic peoples were still scavenging animal remains. Olga Soffer suggests that Upper Paleolithic peoples may have located their settlements near places where many mammoths died naturally in order to make use of the bones for building (see Figure 5). For example, in Moravia, the mammoths may have come to lick deposits of calcite and other sources of magnesium and calcium, particularly during the late spring and early summer when resources were short and mortality was high. Consistent with this idea is that there are few human-made cut marks on mammoth bones in some places. For example, at Dolni Vestonice, where bones of 100 mammoths were found, few bones show cut marks from butchering and few bones were found inside the huts. In contrast, the site is littered with bison, horse, and reindeer bones, suggesting that these other animals were deliberately killed and eaten by humans. If the people had been able to kill all the mammoths we find the remains of, why would they have hunted so many other animals?[90]

Upper Paleolithic Art The earliest discovered traces of art are beads and carvings, and then paintings, from Upper Paleolithic sites. We might expect that early artistic efforts were crude,

Figure 5 Here we see the type of mammoth-bone shelters constructed about 15,000 years ago on the East European Plain. Often mammoth skulls formed part of the foundation for the tusk, long bone, and wooden frame, covered with hide. As many as 95 mammoth mandibles were arranged around the outside in a herringbone pattern.

but the cave paintings of Spain and southern France show a marked degree of skill. So do the naturalistic paintings on slabs of stone excavated in southern Africa. Some of those slabs appear to have been painted as much as 28,000 years ago, which suggests that painting in Africa is as old as painting in Europe.[91] But painting may be even older than that. The early Australians may have painted on the walls of rock shelters and cliff faces at least 30,000 years ago and maybe as much as 60,000 years ago.[92] And at Blombos Cave in South Africa, engraved pieces of red ochre date back to more than 77,000 years ago.[93]

Peter Ucko and Andrée Rosenfeld identified three principal locations of paintings in the caves of western Europe: (1) in obviously inhabited rock shelters and cave entrances—art as decoration or "art for art's sake"; (2) in "galleries" immediately off the inhabited areas of caves; and (3) in the inner reaches of caves, whose difficulty of access has been interpreted by some as a sign that magical-religious activities were performed there.[94]

The subjects of the paintings are mostly animals. The paintings are on bare walls, with no backdrops or environmental trappings. Perhaps, like many contemporary peoples, Upper Paleolithic men and women believed that the drawing of a human image could cause death or injury. That might explain why human figures are rarely depicted in cave art. Another explanation for the focus on animals is that these people sought to improve their luck at hunting. This theory is suggested by evidence of chips in the painted figures, perhaps made by spears thrown at the drawings. Or perhaps the paintings were inspired by the need to increase the supply of animals. Cave art seems to have reached a peak toward the end of the Upper Paleolithic period, when the herds of game were decreasing.

The particular symbolic significance of the cave paintings in southwestern France is more explicitly revealed by the results of Patricia Rice and Ann Paterson's statistical study.[95] The data suggest that the animals portrayed in the cave paintings were mostly the ones that the painters preferred for meat and for materials such as hides. For example, wild cattle (bovines) and horses are portrayed more often than we would expect by chance, probably because they were larger and heavier (meatier) than the other animals in the environment. In addition, the paintings

Paintings of wild horses from Chauvet cave in France. Cave paintings like this demonstrate the remarkable skill of Upper Paleolithic artists.

mostly portray animals that the painters may have feared the most because of their size, speed, natural weapons such as tusks and horns, and unpredictability of behavior (mammoths, bovines, and horses). Thus, the paintings are consistent with the idea that "the art is related to the importance of hunting in the economy of Upper Paleolithic people."[96] Consistent with this idea is the fact that the art of the cultural period that followed the Upper Paleolithic, when getting food no longer depended on hunting large game because they were becoming extinct, the art ceased to focus on portrayals of animals.

Upper Paleolithic Cultures in Africa and Asia

Europe was not the only region where Upper Paleolithic peoples thrived. In North Africa, for example, Upper Paleolithic peoples hunted large animals on the grasslands that covered the region during that period. They lived in small communities located within easy access to water and other resources, and moved regularly, probably to follow the animal herds. Trade took place between local groups, particularly for high-quality stone used in making tools.[97] In eastern and southern Africa, a way of life known as the Later Stone Age developed that persisted in some areas until very recently. People lived in small, mobile groups, hunting large animals and collecting a wide variety of plant foods.

In South Asia, the Upper Paleolithic saw an increasingly sedentary lifestyle developing along the banks of freshwater streams. The Upper Paleolithic peoples in South Asia combined hunting, fishing, and gathering with seasonal movements to exploit seasonally abundant resources.[98] In East and Southeast Asia, ocean resources became vital to coastal-dwelling peoples, whereas those inland lived primarily in caves, hunting and collecting broadly in the local environment. Many of these sites appear to have been occupied for long periods of time, suggesting some degree of sedentism. During the Upper Paleolithic, peoples from Asia also populated Australia, New Guinea, and some of the islands of western Melanesia, clearly demonstrating the ability of these peoples to navigate on the sea and to use its resources.[99]

The Earliest Humans and Their Cultures in the New World

So far, we have dealt only with the Old World—Africa, Europe, and Asia. What about the New World—North and South America? How long have humans lived there, and what were their earliest cultures like?

Because only *Homo sapiens sapiens* fossils have been found in North and South America, migrations of humans to the New World had to have taken place some time after the emergence of *H. sapiens sapiens*. But exactly when these migrations occurred is subject to debate, particularly about when people got to areas south of Alaska. On the basis of similarities in biological traits such as tooth forms and blood types, and on possible linguistic relationships, anthropologists agree that Native Americans originally came from Asia. The traditional assumption is that they came to North America from Siberia, walking across a land bridge (Beringia) that is now under water (the Bering Strait) between Siberia and Alaska. The ice sheets or glaciers that periodically covered most of the high latitudes of the world contained so much of the world's water (the ice sheets were thousands of feet thick in some places) that Beringia was dry land in various periods (see Figure 6).

Figure 6 Beringia and the Ice Sheets

Source: Meltzer 1993.

Until recently, the prevailing view was that humans were not present south of Alaska until after 11,500 years ago. Now it appears from an archaeological site called Monte Verde in Chile that modern humans got to southern South America by at least 12,500 years ago, and maybe as much as 33,000 years ago. The Monte Verde site contains more than 700 stone tools, the remains of hide-covered huts, and a child's footprint next to a hearth.[100] The site suggests that there was at least one wave of human migration into the New World before 11,500 years ago, by walking and/or perhaps in boats. Even when the last glaciers were at their fullest extent, there was a small ice-free corridor through which people could have walked. And there were ice-free corridors earlier.

It was geologically possible then for humans to have walked into the New World at various times, or they could have traveled by boat. Parts of the Beringia land bridge were exposed from about 60,000 years to 25,000 years ago. Not until between 20,000 years and 18,000 years ago was the land bridge at its maximum. When did the last land bridge disappear? It used to be widely believed that the land bridge was flooded around 14,000 years ago, but recent evidence suggests that walking across Beringia was still possible until about 10,000 years ago. An ice-free corridor between the Laurentide and Cordilleran ice sheets may have been present after 25,000 years ago, but that corridor is not likely to have supported big game, and permitted humans to hunt enough for sustenance, until after about 14,000 years ago. So some investigators suggest that moving through the ice-free corridor to what is now south of Canada was not likely until after that time.[101]

The people moving into North America through the ice-free corridor may or may not have hunted big game, but just a little while later people were living in the Amazon jungle of what is now Brazil, and they were definitely not hunters of mammoths and other big game, as the contemporaneous Clovis people of North America were. In other words, it looks like the earliest inhabitants of the New World—in Chile, Brazil, and North America—varied in culture. The people in the Amazon lived by collecting fruits and nuts, fishing, and hunting small game. They lived in caves with painted art on the walls and left 30,000 stone chips from making tips of spears, darts, or harpoons.[102]

There is no disagreement that humans were living south of Canada after 11,000 years ago. The Clovis people, as they are called (after an archaeological site near Clovis, New Mexico), left finely shaped spear points in many locations in North America. And we have human skeletal remains from after 11,000 years ago. Now that the Monte Verde site has been reliably dated to before 12,000 years ago, we know that there were people south of Canada before the Clovis people were in New Mexico. And there are other possible sites of pre-Clovis occupation.[103] For example, the Cactus Hill site in Virginia, the Gault site in Texas, and the Shriver site in Missouri all contain a stratum of blades and other stone tools below a Paleo-Indian stratum containing Clovis tools. Meadowcroft Rockshelter in western Pennsylvania contains the most carefully reported pre-Clovis occupation in North America.[104] In the bottom third of a stratum that seems to date from 19,600 years to 8,000 years ago, the Meadowcroft site shows clear signs of human occupation—a small fragment of human bone, a spearpoint, and chipped knives and scrapers. Surprising physical evidence for pre-Clovis people in the Americas comes from the Paisley Caves in southern Oregon. Here, human coprolites (dried feces) have been found and dated to 14,400 years ago. Because the coprolites contain human DNA, and radiocarbon samples were taken directly from the coprolites, it seems conclusive that at least a small group of humans were in North America more than a thousand years before Clovis people.[105]

According to comparative linguists Joseph Greenberg and Merritt Ruhlen, there were three waves of migration into the New World.[106] They compared hundreds of languages in North and South America, grouping them into three different language families. Because each of these language families has a closer relationship to an Asian language family than to the other New World language families, it would appear that three different migrations came out of Asia. The first arrivals spoke a language that diverged over time into most of the languages found in the New World, the Amerind family of languages; the speakers of these related languages came to occupy all of South and Central America as well as most of North America. Next came the ancestors of the people who speak languages belonging to the Na-Dené family, which today includes Navajo and Apache in the southwestern United States and the various Athapaskan languages of northern California, coastal Oregon, northwestern Canada, and Alaska. Finally, perhaps 4,000 years ago, came the ancestors of the Inuit (Eskimo) and Aleut (the latter came to occupy the islands southwest of Alaska and the adjacent mainland), who speak languages belonging to the Inuit–Aleut family.

Christy Turner's study of New World teeth supports the Greenberg and Ruhlen proposal of three separate migrations. Turner looked at the proportions of shovel-shaped incisors, a common Asian trait, in New World populations. The varying proportions fall into three distinct

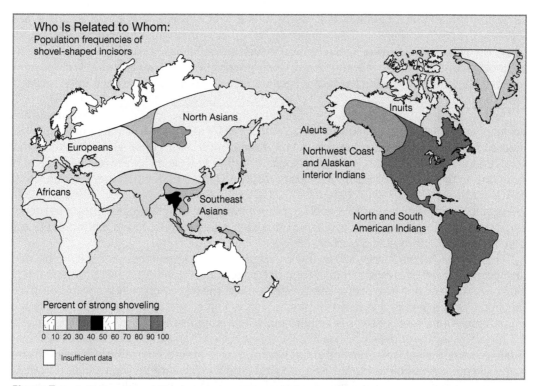

Figure 7 Inuit (Eskimos) and Aleuts, speakers of Na-Dené languages, and other Native American language groups differ in the frequency of shovel-shaped incisors and other genetically based traits. These genetic differences seem to reflect three waves of migration into the New World.

Source: Turner 1987; 2005.

groupings, the same three suggested by the linguists[107] (see Figure 7). But genetic analyses suggest that the peopling of the New World may have been even more complicated. There could have been four separate migrations from the Old World, from different regions of Asia, or there could have been only one, with languages and genes diverging after humans arrived.[108]

The Paleo-Indians Archaeological remains of early New World hunters, called *Paleo-Indians,* have been found in the United States, Mexico, and Canada. Just south of the farthest reaches of the last glaciations, the area east of the Rockies known as the High Plains abounded with mammoths, bison, wild camels, and wild horses. The tools found with mammoth kills are known as the *Clovis complex,* which includes the Clovis projectile point as well as stone scrapers and knives and bone tools. The Clovis projectile point is large and leaf-shaped, flaked on both sides. It has a broad groove in the middle, presumably so that the point could be attached to a wooden spear shaft.[109] Because one mammoth was found with eight Clovis points in it, there is little dispute that Clovis people hunted large game.[110] Recent dating places most Clovis sites between 11,200 years and 10,900 years ago.[111]

The mammoth disappeared about 10,000 years ago, and the largest game animal became the now-extinct large, straight-horned bison. The hunters of that bison used a projectile point called the *Folsom point,* which was much smaller than the Clovis point. Tools are also found with many other kinds of animal remains, including wolf, turtle, rabbit, horse, fox, deer, and camel, so the bison hunters obviously depended on other animals as well.[112] In the Rio Grande valley, the Folsom toolmakers characteristically established a base camp on low dune ridges overlooking both a large pond and broad, open grazing areas. If we assume that the pond provided water for the grazing herds, the people in the camp would have been in an excellent position to watch the herds.[113]

As the climate of what is now the American Southwest became drier, the animals and the cultural adaptations changed somewhat. About 9,000 years ago, the smaller modern bison replaced the earlier straight-horned variety.[114] Base camps began to be located farther from ponds and grazing areas and closer to streams. If the ponds were no longer reliable sources of water during these drier times, the animals probably no longer frequented them, which would explain why the hunters had to change the sites of their base camps. Not much is known about the plant foods these Paleo-Indian people may have exploited, but plant-gathering on the desert fringes may have been vital. In Nevada and Utah, archaeologists have found milling stones and other artifacts for processing plant food.[115]

The Olsen-Chubbuck site, a kill site excavated in Colorado, shows the organization that may have been involved in hunting bison.[116] In a dry gulch dated to 6500 B.C. were the remains of 200 bison. At the bottom were complete skeletons and at the top, completely butchered animals. This find clearly suggests that Paleo-Indian hunters deliberately stampeded the animals into a natural trap—an arroyo, or steep-sided dry gully. The animals in front were probably pushed into the arroyo by the ones behind. Joe Ben Wheat estimated that the hunters may have obtained 55,000 pounds of meat from this one kill. If we judge from nineteenth-century Plains Indians, who could prepare bison meat to last a month, and estimate that each person would eat a pound a day, the kill at the Olsen-Chubbuck site could have fed more than 1,800 people for a month (they probably did not all live together throughout the year). The hunters must have been highly organized not only for the stampede itself but also for butchering. It seems that the enormous carcasses had to be carried to flat ground for that job. In addition, the 55,000 pounds of meat and hides had to be carried back to camp.[117]

Although big game may have been most important on the High Plains, other areas show different adaptations. For example, Paleo-Indian people in woodland regions of what is now the United States seem to have depended more heavily on plant food and smaller game. In some woodland areas, fish and shellfish may have been a vital part of the diet.[118] On the Pacific coast, some Paleo-Indian people developed food-getting strategies more dependent on fish.[119] And in other areas, the lower Illinois River valley being one example, Paleo-Indian people who depended on game and wild vegetable foods managed to get enough food to live in permanent villages of perhaps between 100 and 150 people.[120]

The End of the Upper Paleolithic

After about 10,000 years ago, the glaciers began to disappear, and with their disappearance came other environmental changes. The melting of the glacial ice caused the oceans to rise, and, as the seas moved inland, the waters inundated some of the richest fodder-producing coastal plains, creating islands, inlets, and bays. Other areas were opened up for human occupation as the glaciers retreated and the temperatures rose.[121] The cold, treeless plains, tundras, and grasslands eventually gave way to dense mixed forests, mostly birch, oak, and pine, and the Pleistocene megafauna became extinct. The warming waterways began to be filled with fish and other aquatic resources.[122]

The Emergence of *Homo sapiens*

Archaeologists believe that these environmental changes induced some populations to alter their food-getting strategies. When the tundras and grasslands disappeared, hunters could no longer obtain large quantities of meat simply by remaining close to large migratory herds of animals, as they probably did during Upper Paleolithic times. Even though deer and other game were available, the number of animals per square mile (density) had decreased, and it became difficult to stalk and kill animals sheltered in the thick woods. Thus, in many areas, people seemed to have turned from a reliance on big game hunting to the intensive collecting of wild plants, mollusks, fish, and small game to make up for the extinction of the large game animals they had once relied upon.

The Maglemosian Culture of Northern Europe Some adaptations to the changing environment can be seen in the cultural remains of the settlers in northern Europe who archaeologists call *Maglemosians.* Their name derives from the peat bogs (*magle mose* in Danish means "great bog") where their remains have been found.

To deal with the new, more forested environment, the Maglemosians made stone axes and adzes to chop down trees and form them into various objects. Large timbers appear to have been split for houses; trees were hollowed out for canoes; and smaller pieces of wood were made into paddles. The canoes presumably were built for travel and perhaps for fishing on the lakes and rivers that abounded in the postglacial environment.

We do not know to what extent the Maglemosians relied on wild plant foods, but there were a lot of different kinds available, such as hazelnuts. However, we do know many other things about the Maglemosians' way of life. Although fishing was fairly important, as suggested by the frequent occurrence of bones from pike and other fish, as well as fishhooks, these people apparently depended mainly on hunting for food. Game included elk, wild ox, deer, and wild pig. In addition to many fishing implements and the adzes and axes, the Maglemosians' tool kit included the bow and arrow. Some of their tools were ornamented with finely engraved designs. Ornamentation independent of tools also appears in amber and stone pendants and small figurines representing, for example, the head of an elk.[123]

Like the Maglemosian finds, many of the European post–Upper Paleolithic sites are found near water—lakes, rivers, and ocean. But these sites probably were not inhabited year-round; there is evidence that at least some groups moved seasonally from one place of settlement to another, perhaps between the coast and inland areas.[124] Finds such as kitchen middens (piles of shells) that centuries of post–Upper Paleolithic seafood eaters had discarded, and the remains of fishing equipment, canoes, and boats indicate that these people depended much more heavily on fishing than had their ancestors in Upper Paleolithic times.

The Archaic Cultures of Eastern North America A related set of adaptations to the changing environment can be seen among the peoples who inhabited eastern North America at the end of the ice age. As the climate became warmer and drier, the flora and fauna of North America changed. Megafauna, as elsewhere in the world, went extinct, and were replaced by smaller mammals, particularly deer. The availability of meat was greatly reduced—hunters could count on coming home with pounds, not tons, of meat. Warmer-adapted plants replaced cold-adapted plants, and were used for food to replace the meat that was no longer available. Warmer-adapted plants had advantages as food resources for humans over cold-adapted ones because edible seeds, fruits, and nuts were more common, and often more plentiful and accessible, on the warmer-adapted plants. Thus, the Archaic peoples came to use a much greater diversity of plants and animals.[125]

The Emergence of *Homo sapiens*

The **Archaic** peoples of North America, like the Maglemosian peoples in Europe, began to follow a more sedentary lifestyle. Two forms of Archaic settlement appear to have been typical. One was a residential base camp, which would have been inhabited seasonally by several, probably related, families. The other was a special-purpose camp, which would have been a short-term habitation near a particular resource or perhaps used by a group of hunters for a short period of time.[126] On the Atlantic coast, for example, individual groups apparently moved seasonally along major river valleys, establishing summer base camps in the piedmont and winter camps near the coast. Special-purpose camps were created year-round as groups went out from the base camp to hunt and collect particular resources, such as stone for making tools.[127]

One of the innovations of the Archaic peoples was the development of ground stone woodworking tools. Axes, adzes, and tools for grinding seeds and nuts become more and more common in the tool kit.[128] This probably reflects the emergence of greater areas of forest following the retreat of the glaciers from North America, but it also demonstrates a greater reliance on forest products and, most likely, a greater use of wood and wood products. Fish and shellfish also came to be relied upon in some areas, and this too reflects the adjustment made by the Archaic peoples to the changing conditions they faced at the end of the last ice age.

Some examples of Archaic ground stone woodworking tools from eastern North America (wooden handles are reproductions) Archaic peoples apparently used wood more extensively than the Paleo-Indians.

The innovation of most lasting importance in both the New and Old Worlds, however, was the development of domesticated plants and animals. In both parts of the world, peoples at the end of the ice age began to experiment with plants. By around 14,000 years ago in the Old World, and 10,000 years ago in the New World, some species had been domesticated. This fundamental change in food-getting—the invention of agriculture—is an important subject.

✓—[Study and Review on **myanthrolab.com**

Summary

1. Most anthropologists agree that *Homo erectus* began to evolve into *Homo sapiens* after about 500,000 years ago. But there is disagreement about how and where the transition occurred. The mixed traits of the transitional fossils include large cranial capacities (well within the range of modern humans), together with low foreheads and large browridges, which are characteristic of *H. erectus* specimens.

2. *Homo sapiens* have been found in many parts of the Old World—in Africa and Asia as well as in Europe. Some of these *H. sapiens* may have lived earlier than the Neandertals

of Europe. There is still debate over whether the Neandertals in western Europe became extinct or survived and were ancestral to the modern-looking people who lived in western Europe after about 40,000 years ago.

3. The period of cultural history associated with the Neandertals is traditionally called the Middle Paleolithic in Europe and the Near East and dates from about 300,000 years to about 40,000 years ago. For Africa, the term *Middle Stone Age* is used. The assemblages of flake tools from this period are generally referred to as Mousterian in Europe and the Near East and as post-Acheulian in Africa. Compared with an Acheulian assemblage, a Mousterian tool assemblage has a smaller proportion of large hand axes and cleavers and a larger proportion of small flake tools such as scrapers. Some Mousterian sites show signs of intentional burial.

4. Fossil remains of fully modern-looking humans, *Homo sapiens sapiens,* have been found in Africa, the Near East, Asia, and Australia, as well as in Europe. The oldest of these fossils have been found in East Africa and may be 160,000 years old.

5. Two theories about the origins of modern humans continue to be debated among anthropologists. One, the *single-origin theory,* suggests that modern humans emerged in just one part of the Old World—the Near East and, more recently, Africa have been the postulated places of origin—and spread to other parts of the Old World, superseding Neandertals. The second theory, the *multiregional theory,* suggests that modern humans emerged in various parts of the Old World, becoming the varieties of humans we see today.

6. The period of cultural history known as the Upper Paleolithic in Europe, the Near East, and Asia or the Later Stone Age in Africa dates from about 40,000 years ago to about 14,000 to 10,000 years ago. During this ice age, glaciers covered much of northern Europe and North America, and annual temperatures were much lower than today's temperatures.

7. The Upper Paleolithic tool kit is characterized by the preponderance of blades; there were also burins, bone and antler tools, and (later) microliths. In many respects, lifestyles were similar to lifestyles before. People were still mainly hunters, gatherers, and fishers who probably lived in highly mobile bands. They made their camps out in the open and in caves and rock shelters.

8. The Upper Paleolithic is also characterized by a variety of new developments: new techniques of toolmaking, the emergence of art, population growth, and new inventions such as the bow and arrow, the spear thrower (atlatl), and the harpoon.

9. Only *Homo sapiens sapiens* remains have been found in the New World. The prevailing opinion is that humans migrated to the New World over a land bridge between Siberia and Alaska in the area of what is now the Bering Strait. Until recently, it was thought that humans were not present south of Alaska until after 11,500 years ago. Now it appears that modern humans arrived in southern South America by at least 12,500 years ago and perhaps as much as 33,000 years ago.

10. At the end of the ice age, around 14,000 years ago, the climate began to become more temperate. Many large animals that Upper Paleolithic peoples relied upon for food went extinct, and at the same time new, warmer-adapted plants provided a rich, new food source. Around the world, people began to use more plant foods and a broader range of resources overall. In many parts of the world, people began experimenting with domesticating plants and animals.

The Emergence of *Homo sapiens*

Glossary Terms

Archaic
atlatl
blade
burin
Cro-Magnon
ethnographic analogy

Homo heidelbergensis
Homo neandertalensis
Homo sapiens sapiens
indirect percussion
Levalloisian method
microlith

Middle Paleolithic
Mousterian tool assemblage
Neandertal
pressure flaking
Upper Paleolithic

Critical Questions

1. If the single-origin or "out-of-Africa" theory were correct, by what mechanisms could *Homo sapiens* have been able to replace *Homo erectus* and *Homo neandertalensis* populations?

2. How do Middle Paleolithic cultures differ from Lower Paleolithic cultures?

3. Upper Paleolithic cave paintings arouse our imaginations. We have described some research that tested ideas about what these paintings might mean. Can you think of other ways to understand the significance of cave art?

Read the Original Source on myanthrolab.com

Read the chapter by David Frayer titled "Testing Theories and Hypotheses about Modern Human Origins" on MyAnthroLab. Answer the following questions.

1. What does Frayer identify as the key elements of debate between the "Out of Africa" (or, as he calls it, "Noah's Ark") and "Multiregional" models of modern human origins?

2. What problems does Frayer identify with mitochondrial DNA evidence of modern human origins?

3. Frayer is in the minority among physical anthropologists today in supporting the multiregional model of human evolution. What reasons does he give for rejecting the more broadly accepted "Out of Africa" model?

Photo Credits

Credits are listed in order of appearance.

American Museum of Natural History; Universal Images Group Limited/Alamy; Bettmann/Corbis; Dallas and John Heaton/Stock Connection; David L. Brill Photography; Gianni Dagli Orti/Corbis; Stephane Marc/PHOTOPQR/Le Dauphine/Newscom; DK Images.

Figure 2: From Matthias Krings, et al "Neandertal DNA Sequences and the Origin of Modern Humans" *Cell*, Vol 90: 25 Copyright (c) 1997 Reprinted by permission of Elsevier. Figure 3: From Richard G. Klein, "Ice-Age Hunters of the Ukraine" *Scientific American* (June 1974): 96–105. Copyright (c) 1974 Reprinted with permission. Figure 6: David J. Meltzer, "Pleistocene peopling of the Americas" EVOLUTIONARY ANTHROPOLOGY, Vol 1(5) Copyright 1993 Reprinted by permission of John Wiley & Sons, Inc. Figure 7: From Christy G. Turner, II, "Telltale Teeth." *Natural History* (January 1987):8. Copyright 1987 Reprinted with permission.

Glossary

Archaic Time period in the New World during which food production first developed.

Atlatl Aztec word for "spear thrower."

Blade A thin flake whose length is usually more than twice its width. In the blade technique of toolmaking, a core is prepared by shaping a piece of flint with hammerstones into a pyramidal or cylindrical form. Blades are then struck off until the core is used up.

Burin A chisel-like stone tool used for carving and for making such artifacts as bone and antler needles, awls, and projectile points.

Cro-Magnons Humans who lived in western Europe about 35,000 years ago, they were once thought to be the earliest specimens of modern-looking humans, or *Homo sapiens sapiens.* But it is now known that modern-looking humans appeared earlier outside of Europe; the earliest so far found lived in Africa.

Ethnographic analogy Method of comparative cultural study that extrapolates to the past from recent or current societies.

Homo heidelbergensis A transitional species between *Homo erectus* and *Homo sapiens.*

Homo neandertalensis The technical name for the Neandertals, a group of robust and otherwise anatomically distinct hominids that are close relatives of modern humans—so close that some believe they should be classified as *Homo sapiens neandertalensis.*

Homo sapiens sapiens Modern-looking humans, undisputed examples of which appeared about 50,000 years ago; may have appeared earlier.

Indirect percussion A toolmaking technique common in the Upper Paleolithic. After shaping a core into a pyramidal or cylindrical form, the toolmaker can put a punch of antler or wood or another hard material into position and strike it with a hammer. Using a hammer-struck punch enabled toolmakers to strike off consistently shaped blades.

Levalloisian method A method that allowed flake tools of a predetermined size to be produced from a shaped core. The toolmakers first shaped the core and prepared a "striking platform" at one end. Flakes of predetermined and standard sizes could then be knocked off. Although some Levallois flakes date from as far back as 400,000 years ago, they are found more frequently in Mousterian tool kits.

Microlith A small, razorlike blade fragment that was probably attached in a series to a wooden or bone handle to form a cutting edge.

Middle Paleolithic The time period of the Mousterian stone tool tradition.

Mousterian tool assemblage Named after the tool assemblage found in a rock shelter at Le Moustier in the Dordogne region of southwestern France. Compared with an Acheulian assemblage, the Middle Paleolithic (40,000–300,000 years ago) Mousterian has a smaller proportion of large core tools such as hand axes and cleavers and a bigger proportion of small flake tools such as scrapers. Flakes were often altered or "retouched" by striking small flakes or chips from one or more edges.

Neandertal The common name for the species *Homo neandertalensis*.

Pressure flaking Toolmaking technique whereby small flakes are struck off by pressing against the core with a bone, antler, or wooden tool.

Upper Paleolithic The time period associated with the emergence of modern humans and their spread around the world.

Notes

1. Stringer 1985.
2. Ibid.
3. Rightmire 1997.
4. Carbonell et al. 2008.
5. Fleagle 1999, 535–37; Rightmire 1997.
6. Spencer 1984.
7. Trinkaus 1985.
8. Stringer 2000.
9. Trinkaus and Shipman 1993a; 1993b.
10. Krings et al. 1997.
11. Ibid.
12. Green et al. 2008; Ovchinnikov et al. 2000.
13. Krause et al. 2007
14. Lalueza-Fox et al. 2007.
15. Pennisi 2009.
16. Hodgson and Driscoll 2008; Serre et al. 2004.
17. Gibbons 2001; Tattersall 1999, 115–16.
18. Mellars 1996: 405–19.
19. Mellars 1998.
20. Strauss 1989.
21. Schick and Toth 1993, 288–92.
22. Klein 1989, 291–96.
23. Schick and Toth 1993, 288–92; Whittaker 1994, 30–31.
24. Klein 1989, 421–22.
25. Binford and Binford 1969.
26. Fish 1981, 377.
27. Butzer 1982, 42.
28. Phillipson 1993, 63.
29. For the controversy about whether the inhabitants of the Dordogne Valley lived in their homesites year-round, see Binford 1973.
30. Schick and Toth 1993, 292.
31. Klein 1977.
32. Klein 1974.
33. Bordes 1961.
34. T. Patterson 1981.
35. Phillipson 1993, 64.
36. Klein 1983, 38–39.
37. Binford 1984, 195–97. To explain the lack of complete skeletons of large animals, Klein (1983) suggests that the hunters may have butchered the large animals elsewhere because they could carry home only small cuts.
38. Wilford 1997.

39. Chase and Dibble 1987.
40. Stringer, Hublin, and Vandermeersch 1984, 107.
41. Singer and Wymer 1982, 149.
42. Gibbons 2003.
43. Bräuer 1984, 387–89, 394; Rightmire 1984, 320.
44. Valladas et al. 1988.
45. Stringer et al. 1984, 121.
46. For arguments supporting the single-origin theory, see the chapters by Günter Bräuer, F. Clark Howell, and C. B. Stringer et al., in F. Smith and Spencer 1984. For arguments supporting the multiregional theory, see the chapters by C. L. Brace et al., David W. Frayer, Fred H. Smith, and Milford H. Wolpoff et al. in the same volume.
47. Cann 1988.
48. Cann 1988.
49. Vigilant et al. 1991.
50. Cann, Stoneking, and Wilson 1987.
51. Vigilant et al. 1991.
52. Stoneking 1997.
53. Hammer and Zegura 1996.
54. Hammer and Zegura 2002.
55. Cavalli-Sforza and Feldman 2003.
56. Stringer 2003.
57. Frayer et al. 1993; Wolpoff 1999, 501–04, 727–31.
58. Frayer et al. 1993; Wolpoff 1999, 735–43.
59. D. Lieberman 1995.
60. Templeton 1993.
61. Trinkaus 1986.
62. Eswaran 2002.
63. Templeton 1996; see also Ayala 1995; 1996.
64. Reed et al. 2004.
65. Duarte et al. 1999.
66. Bahn 1998.
67. Tattersall 1999, 198–203.
68. Trinkaus 1986; see also Trinkaus and Howells 1979.
69. Culotta 2005.
70. Klein 2003.
71. R. White 1982.
72. Strauss 1982.
73. Dawson 1992, 24–71.
74. COHMAP 1988.
75. Martin and Wright 1967.
76. Mellars 1994.
77. T. Patterson 1981.
78. Klima 1962.
79. Schick and Toth 1993, 293–99; Whittaker 1994, 33.
80. Whittaker 1994, 31.
81. Bordaz 1970, 68.
82. Whittaker 1994, 33.
83. Phillipson 1993, 60.
84. Bordaz 1970.
85. Ibid.
86. We thank Robert L. Kelly (personal communication) for bringing this possibility to our attention. See also J. D. Clark 1977, 136.
87. Ascher 1961.
88. Semenov 1970, 103. For a more recent discussion of research following this strategy, see Keeley 1980.
89. Klein 1994, 508.
90. Soffer 1993, 38–40.
91. Phillipson 1993, 74.
92. Morell 1995.
93. Henshilwood et al. 2002.
94. Ucko and Rosenfeld 1967.
95. Rice and Paterson 1985; 1986.
96. Rice and Paterson 1985, 98.
97. Hawkins and Kleindienst 2001.
98. Jayaswal 2002.
99. Peregrine and Bellwood 2001.

100. McDonald 1998.
101. Hoffecker, Powers, and Goebel 1993.
102. Gibbons 1995; Roosevelt et al. 1996.
103. Goebel, Waters, and O'Rourke 2008.
104. Dillehay 2000.
105. Gilbert et al. 2008.
106. Greenberg and Ruhlen 1992, 94–99.
107. Turner 1989; see also Kitchen, Miyamoto, and Mulligan (2008) for a more recent reanalysis of genetic and linguistic evidence for a three-stage colonization of the Americas.
108. McDonald 1998; Turner 2005.
109. Wheat 1967.
110. Fagan 1991, 79.
111. Hoffecker et al. 1993.
112. Jennings 1968, 72–88.
113. Judge and Dawson 1972.
114. Wheat 1967.
115. Fagan 1989, 221.
116. Wheat 1967.
117. Ibid.
118. Fagan 1989, 227.
119. Fagan 1991, 192.
120. Fagan 1989, 227.
121. Collins 1976, 88–125.
122. Chard 1969, 171.
123. G. Clark 1975, 101–61.
124. Petersen 1973, 94–96.
125. Daniel 2001.
126. Sassaman 1996, 58–83.
127. Ibid.
128. J. Brown 1983, 5–10.

Bibliography

Ascher, Robert. 1961. Analogy in archaeological interpretation. *Southwestern Journal of Anthropology* 17:317–25.

Ayala, Francisco J. 1995. The myth of Eve: Molecular biology and human origins. *Science* 270 (December 22):1930–36.

Ayala, Francisco J. 1996. Communication. *Science* 274 (November 29):1354.

Bahn, Paul. 1998. Neanderthals emancipated. *Nature* 394 (August 20):719–20.

Binford, Lewis R. 1973. Interassemblage variability: The Mousterian and the "functional" argument. In *The explanation of culture change,* ed. C. Renfrew. Pittsburgh, PA: University of Pittsburgh Press.

Binford, Lewis R. 1984. *Faunal remains from Klasies River mouth.* Orlando, FL: Academic Press.

Binford, Sally R., and Lewis R. Binford. 1969. Stone tools and human behavior. *Scientific American* (April):70–84.

Bordaz, Jacques. 1970. *Tools of the old and new stone age.* Garden City, NY: Natural History Press.

Bordes, François. 1961. Mousterian cultures in France. *Science* 134 (September 22):803–10.

Bräuer, Günter. 1984. A craniological approach to the origin of anatomically modern *Homo sapiens* in Africa and implications for the appearance of modern Europeans. In *The origins of modern humans,* eds. F. Smith and F Spencer. New York: Alan R. Liss.

Brown, James A. 1983. Summary. In *Archaic hunters and gatherers in the American Midwest,* eds. J. L. Phillips and J. A. Brown, 5–10. New York: Academic Press.

Butzer, Karl W. 1982. Geomorphology and sediment stratigraphy. In *The Middle Stone Age at Klasies River Mouth in South Africa,* eds. R. Singer and J. Wymer. Chicago: University of Chicago Press.

Cann, Rebecca. 1988. DNA and human origins. *Annual Review of Anthropology* 17:127–43.

Cann, Rebecca, M. Stoneking, and A. C. Wilson. 1987. Mitochondrial DNA and human evolution. *Nature* 325 (January 1):31–36.

Carbonell, Eudald, José M. Bermúdez de Castro, Josep M. Parés, Alfredo Pérez-González, Gloria Cuenca-Bescós, Andreu Ollé, Marina Mosquera, Rosa Huguet, Jan van der Made, Antonio Rosas, Robert Sala, Josep Vallverdú, Nuria García, Darryl E. Granger, María Martinón-Torres, Xosé P. Rodríguez, Greg M. Stock, Josep M. Vergès, Ethel Allué, Francesc Burjachs, Isabel Cáceres, Antoni Canals, Alfonso Benito, Carlos Díez, Marina Lozano, Ana Mateos, Marta Navazo, Jesús Rodríguez, Jordi Rosell, Juan L. Arsuaga. 2008. The first hominin of Europe. *Nature* 452 (March 27):465–69.

Cavalli-Sforza, L. Luca, and Marcus W. Feldman. 2003. The application of molecular genetic approaches to the study of human evolution. *Nature Genetics Supplement* 33:266–75.

Chard, Chester S. 1969. *Man in prehistory.* New York: McGraw-Hill.

Chase, Philip, and Harold Dibble. 1987. Middle Paleolithic symbolism: A review of current evidence and interpretations. *Journal of Anthropological Archaeology* 6:263–69.

The Emergence of *Homo sapiens*

Clark, J. Desmond. 1977. Interpretations of prehistoric technology from ancient Egyptian and other sources. Pt. II: Prehistoric arrow forms in Africa as shown by surviving examples of the traditional arrows of the San Bushmen. *Paleorient* 3:127–50.

Clark, Grahame. 1975. *The earlier stone age settlement of Scandinavia.* Cambridge, UK: Cambridge University Press.

COHMAP (Cooperative Holocene Mapping Project) Personnel. 1988. Climatic changes of the last 18,000 years. *Science* 241 (August 26):1043–52.

Collins, Desmond. 1976. Later hunters in Europe. In *The origins of Europe,* ed. D. Collins. New York: Thomas Y. Crowell.

Culotta, Elizabeth. 2005. Calorie count reveals Neandertals out-ate hardiest modern humans. *Science* 307 (February 11):840.

Daniel, I. Randolph. 2001. Early Eastern Archaic. In *Encyclopedia of prehistory,* vol. 6: North America, eds. P. N. Peregrine and M. Ember. New York: Kluwer Academic/Plenum Press.

Dawson, Alistair. 1992. *Ice age earth.* London: Routledge.

Dillehay, Thomas. 2000. *The settlement of the Americas.* New York: Basic Books.

Duarte, Cidalia, J. Mauricio, P. B. Pettitt, P. Souto, E. Trinkaus, H. van der Plicht, and J. Zilhao. 1999. The early Upper Paleolithic human skeleton from the Abrigo do Lagar Velho (Portugal) and modern human emergence in Iberia. *Proceedings of the National Academy of Sciences of the United States* 96:7604–09.

Eswaran, Vinayak. 2002. A diffusion wave out of Africa. *Current Anthropology* 43:749–74.

Fagan, Brian M. 1989. *People of the earth: An introduction to world prehistory.* 6th ed. Glenview, IL: Scott, Foresman.

Fagan, Brian M. 1991. *Ancient North America: The archaeology of a continent.* London: Thames and Hudson.

Fish, Paul R. 1981. Beyond tools: Middle Paleolithic debitage analysis and cultural inference. *Journal of Anthropological Research* 37:374–86.

Fleagle, John G. 1999. *Primate adaptation and evolution.* 2nd ed. San Diego, CA: Academic Press.

Frayer, David W., M. Wolpoff, A. Thorne, F. Smith, and G. Pope. 1993. Theories of modern human origins: The paleontological test. *American Anthropologist* 95:24–27.

Gibbons, Ann. 1995. First Americans: Not mammoth hunters, but forest dwellers? *Science* 268 (April 19):346–47.

Gibbons, Ann. 2001. The riddle of co-existence. *Science* 291(March 2):1725–29.

Gibbons, Ann. 2003. Oldest members of *Homo sapiens* discovered in Africa. *Science* 300 (June 13):1641.

Gilbert, M. Thomas P., Dennis L. Jenkins, Anders Götherstrom, Nuria Naveran, Juan J. Sanchez, Michael Hofreiter, Philip Francis Thom-sen, Jonas Binladen, Thomas F. G. Higham, Robert M. Yohe, II, Robert Parr, Linda Scott Cummings, and Eske Willerslev. 2008. DNA from pre-Clovis human coprolites in Oregon, North America. *Science* 320 (May 9):786–89.

Goebel, Ted, Michael Waters, and Dennis O'Rourke. 2008. The late Pleistocene dispersal of modern humans in the Americas. *Science* 319 (March 14):1479–1502.

Green, Richard E., Anna-Sapfo Malaspinas, Johannes Krause, Adrian W. Briggs, Philip L.F. Johnson, Caroline Uhler, Matthias Meyer, Jef-frey M. Good, Tomislav Maricic, Udo Stenzel, Kay Prüfer, Michael Siebauer, Hernán A. Burbano, Michael Ronan, Jonathan M. Rothberg, Michael Egholm, Pavao Rudan, Dejana Brajković, Željko Kućan, Ivan Gušić, Mårten Wikström, Liisa Laakkonen, Janet Kelso, Montgomery Slatkin, and Svante Pääbo. 2008. A complete Neandertal mitochondrial genome sequence determined by high-throughput sequencing. *Cell* 134:416–26.

Greenberg, Joseph H., and Merritt Ruhlen. 1992. Linguistic origins of Native Americans. *Scientific American* (November):94–99.

Hammer, Michael F., and Stephen L. Zegura. 1996. The role of the Y chromosome in human evolutionary studies. *Evolutionary Anthropology* 5:116–34.

Hammer, Michael F., and Stephen L. Zegura. 2002. The human Y chromosome haplogroup tree. *Annual Review of Anthropology* 31:303–21.

Hawkins, Alicia, and M. Kleindienst. 2001. Aterian. In *Encyclopedia of prehistory,* vol. 1: *Africa,* eds. P. N. Peregrine and M. Ember, 23–45. New York: Kluwer Academic/Plenum Press.

Henshilwood, Christopher, et al. 2002. Emergence of modern human behavior: Middle Stone Age engravings from South Africa. *Science* 295 (February 15):1278–80.

Hodgson, Jason, and Todd Driscoll. 2008. No evidence of a Neandertal contribution to modern human diversity. *Genome Biology* 9:206.1–206.7.

Hoffecker, John F., W. Roger Powers, and Ted Goebel. 1993. The colonization of Beringia and the peopling of the New World. *Science* 259 (January 1):46–53.

Jayaswal, Vidula. 2002. South Asian Upper Paleolithic. In *Encyclopedia of prehistory,* vol. 8: *South and Southwest Asia,* eds. P. N. Peregrine and M. Ember. New York: Kluwer Academic/Plenum Press.

Jennings, Jesse D. 1968. *Prehistory of North America.* New York: McGraw-Hill.

Judge, W. James, and Jerry Dawson. 1972. Paleo-Indian settlement technology in New Mexico. *Science* 176 (June 16):1210–16.

Keeley, Lawrence H. 1980. *Experimental determination of stone tool uses: A microwear analysis.* Chicago: University of Chicago Press.

Kelly, Robert L. 1995. *The foraging spectrum: Diversity in hunter-gatherer lifeways.* Washington, DC: Smithsonian Institution Press.

Kitchen, Andrew, Michael Miyamoto, and Connie Mulligan. 2008. A three-stage colonization model for the peopling of the Americas. *PLoS ONE* 3(2):e1596.

Klein, Richard G. 1974. Ice-Age hunters of the Ukraine. *Scientific American* (June):96–105.

Klein, Richard G. 1977. The ecology of early man in Southern Africa. *Science* 197 (July 8):115–26.

Klein, Richard G. 1983. The Stone Age prehistory of Southern Africa. *Annual Review of Anthropology* 12:25–48.

Klein, Richard G. 1989. *The human career: Human biological and cultural origins.* Chicago: University of Chicago Press.

Klein, Richard G. 1994. Southern Africa before the ice age. In *Integrative paths to the past,* eds. R. Corruccini and R. Ciochon. Upper Saddle River, NJ: Prentice Hall.

Klein, Richard G. 2003. Whither the Neanderthals. *Science* 299 (March 7):1525–28.

Klima, Bohuslav. 1962. The first ground-plan of an Upper Paleolithic loess settlement in Middle Europe and its meaning. In *Courses toward urban life,* eds. R. Braidwood and G. Willey. Chicago: Aldine.

Krause, Johannes, Carles Lalueza-Fox, Ludovic Orlando, Wolfgang Enard, Richard E. Green, Hernán A. Burbano, Jean-Jacques Hublin, Catherine Hänni, Javier Fortea, Marco de la Rasilla, Jaume Bertranpetit, Antonio Rosas, and Svante Pääbo. 2007. The derived FOXP2 variant of modern humans was shared with Neandertals. *Current Biology* 17(21):1908–12.

Krings, Matthias, A. Stone, R. W. Schmitz, H. Krainitzki, M. Stoneking, and S. Paabo. 1997. Neandertal DNA sequences and the origin of modern humans. *Cell* 90:19–30.

Lalueza-Fox, Carles, Holger Römpler, David Caramelli, Claudia Stäubert, Giulio Catalano, David Hughes, Nadin Rohland, Elena Pilli, Laura Longo, Silvana Condemi, Marco de la Rasilla, Javier Fortea, Antonio Rosas, Mark Stoneking, Torsten Schöneberg, Jaume

The Emergence of *Homo sapiens*

Bertranpetit, and Michael Hofreiter. 2007. A melanocortin 1 receptor allele suggests varying pigmentation among Neanderthals. *Science* 318 (November 30):1453–55.

Lieberman, Daniel E. 1995. Testing hypotheses about recent human evolution from skulls: Integrating morphology, function, development, and phylogeny. *Current Anthropology* 36:159–97.

Martin, Paul S., and H. E. Wright, eds. 1967. *Pleistocene extinctions: The search for a cause.* New Haven, CT: Yale University Press.

McDonald, Kim A. 1998. New evidence challenges traditional model of how the New World was settled. *Chronicle of Higher Education* (March 13):A22.

Mellars, Paul. 1994. The Upper Paleolithic revolution. In *The Oxford illustrated prehistory of Europe,* ed. B. Cunliffe, 42–78. Oxford, UK: Oxford University Press.

Mellars, Paul. 1996. *The Neanderthal legacy.* Princeton, NJ: Princeton University Press.

Mellars, Paul. 1998. The fate of the Neaderthals. *Nature* 395 (October 8):539–40.

Morell, Virginia. 1995. The earliest art becomes older—and more common. *Science,* 267 (March 31):1908–09.

Ovchinnikov, Igor V., et al. 2000. Molecular analysis of Neanderthal DNA from the Northern Caucasus. *Nature* 404 (March 30):490–94.

Patterson, Thomas C. 1981. *The evolution of ancient societies: A world archaeology.* Upper Saddle River, NJ: Prentice Hall.

Pennisi, Elizabeth. 2009. Tales of a prehistoric human genome. *Science* 323 (February 13):866–71.

Peregrine, Peter N., and Peter Bellwood. 2001. Southeast Asia Upper Paleolithic. In *Encyclopedia of prehistory,* vol. 3: *East Asia and Oceania,* eds. P. N. Peregrine and M. Ember, 307–09. New York: Kluwer Academic/Plenum Press.

Petersen, Erik B. 1973. A survey of the Late Paleolithic and the Mesolithic of Denmark. In *The Mesolithic in Europe,* ed. S. K. Kozlowski. Warsaw: Warsaw University Press.

Phillipson, David W. 1993. *African archaeology.* 2nd ed. New York: Cambridge University Press.

Reed, David, V. Smith, S. Hammond, A. Rogers, and D. Clayton. 2004. Genetic analysis of lice supports direct contact between modern and archaic humans. *PLoS Biology* 2 (November):1972–83.

Rice, Patricia C., and Ann L. Paterson. 1985. Cave art and bones: Exploring the interrelationships. *American Anthropologist* 87:94–100.

Rice, Patricia C., and Ann L. Paterson. 1986. Validating the cave art—Archeofaunal relationship in Cantabrian Spain. *American Anthropologist* 88:658–67.

Rightmire, G. Philip. 1984. *Homo sapiens* in sub-Saharan Africa. In *The origins of modern humans,* eds. F. H. Smith and F. Spencer. New York: Alan R. Liss.

Rightmire, G. Philip. 1997. Human evolution in the Middle Pleistocene: The role of *Homo heidelbergensis. Evolutionary Anthropology* 6:218–27.

Roosevelt, Anna C., et al. 1996. Paleoindian cave dwellers in the Amazon: The peopling of the Americas. *Science* 272 (April 19):373–84.

Sassaman, Kenneth. 1996. Early Archaic settlement in the South Carolina coastal plain. In *The Paleoindian and early Archaic Southeast,* eds. D. G. Anderson and K. E. Sassaman, 58–83. Tuscaloosa: University of Alabama Press.

Schick, Kathy D., and Nicholas Toth. 1993. *Making silent stones speak.* New York: Simon & Schuster.

Semenov, Sergei A. 1970. *Prehistoric technology.* Trans. M. W. Thompson. Bath, UK: Adams & Dart.

Serre, David, André Langaney, Mario Chech, Maria Teschler-Nicola, Maja Paunovic, Philippe Mennecier, Michael Hofreiter, Göran Possnert, and Svante Pääbo. 2004. No evidence of Neandertal mtDNA contribution to early modern humans. *PLoS Biology* 2:313–17.

Singer, Ronald, and John Wymer. 1982. *The Middle Stone Age at Klasies River mouth in South Africa.* Chicago: University of Chicago Press.

Smith, Fred H., and Frank Spencer, eds. 1984. *The origins of modern humans: A world survey of the fossil evidence.* New York: Alan R. Liss.

Soffer, Olga. 1993. Upper Paleolithic adaptations in central and eastern Europe and man-mammoth interactions. In *From Kostenki to Clovis,* eds. O. Soffer and N. D. Praslov. New York: Plenum Press.

Spencer, Frank. 1984. The Neandertals and their evolutionary significance: A brief historical survey. In *The origins of modern humans,* eds. F. H. Smith and F. Spencer. New York: Alan R. Liss.

Stoneking, Mark. 1997. Recent African origin of human mitochondrial DNA. In *Progress in population genetics and human evolution,* eds. P. Donnelly and S. Tavaré, 1–13. New York: Springer.

Strauss, Lawrence Guy. 1982. Comment on White. *Current Anthropology* 23:185–86.

Strauss, Lawrence Guy. 1989. On early hominid use of fire. *Current Anthropology* 30:488–91.

Stringer, Christopher B. 1985. Evolution of a species. *Geographical Magazine* 57:601–07.

Stringer, Christopher B. 2000. Neandertals. In *Encyclopedia of human evolution and prehistory,* eds. I. Tattersall, E. Delson, and J. van Couvering. New York: Garland.

Stringer, Christopher. B. 2003. Out of Ethiopia. *Nature* 423 (June 12):692–95.

Stringer, Christopher B., J. J. Hublin, and B. Vandermeersch. 1984. The origin of anatomically modern humans in western Europe. In *The origins of modern humans,* eds. F. H. Smith and F. Spencer. New York: Alan R. Liss.

Tattersall, Ian. 1999. *The last Neanderthal.* Boulder, CO: Westview Press.

Templeton, Alan R. 1993. The "Eve" hypotheses: A genetic critique and reanalysis. *American Anthropologist* 95:51–72.

Templeton, Alan R. 1996. Gene lineages and human evolution. *Science* 272 (May 31):1363.

Trinkaus, Erik. 1985. Pathology and the posture of the La Chapelle-aux-Saints Neandertal. *American Journal of Physical Anthropology* 67:19–41.

Trinkaus, Erik. 1986. The Neandertals and modern human origins. *Annual Review of Anthropology* 15:193–218.

Trinkaus, Erik, and William W. Howells. 1979. The Neanderthals. *Scientific American* (December):118–33.

Trinkaus, Erik, and Pat Shipman. 1993a. *The Neandertals: Changing the image of mankind.* New York: Knopf.

Trinkaus, Erik, and Pat Shipman. 1993b. Neandertals: Images of ourselves. *Evolutionary Anthropology* 1:194–201.

Turner, Christy G., II. 1989. Teeth and prehistory in Asia. *Scientific American* (February):88–95.

Turner, Christy. G., II. 2005. A synoptic history of physical anthropological studies on the peopling of Alaska and the Americas. *Alaska Journal of Anthropology* 3:157–70.

Ucko, Peter J., and Andrée Rosenfeld. 1967. *Paleolithic cave art.* New York: McGraw-Hill.

Valladas, Helene, J. L. Joron, G. Valladas, O. Bar-Yosef, and B. Vandermeersch. 1988. Thermoluminescence dating of Mousterian "Proto-Cro-Magnon" remains from Israel and the origin of modern man. *Nature* 337 (February 18):614–16.

Vigilant, Linda, Mark Stoneking, Henry Harpending, Kristen Hawkes, and Allan C. Wilson. 1991. African populations and the evolution of human mitochrondrial DNA. *Science* 253 (September 27):1503–07.

Wheat, Joe B. 1967. A Paleo-Indian bison kill. *Scientific American* (January):44–52.

Whittaker, John C. 1994. *Flintknapping: Making and understanding stone tools.* Austin: University of Texas Press.

White, Randall. 1982. Rethinking the Middle/Upper Paleolithic transition. *Current Anthropology* 23:169–75.
Wilford, John Noble. 1997. Ancient German spears tell of mighty hunters of Stone Age. *New York Times,* March 4, p. C6.
Wolpoff, Milford H. 1999. *Paleoanthropology.* 2nd ed. Boston: McGraw-Hill.

Culture and Culture Change

From Chapter 2 of *Human Culture,* Second Edition. Carol R. Ember, Melvin Ember. Copyright © 2012 by Pearson Education, Inc. All rights reserved.

Culture and Culture Change

CHAPTER OUTLINE

Defining Culture

Attitudes That Hinder the Study of Cultures

Cultural Relativism

Describing a Culture

Culture is Patterned

How and Why Cultures Change

Globalization: Problems and Opportunities

Culture Diversity in the Future

Culture and Culture Change

We all consider ourselves to be unique individuals with our own set of personal opinions, preferences, habits, and quirks. Indeed, all of us are unique; and yet most of us also share many feelings, beliefs, and habits with most of the people who live in our society. If we live in North America, we are likely to have the feeling that eating dogs is wrong, have the belief that bacteria or viruses cause illness, and have the habit of sleeping on a bed. These ideas and behaviors are part of what we mean by *culture*.

We only begin to become aware that our culture is different when we become aware that other peoples have different feelings, different beliefs, and different habits from ours. So most North Americans would never even think of the possibility of eating dog meat if they did not know that people in some other societies commonly do so. They would not realize that their belief in germs was cultural if they were not aware that people in some societies think that witchcraft or evil spirits causes illness. They might not become aware that it is their custom to sleep on beds if they were not aware that people in many societies sleep on the floor or on the ground. Only when we compare ourselves with people in other societies may we become aware of cultural differences and similarities. This is, in fact, the way that anthropology as a profession began. When Europeans began to explore and move to faraway places, they were forced to confront the sometimes striking facts of cultural variation.

Most of us are aware that "times have changed," especially when we compare our lives with those of our parents. Some of the most dramatic changes have occurred in attitudes about sex and marriage, changes in women's roles, and changes in technology. But such culture change is not unusual. Throughout history, humans have replaced or altered customary behaviors and attitudes as their needs have changed. Just as no individual is immortal, no particular cultural pattern is impervious to change. Anthropologists want to understand how and why such change occurs. Culture change may be gradual or rapid. Although there has always been contact between different societies, contact between faraway cultures through exploration, colonization, trade, and more recently multinational business has accelerated the pace of change within the last 600 years or so. Globalization has made the world more and more interconnected. We conclude here with a discussion of the future of cultural diversity.

Defining Culture

In everyday usage, the word *culture* refers to a desirable quality we can acquire by attending a sufficient number of plays and concerts and visiting art museums and galleries. Anthropologists, however, have a different definition, as Ralph Linton explained:

> *Culture* refers to the total way of life of any society, not simply to those parts of this way which the society regards as higher or more desirable. Thus culture, when applied to our own way of life, has nothing to do with playing the piano or reading Browning. For the social scientist such activities are simply elements within the totality of our culture. This totality also includes such mundane activities as washing dishes or driving an automobile, and for the purposes of cultural studies these stand quite on a par with "the finer things of life." It follows that for the social scientist there are no uncultured societies or even individuals. Every society has a culture, no matter how simple this culture may be, and every human being is cultured, in the sense of participating in some culture or other.[1]

Culture, then, refers to innumerable aspects of life, including many things we consider ordinary. Linton emphasized common habits and behaviors in what he considered culture, but the totality of life also includes not just what people do, but also how they commonly think and feel. As we define it here, **culture** is the set of learned behaviors and ideas (including beliefs, attitudes, values, and ideals) that are characteristic of a particular society or other social group. Behaviors can also produce products or *material culture*—things like houses, musical instruments, and tools that are the products of customary behavior.

Different kinds of groups can have cultures. People come to share behaviors and ideas because they communicate with and observe each other. Although groups from families to societies share cultural traits, anthropologists have traditionally been concerned with the cultural characteristics of *societies*. Many anthropologists define **society** as a group of people who occupy a particular territory and speak a common language not generally understood by neighboring peoples. By this definition, societies may or may not correspond to countries. There are many countries, particularly newer ones, that have within their boundaries different peoples speaking mutually unintelligible languages. By our definition of society, such countries are composed of many different societies and therefore many cultures. Also, by our definition of society, some societies may even include more than one country. For example, we would have to say that Canada and the United States form a single society because the two groups generally speak English, live next to each other, and share many common ideas and behaviors. That is why we refer to "North American culture." The terms *society* and *culture* are not synonymous. Society refers to a group of people; culture refers to the learned and shared behaviors, ideas, and characteristics of those people. As we will discuss shortly, we also have to be careful to describe culture as of a particular time period; what is characteristic of one time may not be characteristic of another.

Culture Is Commonly Shared

If only one person thinks or does a certain thing, that thought or action represents a personal habit, not a pattern of culture. For a thought or action to be considered cultural, some social group must commonly share it. We usually share many behaviors and ideas with our families and friends. We commonly share cultural characteristics with those whose ethnic or regional origins, religious affiliations, and occupations are the same as or similar to our own. We share certain practices and ideas with most people in our society. We also share some cultural traits with people beyond our society who have similar interests (such as rules for international sporting events) or similar roots (as do the various English-speaking nations).

When we talk about the commonly shared customs of *a* society, which constitute the traditional and central concern of cultural anthropology, we are referring to *a* culture. When we talk about the commonly shared customs of a group within a society, which are a central concern of sociologists and increasingly of concern to anthropologists, we are referring to a **subculture**. (A subculture is not necessarily the same as an ethnic group.) When we study the commonly shared customs of some group that includes different societies, we are talking about a phenomenon for which we do not have a single word—for example, as when we refer to *Western culture* (the cultural characteristics of societies in or derived from Europe) or the *culture of poverty* (the presumed cultural characteristics of poor people the world over).

We must remember that, even when anthropologists refer to something as cultural, there is always individual variation, which means that not everyone in a society shares a particular cultural characteristic of that society. For example, it is cultural in North American society for adults to live apart from their parents. But not all adults in our society do so, nor do all adults wish to do so. The custom of living apart from parents is considered cultural because most adults practice that custom. In every society studied by anthropologists—in the simplest as well as the most complex—individuals do not all think and act the same.[2] Indeed, individual variation is a major source of new culture.[3]

Culture Is Learned

Not all things shared generally by a group are cultural. Typical hair color is not cultural, nor is eating. For something to be considered cultural, it must be learned as well as shared. A typical hair color (unless dyed) is not cultural because it is genetically determined. Humans eat because they must; but what and when and how they eat are learned and vary from culture to culture. Most North Americans do not consider dog meat edible, and indeed the idea of eating dogs horrifies them. But in China, as in some other societies, dog meat is considered delicious. In North American culture, many people consider a baked ham to be a holiday dish. In several societies of the Middle East, however, including those of Egypt and Israel, eating the meat of a pig is forbidden by sacred writings.

To some extent, all animals exhibit learned behaviors, some of which most individuals in a population may share and may therefore consider cultural. But different animal species vary in the degree to which their shared behaviors are learned or are instinctive. The sociable ants, for instance, despite all their patterned social behavior, do not appear to have much, if any, culture. They divide their labor, construct their nests, form their raiding columns, and carry off their dead—all without having been taught to do so and without imitating the behavior of other ants. Our closest biological relatives, the monkeys and the apes, not only learn a wide variety of behaviors on their own, they also learn from each other. Some of their learned responses are as basic as those involved in maternal care; others are as frivolous as the taste for candy. Frans de Waal reviewed seven long-term studies of chimpanzees and identified at least 39 behaviors that were clearly learned from others.[4] If shared and socially learned, these behaviors could be described as cultural.

A daughter braids her doll's hair, imitating what her mother is doing.

Although humans may acquire much learned behavior by trial and error and imitation, as do monkeys and apes, most human ideas and behaviors are learned from others. Much of it is probably acquired with the aid of spoken, symbolic language. Using language, a human parent can describe a snake and tell a child that a snake is dangerous and should be avoided. If symbolic language did not exist, the parent would have to wait until the child actually saw a snake and then, through example, show the child that such a creature is to be avoided. To sum up, we may say that something is cultural if it is a learned behavior or idea (belief, attitude, value, ideal) that the members of a society or other social group generally share.

Attitudes That Hinder the Study of Cultures

Many of the Europeans who first traveled to faraway places were revolted or shocked by customs they observed. Such reactions are not surprising. People

Because we are ethnocentric about many things, it is often difficult to criticize our own customs, some of which might seem shocking to a member of another society. The elderly in America often spend their days alone. In contrast, the elderly in Japan often live in a three-generational family.

commonly feel that their own behaviors and attitudes are the correct ones and that people who do not share those patterns are immoral or inferior.[5] People who judge other cultures solely in terms of their own culture are **ethnocentric**—that is, they hold an attitude called **ethnocentrism**. Most North Americans would think that eating dogs or insects is disgusting, but most do not feel the same way about eating beef. Similarly, they would react negatively to child betrothal or digging up the bones of the dead.

Our own customs and ideas may appear bizarre or barbaric to an observer from another society. Hindus in India, for example, would consider our custom of eating beef disgusting. In their culture, the cow is a sacred animal and may not be slaughtered for food. In many societies, a baby is almost constantly carried by someone, in someone's lap, or asleep next to others.[6] People in such societies may think it is cruel of us to leave babies alone for long periods of time, often in devices that resemble cages (cribs and playpens). Even our most ordinary customs—the daily rituals we take for granted—might seem thoroughly absurd when viewed from an outside perspective. An observer of our society might justifiably take notes on certain strange behaviors that seem quite ordinary to us, as the following description shows:

The daily body ritual performed by everyone includes a mouth-rite. Despite the fact that these people are so punctilious about the care of the mouth, this rite involves a practice which strikes the uninitiated stranger as revolting. It was reported to me that the ritual consists of inserting a small bundle of hog hairs into the mouth, along with certain magical powders, and then moving the bundle in a highly formalized series of gestures. In addition to the private mouth-rite, the people seek out a holy-mouth man once or twice a year. These practitioners have an impressive set of paraphernalia, consisting of a variety of augers, awls, probes, and prods. The use of these objects in the exorcism of the evils of the mouth involves almost unbelievable ritual torture of the client. The holy-mouth man opens the client's mouth and, using the above-mentioned tools, enlarges any holes which decay may have created in teeth. Magical materials are put into these holes. If there are no naturally occurring holes in the teeth, large sections of one or more teeth are gouged out so that the supernatural substance can be applied. In the client's view, the purpose of these ministrations is to arrest decay and to draw friends. The extremely sacred and traditional character of the rite is evident in the fact that the natives return to the holy-mouth man year after year, despite the fact that their teeth continue to decay.[7]

We are likely to protest that to understand the behaviors of a particular society—in this case, our own—the observer must try to find out what the people in that society say about why they do things. For example, the observer might find out that periodic visits to the "holy-mouth man" are for medical, not magical, purposes. Indeed, the observer, after some questioning, might discover that the "mouth-rite" has no sacred or religious connotations whatsoever. Actually, Horace Miner, the author of the passage on the "daily rite ritual," was not a foreigner. An American, he described the "ritual" the way he did to show how the behaviors involved might be interpreted by an outside observer.

Ethnocentrism hinders our understanding of the customs of other people and, at the same time, keeps us from understanding our own customs. If we think that everything we do is best, we are not likely to ask why we do what we do or why "they" do what "they" do.

We may not always glorify our own culture. Other ways of life may sometimes seem more appealing. Whenever we are weary of the complexities of civilization, we may long for a way of life that is "closer to nature" or "simpler" than our own. For instance, a young North American whose parent is holding two or three jobs just to provide the family with bare necessities might briefly be attracted to the lifestyle of the San of the Kalahari Desert in the 1950s. The San shared their food and therefore were often free to engage in leisure activities during the greater part of the day. They obtained all their food by men hunting animals and women gathering wild plants. They had no facilities for refrigeration, so sharing a large freshly killed animal was clearly more sensible than hoarding meat that would soon rot. Moreover, the sharing provided a kind of social security system for the San. If a hunter was unable to catch an animal on a certain day, he could obtain food for himself and his family from someone else in his band. Then, at some later date, the game he caught would provide food for the family of another, unsuccessful hunter. This system of sharing also ensured that people too young or too old to help with collecting food would still be fed.

Could we learn from the San? Perhaps we could in some respects, but we must not glorify their way of life either or think that their way of life might be easily imported into our own society. Other aspects of San life would not appeal to many North Americans. For example, when the nomadic San decided to move their camps, they had to carry all the family possessions, substantial amounts of food and water, and all young children below age 4 or 5. This is a sizable burden to carry for any distance. The nomadic San traveled about 1,500 miles in a single year and families had few possessions.[8] It is unlikely that most North Americans would find the San way of life enviable in all respects.

Both ethnocentrism and its opposite, the glorification of other cultures, hinder effective anthropological study.

Cultural Relativism

The early evolutionists tended to think of Western cultures as being at the highest or most progressive stage of evolution. Not only were these early ideas based on very poor evidence of the details of world ethnography, they could also be ethnocentric glorifications of Western culture.

But Franz Boas and many of his students—like Ruth Benedict, Melville Herskovits, and Margaret Mead—challenged the attitude that Western cultures were obviously superior. The anthropological attitude that a society's customs and ideas should be described objectively and understood in the context of that society's problems and opportunities became known as **cultural relativism**. Does cultural relativism mean that the actions of another society, or of our own, should not be judged? Does our insistence on objectivity mean that anthropologists should not make moral judgments about the cultural phenomena they observe and try to explain? Does it mean that anthropologists should not try to bring about change? Not necessarily. Although the concept of cultural relativism remains an important anthropological tenet, anthropologists differ in their interpretation of the principle of cultural relativism.

Many anthropologists are uncomfortable with the strong form of cultural relativism that suggests that all patterns of culture are equally valid. What if the people practice slavery, violence against women, torture, or genocide? If the strong doctrine of relativism is adhered to, then these cultural practices are not to be judged, and we should not try to eliminate them. A weaker form of cultural relativism asserts that anthropologists should strive for objectivity in describing a people and should be wary of superficial or quick judgment in their attempts to understand the reasons for cultural behavior. Tolerance should be the basic mode unless there is strong reason to behave otherwise.[9] The weak version of cultural relativity does not preclude anthropologists from making judgments or from trying to change behavior they think is harmful. But judgments need not, and should not, preclude accurate description and explanation.

Now that we have defined what is cultural, we must ask a further question: How does an anthropologist go about deciding which particular behaviors, values, and beliefs of individuals are cultural?

Describing a Culture

Participant-observation and some other methods of research are used by cultural anthropologists in doing fieldwork.

But here we focus on another question: If all individuals are unique and all cultures have some internal variation, how do anthropologists discover what may be cultural? Understanding what is cultural involves two parts: separating what is shared from what is very individually variable, and understanding whether common behaviors and ideas are learned.

Individual Variation

To understand better how an anthropologist might make sense of diverse behaviors, let us examine the diversity at a professional football game in the United States. When people attend a football game, various members of the crowd behave differently while "The Star-Spangled Banner" is being played. As they stand and listen, some people remove their hats; a child munches popcorn; a veteran of the armed forces stands at attention; a teenager searches the crowd for a friend; and the coaches take a final opportunity to intone secret chants and spells designed to sap the strength of the opposing team. Yet, despite these individual variations, most of the people at the game respond in a basically similar manner: Nearly everyone stands silently, facing the flag. Moreover, if you go to several football games, you will observe that many aspects of the event are notably similar. Although the plays will vary from game to game, the rules of the game are never different, and although the colors of the uniforms of the teams are different, the players never appear on the field dressed in swimsuits.

Although the variations in individual reactions to a given stimulus are theoretically limitless, in fact they tend to fall within easily recognizable limits. A child listening to the anthem may continue to eat popcorn but will probably not do a rain dance. Similarly, the coaches

Culture and Culture Change

In deciding what is cultural behavior, anthropologists look for commonalities, understanding that there is always considerable variation. In North American culture, unmarried couples are allowed and even encouraged to spend time with each other, but how they spend their time varies.

will unlikely react to that same stimulus by running onto the field and embracing the singer. Variations in behavior, then, are confined within socially acceptable limits, and part of the anthropologists' goals is to find out what those limits are. They may note, for example, that some limitations on behavior have a practical purpose: A spectator who disrupts the game by wandering onto the field would be required to leave. Other limitations are purely traditional. In our society, it is considered proper for a man to remove his overcoat if he becomes overheated, but others would undoubtedly frown upon his removing his trousers even if the weather were quite warm. Using observation and interviewing, anthropologists discover the customs and the ranges of acceptable behavior that characterize the society under study.

Similarly, anthropologists interested in describing courtship and marriage in our society would encounter a variety of behaviors. Dating couples vary in where they go (coffee shops, movies, restaurants, bowling alleys), what behaviors they engage in on dates, how long they date before they split up or move on to more serious relationships. If they decide to marry, ceremonies may be simple or elaborate and involve either religious or secular rituals. Despite this variability, anthropologists would begin to detect certain regularities in courting practices. Although couples may do many different things on their first and subsequent dates, they nearly always arrange the dates by themselves; they try to avoid their parents when on dates; they often manage to find themselves alone at the end of a date; they put their lips together frequently; and so forth. After a series of more and more closely spaced encounters, a man and woman may decide to declare themselves publicly as a couple, either by announcing that they are engaged or by revealing that they are living together or intend to do so. Finally, if the two of them decide to marry, they must in some way have their union recorded by the civil authorities.

In our society, a person who wishes to marry cannot completely disregard the customary patterns of courtship. If a man saw a woman on the street and decided he wanted to marry her, he could conceivably choose a quicker and more direct form of action than the usual dating procedure. He could get on a horse, ride to the woman's home, snatch her up in his arms, and gallop away with her. In Sicily, until the 1960s, such a couple would have been considered legally married, even if the woman had never met the man before or had no intention of marrying. But in North American society, any man who acted in such a fashion would be arrested and jailed for kidnapping and would probably have his sanity challenged. Although individual behaviors may vary, most social behavior falls within culturally acceptable limits.

In the course of observing and interviewing, anthropologists also try to distinguish actual behavior from the ideas about how people in particular situations ought to feel and behave. In everyday terms, we speak of these ideas as *ideals*; in anthropology, we refer to them as *ideal cultural traits*. Ideal cultural traits may differ from actual behavior because the ideal is based on the way society used to be. (Consider the ideal of "free enterprise," that industry should be totally free of governmental regulation.) Other ideals may never have been actual patterns and may represent merely what people would like to see as correct behavior. Consider the idealized belief, long cherished in North America, that everybody is "equal before the law," that everybody should be treated in the same way by the police and courts. Of course, we know that this is not always true. The rich, for example, may receive less jail time and be sent to nicer prisons. Nevertheless, the ideal is still part of our culture; most of us continue to believe that the law should be applied equally to all.

Cultural Constraints

Noted French sociologist Émile Durkheim stressed that culture is something *outside* us, exerting a strong coercive power on us. We do not always feel the constraints of our culture because we generally conform to the types of conduct and thought it requires. Social scientists refer to standards or rules about what is acceptable behavior as **norms**. The importance of a norm usually can be judged by how members of a society respond when the norm is violated.

Cultural constraints are of two basic types, *direct* and *indirect*. Naturally, the direct constraints are the more obvious. For example, if you choose to wear a casual shorts outfit to a wedding, you will probably be subject to some ridicule and a certain amount of social isolation. But if you choose to wear nothing, you may be exposed to a stronger, more direct cultural constraint—arrest for indecent exposure.

Although indirect forms of cultural constraint are less obvious than direct ones, they are no less effective. Durkheim illustrated this point when he wrote, "I am not obliged to speak French with my fellow-countrymen, nor to use the legal currency, but I cannot possibly do otherwise. If I tried to escape this necessity, my attempt would fail miserably."[10] In other words, if Durkheim had decided he would rather speak Icelandic than French, nobody would have tried to stop him. But hardly anyone would have understood him either. And although he would not have been put into prison for trying to buy groceries with Icelandic money, he would have had difficulty convincing the local merchants to sell him food.

In a series of classic experiments on conformity, Solomon Asch revealed how strong social pressure can be. Asch coached the majority of a group of college students to give deliberately incorrect answers to questions involving visual stimuli. A "critical subject," the one student in the room who was not so coached, had no idea that the other participants would purposely misinterpret the evidence presented to them. Asch found that, in one-third of the experiments, the critical subjects consistently gave incorrect answers, seemingly allowing their own correct perceptions to be distorted by the obviously incorrect statements of the others. And in another 40 percent of the experiments, the critical subject yielded to the opinion of the group some of the time.[11] These studies have been replicated in the United States and elsewhere. Although the degree of conformity appears to vary in different societies, most studies still show conformity effects.[12] Many individuals still do not give in to the wishes of the majority, but a recent study using magnetic resonance imaging has shown that perceptions can actually be altered if participants consciously alter their answers to conform to others.[13]

How to Discover Cultural Patterns

There are two basic ways in which an anthropologist can discover cultural patterns. When dealing with customs that are overt or highly visible within a society—for example, the custom of sending children to school—an investigator can determine the existence of such practices by direct observation and by interviewing a few knowledgeable people. But when dealing with a domain of behavior that may include many individual variations, or when the people studied are unaware of their pattern of behavior and cannot answer questions about it, the anthropologist may need to collect information from a larger sample of individuals to establish what the cultural trait is.

One example of a cultural trait that most people in a society are not aware of is how far apart people stand when they are having a conversation. Yet there is considerable reason to believe that unconscious cultural rules govern such behavior. These rules become obvious when we interact with people who have different rules. We may experience considerable discomfort when another person stands too close (indicating too much intimacy) or too far (indicating unfriendliness). Edward Hall reported that Arabs customarily stand quite close to others, close enough, as we have noted, to be able to smell the other person. In interactions between Arabs and North Americans, then, the Arabs will move closer at the same time that the North Americans back away.[14]

If we wanted to arrive at the cultural rule for conversational distance between casual acquaintances, we could study a sample of individuals from a society and determine the *modal response,* or *mode.* The mode is a statistical term that refers to the most frequently encountered response in a given series of responses. So, for the North American pattern of casual conversational distance, we would plot the actual distance for many observed pairs of people. Some pairs may be 2 feet apart, some 2.5, and some 4 feet apart. If we count the number of times every particular distance is observed, these counts provide what we call a *frequency distribution.* The distance with the highest frequency is the *modal pattern.* Very often the frequency distribution takes the form of a *bell-shaped curve,* as shown in Figure 1.

There, the characteristic being measured is plotted on the horizontal axis (in this case, the distance between conversational pairs), and the number of times each distance is observed

Distance between people conversing varies cross-culturally. The faces of the Rajput Indian men on the left are much closer than the faces of the American women on the right.

(its frequency) is plotted on the vertical axis. If we were to plot how a sample of North American casual conversational pairs is distributed, we would probably get a bell-shaped curve that peaks at around 3 feet.[15] Is it any wonder, then, that we sometimes speak of keeping others "at arm's length"?

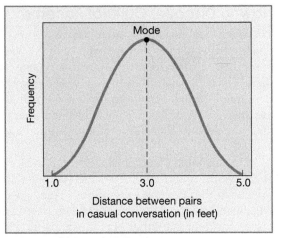

Figure 1 **Frequency Distribution Curve**

Although we may be able to discover by interviews and observation that a behavior, thought, or feeling is widely shared within a society, how do we establish that something commonly shared is learned, so that we can call it cultural? Establishing that something is or is not learned may be difficult. Because children are not reared apart from adult caretakers, the behaviors they exhibit as part of their genetic inheritance are not clearly separated from those they learn from others around them. We suspect that particular behaviors and ideas are largely learned if they vary from society to society. We also suspect genetic influences when particular behaviors or ideas are found in all societies. For example, children the world over seem to acquire language at about the same age, and the structure of their early utterances seems to be similar. These facts suggest that human children are born with an innate grammar. However, although early childhood language seems similar the world over, the particular languages spoken by adults in different societies show considerable variability. This variability suggests that particular languages have to be learned. Similarly, if the courtship patterns of one society differ markedly from those of another, we can be fairly certain that those courtship patterns are learned and therefore cultural.

Culture Is Patterned

Anthropologists have always known that culture is not a hodgepodge of unrelated behaviors and ideas—that a culture is mostly integrated. In saying that a culture is mostly *integrated*, we mean that the elements or traits that make up that culture are not just a random assortment of customs but are mostly adjusted to or consistent with one another.

A culture may also tend to be integrated for psychological reasons. The ideas of a culture are stored in the brains of individuals. Research in social psychology has suggested that people tend to modify beliefs or behaviors that are not cognitively or conceptually consistent with other information.[16] We do not expect cultures to be completely integrated, just as we do not expect individuals to be completely consistent. But if a tendency toward cognitive consistency is found in humans, we might expect that at least some aspects of a culture would tend to be integrated for that reason alone.

Humans are also capable of rational decision making; they can usually figure out that certain things are not easy to do because of other things they do. For example, if a society has a long postpartum sex taboo (a custom in which couples abstain from sex for a year or more after the birth of a baby), we might expect that most people in the society could figure out that it would be easier to observe the taboo if husband and wife did not sleep in the same bed. Or if people drive on the left side of the road, as in England, it is easier and less dangerous to drive a car with a steering wheel on the right because that placement allows you to judge more accurately how close you are to cars coming at you from the opposite direction. Consistency or integration of culture traits may also be produced by less conscious psychological processes. For example, in religion or magic and the arts, people may generalize (transfer) their experiences from one area of life to another.

Adaptation to the environment is another major reason for traits to be patterned. Customs that diminish the survival chances of a society are not likely to persist. Either the people clinging to those customs will become extinct, taking the customs with them, or the customs will be replaced, thereby possibly helping the people to survive. By either process, **maladaptive customs**—those that diminish the chances of survival and reproduction—are likely to disappear. The customs of a society that enhance survival and reproductive success are **adaptive customs** and are likely to persist. Hence, we assume that if a society has survived long enough to be described in the annals of anthropology (the "ethnographic record"), much, if not most, of its cultural repertoire is adaptive, or was at one time.

When we say that a custom is adaptive, however, we mean it is adaptive only with respect to a specific physical and social environment. What may be adaptive in one environment may not be adaptive in another. Therefore, when we ask why a society may have a particular custom, we really are asking if that custom makes sense as an adaptation to that society's particular environmental conditions. If certain customs are more adaptive in particular settings, then those "bundles" of traits will generally be found together under similar conditions. For example, the San, as we have mentioned, subsisted by hunting wild animals and gathering wild plants. Because wild game is mobile and different plants mature at different times, a nomadic way of life may be an adaptive strategy. That food-getting strategy cannot support that many people in one area, so small social groups make more sense than large communities. Because people move frequently, it is probably more adaptive to have few material possessions. These cultural traits usually occur together when people depend on hunting and gathering for their food.

We must remember that not all aspects of culture are consistent, nor is a society forced to adapt its culture to changing environmental circumstances.

How and Why Cultures Change

When you examine the history of a society, it is obvious that its culture has changed over time. Some of the shared behaviors and ideas that were common at one time are modified or replaced at another time. That is why, in describing a culture, it is important to understand that a description pertains to a particular time period. For example, the San of the 1950s were mostly dependent on the collection of wild plants and animals and moved their campsites frequently, but later they became more sedentary to engage in wage labor.

When we compare our lives with those of our parents, it is obvious that many culture changes have occurred. Witness the recent changes in attitudes about sex and marriage, as well as the changes in women's roles. But such culture change is not unusual. Throughout history humans have replaced or altered customary behaviors and attitudes as their needs have changed. Anthropologists want to understand how and why cultures change.

Three general questions can be asked about culture change: What is the source of a new trait? Why are people motivated unconsciously, as well as consciously, to adopt it? And is the new trait adaptive? In general, the impetus for change may come from within the society or from without. From within, the unconscious or conscious pressure for consistency will produce culture change if enough people adjust old behavior and thinking to new. And change can also occur if people try to invent better ways of doing things. Michael Chibnik suggests that people who confront a new problem conduct mental or small "experiments" to decide how to behave. These experiments may give rise to new cultural traits.[17] A good deal of culture change may be stimulated by changes in the external environment. Many North Americans, for example, started to think seriously about conserving energy and about using sources of energy other than oil only after oil supplies from the Middle East were curtailed in 1973 and 1974. A significant amount of the radical and rapid culture change that has occurred in the last few hundred years has been due to the imperial expansion of Western societies into other areas of the world. Native Americans, for instance, were forced to alter their lifestyles drastically when they were driven off their lands and confined to reservations.

Discovery and Invention

The new thing discovered or invented, the innovation, may be an object—the wheel, the plow, the computer—or it may involve behavior and ideas—buying and selling, democracy, monogamy. According to Ralph Linton, a discovery is any addition to knowledge, and an invention is a new application of knowledge.[18] Thus, a person might discover that children can be persuaded to eat nourishing food if the food is associated with an imaginary character that appeals to them. And then someone might exploit that discovery by inventing a character named Popeye who appears in a series of animated cartoons, acquiring miraculous strength by devouring cans of spinach.

Unconscious Invention In discussing the process of invention, we should differentiate between various types of inventions. One type is the consequence of a society's setting itself a specific goal, such as eliminating tuberculosis or placing a person on the moon. Another type emerges less intentionally. This second process of invention is often referred to as *accidental juxtaposition* or *unconscious invention.* Linton suggested that some inventions, especially those of prehistoric days, were probably the consequences of literally dozens of tiny initiatives by "unconscious" inventors. These inventors made their small contributions, perhaps over many hundreds of years, without being aware of the part they were playing in bringing one invention, such as the wheel or a better form of hand ax, to completion.[19] In reconstructing the process of invention in prehistoric times, however, we should be careful not to look back on our ancestors with a smugness generated by our more highly developed technology. We have become accustomed to reading science news in magazines, newspapers and online, finding, almost daily, reports of miraculous new discoveries and inventions. From our point of view, it is difficult to imagine such a simple invention as the wheel taking so many centuries to come into being. We are tempted to surmise that early humans were less intelligent than we are. But the capacity of the human brain has been the same for perhaps 100,000 years; there is no evidence that the inventors of the wheel were any less intelligent than we are.

Intentional Innovation Some discoveries and inventions arise out of deliberate attempts to produce a new idea or object. It may seem that such innovations are obvious responses to perceived needs. For example, during the Industrial Revolution, there was a great demand for inventions that would increase productivity. James Hargreaves, in eighteenth-century England, is an example of an inventor who responded to an existing demand. Textile manufacturers were clamoring for such large quantities of spun yarn that cottage laborers, working with foot-operated spinning wheels, could not meet the demand. Hargreaves, realizing that prestige and financial rewards would come to the person who invented a method of spinning large quantities of yarn in a short time, set about the task and developed the spinning jenny.

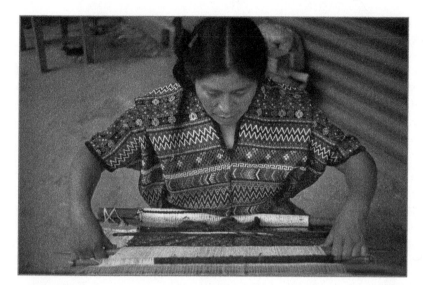

Mayan woman from San Martin Jilotepeque working on a hip-strap loom. Designs became more individual and complex by the 1990s.

A study of innovation among Ashanti artist carvers in Ghana suggests that creativity is more likely in some socioeconomic groups than in others.[20] Some carvers produced only traditional designs; others departed from tradition and produced "new" styles of carving. Two groups were found to innovate the most—the wealthiest and the poorest carvers. These two groups of carvers may tolerate risk more than the middle socioeconomic group. Innovative carving entails some risk because it may take more time and it may not sell. Wealthy carvers can afford the risk, and they may gain some prestige as well as income if their innovation is appreciated. The poor are not doing well anyway, and they have little to lose by trying something new.

Some societies encourage innovativeness more than others, and this can vary substantially over time. Patricia Greenfield and her colleagues describe the changes in weaving in a Mayan community in the Zinacantán region of Chiapas, Mexico.[21] In 1969 and 1970, innovation was not valued. Rather, tradition was; there was the old "true way" to do everything, including how one dressed. There were only four simple weaving patterns, and virtually all males wore ponchos with the same pattern. By 1991, virtually no poncho was the same and the villagers had developed elaborate brocaded and embroidered designs. In a period of 20 years, innovation had increased dramatically.

Who Adopts Innovations? Once someone discovers or invents something, there is still the question of whether others will adopt the innovation. Many researchers have studied the characteristics of "early adopters." Such individuals tend to be educated, high in social status, upwardly mobile, and, if they are property owners, have large farms and businesses. The individuals who most need technological improvements—those who are less well off—are generally the last to adopt innovations. The theory is that only the wealthy can afford to take the substantial risks associated with new ways of doing things. In periods of rapid technological change, therefore, the gap between rich and poor is likely to widen because the rich adopt innovations sooner, and benefit more from them, than the poor.[22]

Costs and Benefits An innovation that is technologically superior is not necessarily going to be adopted. There are costs as well as benefits for both individuals and large-scale industries. Take the computer keyboard. The keyboard used most often on computers today is called the

QWERTY keyboard (named after the letters on the left side of the line of keys below the row of number keys). This keyboard was actually invented to slow typing speed down! Early typewriters had mechanical keys that jammed if the typist went too fast.[23] Computer keyboards don't have that problem, so an arrangement of keys that allowed faster typing would probably be better. Different keyboard configurations have been invented, but they haven't caught on. Most people probably would find it too hard or too time-consuming to learn a new style of typing, so the original style of keyboard persists.

Diffusion

The source of new cultural elements in a society may also be another society. The process by which cultural elements are borrowed from another society and incorporated into the culture of the recipient group is called **diffusion**. Borrowing sometimes enables a group to bypass stages or mistakes in the development of a process or institution. For example, Germany was able to accelerate its program of industrialization in the nineteenth century because it was able to avoid some of the errors its English and Belgian competitors made by taking advantage of technological borrowing. Japan did the same somewhat later. Indeed, in recent years, some of the earliest industrialized countries have fallen behind their imitators in certain areas of production, such as automobiles, televisions, cameras, and computers.

In a well-known passage, Linton conveyed the far-reaching effects of diffusion by considering the first few hours in the day of an American man in the 1930s. This man

> . . . awakens in a bed built on a pattern which originated in the Near East but which was modified in northern Europe before it was transmitted to America. He throws back covers made from cotton, domesticated in India, or linen, domesticated in the Near East, or silk, the use of which was discovered in China. All of these materials have been spun and woven by processes invented in the Near East. . . . He takes off his pajamas, a garment invented in India, and washes with soap invented by the ancient Gauls. He then shaves, a masochistic rite which seems to have derived from either Sumer or ancient Egypt.

A Masai man in Kenya can call home or around the world from the plains of Kenya.

Before going out for breakfast he glances through the window, made of glass invented in Egypt, and if it is raining puts on overshoes made of rubber discovered by the Central American Indians and takes an umbrella, invented in southeastern Asia. . . .

On his way to breakfast he stops to buy a paper paying for it with coins, an ancient Lydian invention. . . . His plate is made of a form of pottery invented in China. His knife is of steel, an alloy first made in southern India, his fork a medieval Italian invention, and his spoon a derivative of a Roman original. . . . After his fruit (African watermelon) and first coffee (an Abyssinian plant), . . . he may have the egg of a species of bird domesticated in Indo-China, or thin strips of the flesh of an animal domesticated in eastern Asia which have been salted and smoked by a process developed in northern Europe. . . .

While smoking (an American Indian habit), he reads the news of the day, imprinted in characters invented by the ancient Semites upon a material invented in China by a process invented in Germany. As he absorbs the accounts of foreign troubles he will, if he is a good conservative citizen, thank a Hebrew deity in an Indo-European language that he is 100 percent American.[24]

The Selective Nature of Diffusion Although there is a temptation to view the dynamics of diffusion as similar to a stone sending concentric ripples over still water, this would be an over-simplification of the way diffusion actually occurs. Not all cultural traits are borrowed as readily as the ones we have mentioned, nor do they usually expand in neat, ever-widening circles. Rather, diffusion is a selective process. The Japanese, for instance, accepted much from Chinese culture, but they also rejected many traits. Rhymed tonal poetry, civil service examinations, and foot binding, which the Chinese favored, were never adopted in Japan. The poetry form was unsuited to the structure of the Japanese language; the examinations were unnecessary in view of the entrenched power of the Japanese aristocracy; and foot binding was repugnant to a people who abhorred body mutilation of any sort.

Not only would we expect societies to reject items from other societies that are repugnant, we would also expect them to reject ideas and technology that do not satisfy some psychological, social, or cultural need. After all, people are not sponges; they don't automatically soak up the things around them. If they did, the amount of cultural variation in the world would be extremely small, which is clearly not the case. Finally, diffusion is selective because the overt form of a particular trait, rather than its function or meaning, frequently seems to determine how the trait will be received. For example, the enthusiasm in women for bobbed hair (short haircuts) that swept through much of North America in the 1920s never caught on among the Native Americans of northwestern California. To many women of European ancestry, short hair was a symbolic statement of their freedom. To Native American women, who traditionally cut their hair short when in mourning, it was a reminder of death.[25]

Acculturation

On the surface, the process of change called **acculturation** seems to include much of what we have discussed under the label of diffusion because acculturation refers to the changes that occur when different cultural groups come into intensive contact. As in diffusion, the source of new cultural items is the other society. But more often than not, anthropologists use the term *acculturation* to describe a situation in which one of the societies in contact is much more powerful than the other. Thus, acculturation can be seen as a process of extensive cultural borrowing in the context of superordinate–subordinate relations between societies.[26] There is probably always some borrowing both ways, but generally the subordinate or less powerful society borrows the most.

Culture and Culture Change

External pressure for culture change can take various forms. In its most direct form—conquest or colonialization—the dominant group uses force or the threat of force to try to bring about culture change in the other group. For example, in the Spanish conquest of Mexico, the conquerors forced many of the native groups to accept Catholicism. Although such direct force is not always exerted in conquest situations, dominated peoples often have little choice but to change. Examples of such indirectly forced change abound in the history of Native Americans in the United States. Although the federal government made few direct attempts to force people to adopt American culture, it did drive many native groups from their lands, thereby obliging them to give up many aspects of their traditional ways of life. To survive, they had no choice but to adopt many of the dominant society's traits. When Native American children were required to go to school, which taught the dominant society's values, the process was accelerated.

A subordinate society may acculturate to a dominant society even in the absence of direct or indirect force. Perceiving that members of the dominant society enjoy more secure living conditions, the dominated people may identify with the dominant culture in the hope that they will be able to share some of its benefits by doing so. Or, they may elect to adopt cultural elements from the dominant society because they perceive that the new element has advantages. For example, in Arctic areas, many Inuit and Saami (or Lapp) groups seemed eager to replace dog sleds with snowmobiles without any coercion.[27] There is evidence that the Inuit weighed the advantages and disadvantages of the snowmobile versus the dog sled and that its adoption was gradual. Similarly, rifles were seen as a major technological improvement, increasing the success rate in hunting, but the Inuit did not completely abandon their former ways of hunting. More recently the Inuit are trying out GPS devices for navigating.[28]

Acculturation processes vary considerably depending on the wishes of the more powerful society, the attitudes of the less powerful, and whether there is any choice. More powerful societies do not always want individuals from another culture to assimilate or "melt into" the dominant culture completely; instead, they may prefer and even actively promote a *multicultural* society. Multiculturalism can be voluntary or it may arise out of deliberate segregation.

Many millions of people, however, never had a chance to acculturate after contact with Europeans. They simply died, sometimes directly at the hands of the conquerors, but probably more often as a result of the new diseases the Europeans inadvertently brought with them. Depopulation because of measles, smallpox, and tuberculosis was particularly common in North and South America and on the islands of the Pacific. Those areas had previously been isolated from contact with Europeans and from the diseases of that continuous landmass we call the Old World—Europe, Asia, and Africa.[29]

Nowadays, many powerful nations—and not just Western ones—may seem to be acting in more humanitarian ways to improve the life of previously subjugated as well as other "developing" peoples. For better or worse, these programs, however, are still forms of external pressure. The tactic used may be persuasion rather than force, but most of the programs are nonetheless designed to bring about acculturation in the direction of the dominant societies' cultures. For example, the introduction of formal schooling cannot help but instill new values that may contradict traditional cultural patterns. Even health care programs may alter traditional ways of life by undermining the authority of shamans and other leaders and by increasing population beyond the number that can be supported in traditional ways. Confinement to "reservations" or other kinds of direct force are not the only ways a dominant society can bring about acculturation.

The process of acculturation also applies to immigrants, most of whom, at least nowadays, choose to leave one country for another. Immigrants are almost always a minority in the new country and therefore are in a subordinate position. If the immigrant's culture changes, it is almost always in the direction of the dominant culture. Immigrant groups vary considerably in the degree and speed with which they adopt the new culture and the social roles of the new society in which they live. An important area of research is explaining the variation in acculturation and assimilation. (*Assimilation* is a concept very similar to acculturation, but *assimilation* is a term more often used by sociologists to describe the process by which individuals acquire the social roles and culture of the dominant group.) Why do some immigrant groups acculturate or assimilate faster than others? A comparative study by Robert Schrauf assessed the degree to which immigrant groups coming to North America retained their native language over time. He looked at whether they lived in tightly knit communities, retained religious rituals, had separate schools and special festivals, visited their homeland, did not intermarry, or worked with others of their ethnic group. All of these factors might be expected to lead to retention of the native language (and presumably other cultural patterns), but only living in tightly knit communities and retaining religious rituals strongly predicted retaining the native language over a long period of time.[30]

Culture Change and Adaptation

Earlier in this chapter when we discussed the fact that culture is patterned, we indicated that adaptation to the environment is one reason why certain culture traits will cluster because more than one trait is likely to be *adaptive* in a particular environment. We make the assumption that most of the customary behaviors of a culture are probably *adaptive*, or at least not maladaptive, in that environment. Even though customs are learned and not genetically inherited, cultural adaptation may resemble biological adaptation in one major respect. The frequency of certain genetic alternatives is likely to increase over time if those genetic traits increase their carriers' chances of survival and reproduction. Similarly, the frequency of a new learned behavior will increase over time and become customary in a population if the people with that behavior are most likely to survive and reproduce.

One of the most important differences between cultural evolution and genetic evolution is that individuals often can decide whether or not to accept and follow the way their parents behave or think, whereas they cannot decide whether or not to inherit certain genes. When enough individuals change their behavior and beliefs, we say that the culture has changed. Therefore, it is possible for culture change to occur much more rapidly than genetic change.

A dramatic example of intentional cultural change was the adoption and later elimination of the custom of *sepaade* among the Rendille, a pastoral population that herds camels, goats, and sheep in the desert in northern Kenya. According to the *sepaade* tradition, some women had to wait to marry until all their brothers were married. These women could well have been over 40 by the time they married. The Rendille say that this tradition was a result of intense warfare between the Rendille and the Borana during the mid-nineteenth century. Attacked by Borana on horseback, the male warriors had to leave their camels unattended and the frightened camels fled. The daughters of one male age-set were appointed to look after the camels, and the *sepaade* tradition developed. In 1998, long after warfare with the Borana ceased, the elders decided to free the *sepaade* from their obligation to postpone their own marriages. Interviews with the Rendille in the 1990s revealed that many individuals were fully aware of the reason for the tradition in the first place. Now, they said, there was peace, so there was no longer any reason for the *sepaade* tradition to continue.[31]

The adoption of the *sepaade* is an example of culture change in a changing environment. But what if the environment is stable? Is culture change more or less likely? Robert Boyd and Peter Richerson have shown mathematically that, when the environment is relatively stable and individual mistakes are costly, staying with customary modes of behavior (usually transmitted by parents) is probably more adaptive than changing.[32] But what happens when the environment, particularly the social environment, is changing? It is particularly when circumstances change that individuals are likely to try ideas or behaviors that are different from those of their parents. We can expect that the choices individuals make may often be adaptive ones. But it is important to note that adopting an innovation from someone in one's own society or borrowing an innovation from another society is not always or necessarily beneficial, either in the short or the long run. Why, for example, have smoking and drug use diffused so widely even though they are likely to reduce a person's chances of survival? Second, even if people are correct in their short-term judgment of benefit, they may be wrong in their judgment about long-run benefit. A new crop may yield more than the old crop for five consecutive years, but the new crop may fail miserably in the sixth year because of lower-than-normal rainfall or because the new crop depleted soil nutrients. Third, people may be forced by the more powerful to change, with few if any benefits for themselves.

Whatever the motives for humans to change their behavior, the theory of natural selection suggests that new behavior is not likely to become cultural or remain cultural over generations if it has harmful reproductive consequences, just as a genetic mutation with harmful consequences is not likely to become frequent in a population.[33] Still, we know of many examples of culture change that seem maladaptive—the switch to bottle-feeding rather than nursing infants, which may spread infection because contaminated water is used, or the adoption of alcoholic beverages, which may lead to alcoholism and early death.

Revolution

Certainly the most drastic and rapid way a culture can change is as a result of **revolution**— replacement, usually violent, of a country's rulers. Historical records, as well as our daily newspapers, indicate that people frequently rebel against established authority. Rebellions, if they occur, almost always occur in state societies, where there is a distinct ruling elite. They take the form of struggles between rulers and ruled, between conquerors and conquered, or between representatives of an external colonial power and segments of the native society. Rebels do not always succeed in overthrowing their rulers, so rebellions do not always result in revolutions. And even successful rebellions do not always result in culture change; the individual rulers may change, but customs or institutions may not. The sources of revolution may be mostly internal, as in the French Revolution, or partly external, as in the Russian-supported 1948 revolution in Czechoslovakia and the United States-supported 1973 revolution against President Allende in Chile.

The American War of Independence toward the end of the eighteenth century is a good example of a colonial rebellion, the success of which was at least partly a result of foreign intervention. The American rebellion was a war of neighboring colonies against the greatest imperial power of the time, Great Britain. In the nineteenth century and continuing into the middle and later years of the twentieth century, there would be many other wars of independence, in Latin America, Europe, Asia, and Africa. We don't always remember that the American rebellion was the first of these anti-imperialist wars in modern times, and the model for many that followed. And just like many of the most recent liberation movements, the American rebellion was also

Culture and Culture Change

Revolutionary leaders are often from high-status backgrounds. Here we see a depiction of Patrick Henry giving his famous speech to the aristocratic landowners in the Virginia General Assembly on March 23, 1775. Urging the Virginians to fight the British, Henry said that the choice was "liberty or death."

Source: Currier & Ives, "Give Me Liberty or Give Me Death!", 1775. Lithograph, 1876. c. The Granger Collection, New York.

part of a larger worldwide war, involving people from many rival nations. Thirty thousand German-speaking soldiers fought, for pay, on the British side; an army and navy from France fought on the American side. There were volunteers from other European countries, including Denmark, Holland, Poland, and Russia.

One of these volunteers was a man named Kosciusko from Poland, which at the time was being divided between Prussia and Russia. Kosciusko helped win a major victory for the Americans, and subsequently directed the fortification of what later became the American training school for army officers, West Point. After the war, he returned to Poland and led a rebellion against the Russians, which was only briefly successful. In 1808, he published the *Manual on the Maneuvers of Horse Artillery*, which was used for many years by the American army. When he died, he left money to buy freedom and education for American slaves. The executor of Kosciusko's will was Thomas Jefferson.

As in many revolutions, those who were urging revolution were considered "radicals." At a now-famous debate in Virginia in 1775, delegates from each colony met at a Continental Congress. Patrick Henry put forward a resolution to prepare for defense against the British armed forces. The motion barely passed, by a vote of 65 to 60. Henry's speech is now a part of American folklore. He rose to declare that it was insane not to oppose the British and that he was not afraid to test the strength of the colonies against Great Britain. Others might hesitate, he said, but he would have "liberty or death." The "radicals" who supported Henry's resolution included many aristocratic landowners, two of whom, George Washington and Thomas Jefferson, became the first and third occupants of the highest political office in what became the United States of America.[34]

Not all peoples who are suppressed, conquered, or colonialized eventually rebel against established authority. Why this is so, and why rebellions and revolts are not always successful in bringing about culture change, are still open questions. The classic revolutions of the past occurred in countries that were industrialized only incipiently at best. For the most part, the same is true of the rebellions and revolutions in recent years; they have occurred mostly in countries we call "developing." The evidence from a worldwide survey of developing countries suggests that rebellions have tended to occur where the ruling classes depended mostly on the produce or income from land, and therefore were resistant to demands for reform from the rural classes that worked the land. In such agricultural economies, the rulers are not likely to yield political power or give greater economic returns to the workers because to do so would eliminate the basis (landownership) of the rulers' wealth and power.[35]

Globalization: Problems and Opportunities

Investment capital, people, and ideas are moving around the world at an ever faster rate.[36] Transportation now allows people and goods to circle the globe in days; telecommunications and the Internet make it possible to send a message around the world in seconds and minutes. Economic exchange is enormously more global and transnational. The word **globalization** is often used nowadays to refer to "the massive flow of goods, people, information, and capital across huge areas of the earth's surface."[37] The process of globalization has resulted in the worldwide spread of cultural features, particularly in the domain of economics and international trade. We buy from the same companies (that have factories all over the world), we sell our products and services for prices that are set by world market forces. We can eat pizza, hamburgers, curry, or sushi in most urban centers. In some ways, cultures are changing in similar directions. They have become more commercial, more urban, and more international. The job has become more important, and kinship less important, as people travel to and work in other countries, and return just periodically to their original homes. Ideas about democracy, the rights of the individual, and alternative medical practices and religions have become more widespread; people in many countries of the world watch the same TV shows, wear similar fashions, and listen to the same or similar music. In short, people are increasingly sharing behaviors and beliefs with people in other cultures, and the cultures of the world are less and less things "with edges," as Paul Durrenberger says.[38]

But diffusion of a culture trait does not mean that it is incorporated in exactly the same way, and the spread of certain products and activities through globalization does not mean that change happens in the same way everywhere. For example, the spread of multinational fast-food restaurants like McDonald's or Kentucky Fried Chicken has come to symbolize globalization. But the

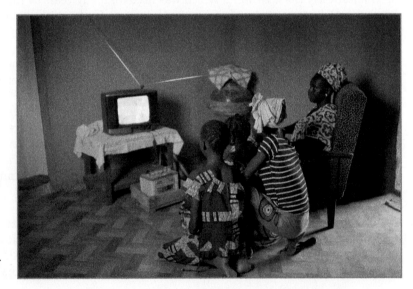

Television has dramatically enhanced world communication. Using other new inventions, a family in the village of Tiele in Mali watch TV powered by a car battery which was recharged with a solar home system.

Culture and Culture Change

behavior of the Japanese in such restaurants is quite different from behavior in the United States. Perhaps the most surprising difference is that the Japanese in McDonald's actually have more familial intimacy and sharing than in more traditional restaurants. We imagine that establishments like McDonald's promote fast eating. But Japan has long had fast food—noodle shops at train stations, street vendors, and boxed lunches. Sushi, which is usually ordered in the United States at

MIGRANTS AND IMMIGRANTS

Increasing Cultural Diversity within the Countries of the World

The modern world is culturally diverse in two ways. There are native cultures in every part of the world, and today most countries have people from different cultures who have arrived relatively recently. Recent arrivals may be migrants coming for temporary work, or they may be refugees, forced by persecution or genocide to migrate, or they may be immigrants who voluntarily come into a new country. Parts of populations have moved away from their native places since the dawn of humanity. The first modern-looking humans moved out of Africa only in the last 100,000 years. People have been moving ever since. The people we call Native Americans were actually the first to come to the New World; most anthropologists think they came from northeast Asia. In the last 200 years, the United States and Canada have experienced extensive influxes of people. As is commonly said, they have become nations of migrants and immigrants, and Native Americans are now vastly outnumbered by the people and their descendants who came from Europe, Africa, Asia, Latin America, and elsewhere. North America not only has native and regional subcultures, but also ethnic, religious, and occupational subcultures, each with its own distinctive set of culture traits. Thus, North American culture is partly a "melting pot" and partly a mosaic of cultural diversity. Many of us, not just anthropologists, like this diversity. We like to go to ethnic restaurants regularly. We like salsa, sushi, and spaghetti. We compare and enjoy the different geographic varieties of coffee. We like music and artists from other countries. We often choose to wear clothing that may have been manufactured halfway around the world. We like all of these things not only because they may be affordable. We like them mostly, perhaps, because they are different.

Many of the population movements in the world today, as in the past, are responses to persecution and war. The word *diaspora* is often used nowadays to refer to these major dispersions. Most were and are involuntary; people are fleeing danger and death. But not always. Scholars distinguish different types of diaspora, including "victim," "labor," "trade," and "imperial" diasporas. The Africans who were sold into slavery, the Armenians who fled genocide in the early twentieth century, the Jews who fled persecution and genocide in various places over the centuries, the Palestinians who fled to the West Bank, Gaza, Jordan, and Lebanon in the mid-twentieth century, and the Rwandans who fled genocide toward the end of the twentieth century may have mostly been victims. The Chinese, Italians, and the Poles may have mostly moved to take advantage of job opportunities, the Lebanese to trade, and the British to extend and service their empire. Often these categories overlap; population movements can and have occurred for more than one reason. Some of the recent diasporas are less one-way than in the past. People are more "transnational," just as economics and politics are more "globalized." The new global communications have facilitated the retention of homeland connections—socially, economically, and politically. Some diasporic communities play an active role in the politics of their homelands, and some nation-states have begun to recognize their far-flung emigrants as important constituencies.

As cultural anthropologists increasingly study migrant, refugee, and immigrant groups, they focus on how the groups have adapted their cultures to new surroundings, what they have retained, how they relate to the homeland, how they have developed an ethnic consciousness, and how they relate to other minority groups and the majority culture.

Sources: M. Ember et al. 2005; Levinson and M. Ember 1997.

a sit-down restaurant, is usually served in Japan at a bar with a conveyor belt—individuals only need to pluck off the wanted dish as it goes by. Observations at McDonald's in Japan suggest that mothers typically order food for the family while the father spends time with the children at a table, a rare event since fathers often work long hours and cannot get home for dinner often. Food, such as French fries, is typically shared by the family. Even burgers and drinks are passed around, with many people taking a bite or a sip. Such patterns typify long-standing family practices. Japan has historically borrowed food, such as the Chinese noodle soup, now called ramen. Indeed, in a survey, ramen was listed as the most representative Japanese food. The burger was the second most-often listed. McDonald's has become Japanese—the younger generation does not even know that McDonald's is a foreign company—they think it is Japanese.[39]

Globalization is not new. The world has been global and interdependent since the sixteenth century.[40] What we currently call "globalization" is a more widespread version of what we used to call by various other names—diffusion, acculturation, colonialism, imperialism, or commercialization. But globalization is now on a much grander scale; enormous amounts of international investment fuel world trade. Shifts in the world marketplace may drastically affect a country's well-being more than ever before. For example, 60 percent of Pakistan's industrial employment is in textile and apparel manufacturing, but serious unemployment resulted when that manufacturing was crippled by restrictive American import policies and fears about war between India and Afghanistan.[41]

As we have seen in this chapter, there are many negative effects of colonialism, imperialism, and globalization. Many native peoples in many places lost their land and have been forced to work for inadequate wages in mines and plantations and factories that foreign capitalists own. Frequently, there is undernutrition if not starvation. Global travel has resulted in the quick spread of diseases such as HIV and severe acute respiratory syndrome (SARS), and increasing deforestation has led to a spread of malaria.[42] But are there any positive consequences? The "human development indicators" collected by the United Nations suggest an improvement in many respects, including increases in life expectancy and literacy in most countries. Much of the improvement in life expectancy is undoubtedly due to the spread of medicines developed in the advanced economies of the West. There is generally less warfare as colonial powers enforced pacification within the colonies that later became independent states. Most important, perhaps, has been the growth of middle classes all over the world, whose livelihoods depend on globalizing commerce. The middle classes in many countries have become strong and numerous enough to pressure governments for democratic reforms and the reduction of injustice.

World trade is the primary engine of economic development. Per capita income is increasing. Forty years ago, the countries of Asia were among the poorest countries in the world in terms of per capita income. Since then, because of their involvement in world trade, their incomes have risen enormously. In 1960, South Korea was as poor as India. Now its per capita income is 20 times higher than India's. Singapore is an even more dramatic example. In the late 1960s, its economy was a disaster. Today, its per capita income is higher than Britain's.[43] Mexico used to be a place where North Americans built factories to produce garments for the North American market. Now its labor is no longer so cheap. But because it has easy access to the North American market and because its plentiful labor is acquiring the necessary skills, Mexico is now seeing the development of high-tech manufacturing with decent salaries.[44]

There is world trade also in people. Many countries of the world now export people to other countries. Mexico has done so for a long time. Virtually every family in a Bangladesh village depends on someone who works overseas and sends money home. Without those remittances, many would face starvation. The government encourages people to go abroad to work. Millions of people from Bangladesh are now overseas on government-sponsored work contracts.[45]

Culture and Culture Change

But does a higher per capita income mean that life has improved generally in a country? Not necessarily. Inequality within countries can increase with technological improvements because the rich often benefit the most. In addition, economic wealth is increasingly concentrated in a relatively small number of countries. Obviously, then, not everyone is better off even if most countries are doing better on average. Poverty has become more common as countries have become more unequal.

Although many of the changes associated with globalization seem to be driven by the economic and political power of the richer countries, the movement of ideas, art, music, and food is more of a two-way process. A large part of that process involves the migration of people who bring their culture with them. Movements of people have played a large role in the entry of food such as tortilla chips and salsa, sushi, and curries into the United States; music like reggae and many types of dance music from Latin America; and African carvings and jewelry such as beaded necklaces. Recently there has even been increased interest in acquiring indigenous knowledge of plants, the knowledge of indigenous healers, and learning about shamanistic trances.

It is probably not possible to go back to a time when societies were not so dependent on each other, not so interconnected through world trade, not so dependent on commercial exchange. Even those who are most upset with globalization find it difficult to imagine that it is possible to return to a less connected world. For better or worse, the world is interconnected and will remain so. The question now is whether the average economic improvements in countries will eventually translate into economic improvements for most individuals.

Many of the processes that we have discussed—the expansion and domination by the West and other powerful nations, the deprivation of the ability of peoples to earn their livelihoods by traditional means, the imposition of schools or other methods to force acculturation, the attempts to convert people to other religions, and globalization—have led to profound changes in culture. But if culture change in the modern world has made cultures more alike in some ways, it has not eliminated cultural differences. Often, in the aftermath of violent events such as depopulation, relocation, enslavement, and genocide by dominant powers, deprived peoples have created new cultures in a process called **ethnogenesis**.[46]

Some of the most dramatic examples of ethnogenesis come from areas where escaped slaves (called Maroons) created new cultures. Maroon societies emerged in the past few hundred years in a variety of New World locations, from the United States to the West Indies and northern parts of South America. One of the new cultures, now known as Aluku, emerged when slaves fled from coastal plantations in Suriname to the swampy interior country along the Cottica River. After a war with the Dutch colonists, this particular group moved to French Guiana. The escaped slaves, originating from widely varying cultures in Africa or born on Suriname plantations, organized themselves into autonomous communities with military headmen.[47] They practiced slash-and-burn cultivation, with women doing most of the work. Although settlements shifted location as a way of evading enemies, coresidence in a community and collective ownership of land became important parts of the emerging identities. Communities took on the names of the specific plantations from which their leaders had escaped. Principles of inheritance through the female line began to develop, and full-fledged matriclans became the core of each village. Each village had its own shrine, the *faaka tiki*, where residents invoked the clan ancestors, as well as a special house where the deceased were brought to be honored and feted before being taken to the forest for burial. Clans also inherited avenging spirits with whom they could communicate through mediums. The Aluku case is a clear example of ethnogenesis because the culture did not exist 350 years ago. It emerged and was created by people trying to adapt to circumstances not of their own making. In common with other cases of emerging ethnic identity, the Aluku came not only to share new patterns of behavior but also to see themselves as having a common origin (a common ancestor), a shared history, and a common religion.[48]

Cultural Diversity in the Future

Measured in terms of travel time, the world today is much smaller than it has ever been. It is possible now to fly halfway around the globe in the time it took people to travel to the next state less than a century ago. In the realm of communication, the world is even smaller. We can talk to someone on the other side of the globe in a matter of minutes, we can send that person a message (by fax or e-mail) in seconds, and through television we can see live coverage of events in that person's country. More and more people are drawn into the world market economy, buying and selling similar things and, as a consequence, altering the patterns of their lives in sometimes similar ways. Still, although modern transportation and communication facilitate the rapid spread of some cultural characteristics to all parts of the globe, it is highly unlikely that all parts of the world will end up the same culturally. Cultures are bound to retain some of their original characteristics or develop distinctive new adaptations. Even though television has diffused around the world, local people continue to prefer local programs when they are available. And even when people all over the world watch the same program, they may interpret it in very different ways. People are not just absorbing the messages they get; they often resist or revise them.[49]

Until recently, researchers studying culture change generally assumed that the differences between people of different cultures would become minimal. But in the last 30 years or so, it has become increasingly apparent that, although many differences disappear, many people are affirming ethnic identities in a process that often involves deliberately introducing cultural difference.[50] Eugeen Roosens describes the situation of the Huron of Quebec, who in the late 1960s seemed to have disappeared as a distinct culture. The Huron language had disappeared and the lives of the Huron were not obviously distinguishable from those of the French Canadians around them. The Huron then developed a new identity as they actively worked to promote the rights of indigenous peoples like themselves. That their new defining cultural symbols bore no resemblance to the past Huron culture is beside the point.

One fascinating possibility is that ethnic diversity and ethnogenesis may be a result of broader processes. Elizabeth Cashdan found that the degree of ethnic diversity appears to be related to environmental unpredictability, which is associated with greater distance from the equator.[51] There appear to be many more cultural groups nearer to the equator than in very northern and southern latitudes. Perhaps, Cashdan suggests, environmental unpredictability in the north and south necessitates wider ties between social groups to allow cooperation in case local resources fail. This may minimize the likelihood of cultural divergence, that is, ethnogenesis. Hence, there will be fewer cultures further from the equator.

Future research on culture change should increase our understanding of how and why various types of change are occurring. If we can increase our understanding of culture change in the present, we should be better able to understand similar processes in the past. We may be guided in our efforts to understand culture change by the large number of cross-cultural correlations that have been discovered between a particular cultural variation and its presumed causes.[52] All cultures have changed over time; variation is the product of differential change. Thus, the variations we see are the products of change processes, and the discovered predictors of those variations may suggest how and why the changes occurred.

Culture and Culture Change

Summary

1. Culture may be defined as the set of learned behaviors and ideas (including beliefs, attitudes, values, and ideals) that are characteristic of a particular society or other social group.

2. When anthropologists refer to *a* culture, they usually are referring to the cultural patterns of a particular society—that is, a particular territorial population speaking a language not generally understood by neighboring territorial populations.

3. Ethnocentrism, judging other cultures in terms of your own, and its opposite—the glorification of other cultures—impede anthropological inquiry. An important tenet in anthropology is the principle of cultural relativism: the attitude that a society's customs and ideas should be studied objectively and understood in the context of that society's culture. But when it comes to some cultural practices such as violence against women, torture, slavery, or genocide, most anthropologists can no longer adhere to the strong form of cultural relativism that asserts that all cultural practices are equally valid.

4. Anthropologists seek to discover the customs and ranges of acceptable behavior that constitute the culture of a society under study. In doing so, they focus on general or shared patterns of behavior rather than on individual variations.

5. Cultures have patterns or clusters of traits. They tend to be integrated for psychological and adaptive reasons.

6. Culture is always changing. Because culture consists of learned behaviors and ideas, cultural traits can be unlearned and learned anew as human needs change.

7. Discoveries and inventions, though ultimately the sources of all culture change, do not necessarily lead to change. Only when society accepts an invention or discovery and uses it regularly can culture change be said to have occurred.

8. The process by which cultural elements are borrowed from another society and incorporated into the culture of the recipient group is called diffusion. Cultural traits do not necessarily diffuse; that is, diffusion is a selective, not automatic, process. A society accepting a foreign cultural trait is likely to adapt it in a way that effectively harmonizes it with the society's own traditions.

9. When a group or society is in contact with a more powerful society, the weaker group is often obliged to acquire cultural elements from the dominant group. This process of extensive borrowing in the context of superordinate–subordinate relations between societies is called acculturation. Acculturation processes vary considerably depending on the wishes of the more powerful society, the attitudes of the less powerful, and whether there is any choice.

10. Even though customs are not genetically inherited, cultural adaptation may be similar to biological adaptation in one major respect. Traits (cultural or genetic) that are more likely to be reproduced (learned or inherited) are likely to become more frequent in a population over time. Particularly when the environment changes, individuals may try out ideas and behaviors that are different than their parents.

11. Perhaps the most drastic and rapid way a culture can change is by revolution—a usually violent replacement of the society's rulers. Rebellions occur primarily in state societies,

Culture and Culture Change

where there is a distinct ruling elite. However, not all peoples who are suppressed, conquered, or colonized eventually rebel or successfully revolt against established authority.

12. Globalization—the widespread flow of people, information, technology, and capital over the earth's surface—has minimized cultural diversity in some respects, but it has not eliminated it.

Glossary Terms

acculturation
adaptive customs
cultural relativism
culture
diffusion

ethnocentric
ethnocentrism
ethnogenesis
globalization
maladaptive customs

norms
revolution
society
subculture

Critical Questions

1. Would it be adaptive for a society to have everyone adhere to the cultural norms? Explain your answer.

2. Not all people faced with external pressure to change do so or do so at the same rate. What factors might explain why some societies rapidly change their culture?

3. Does the concept of cultural relativism promote international understanding, or does it hinder attempts to have international agreement on acceptable behavior, such as human rights?

Read the Original Source on myanthrolab.com

Read the case study by Regina Smith Oboler, "Nandi: From Cattle-Keepers to Cash-Crop Farmers," on MyAnthroLab, and answer the following questions.

1. Who are the Nandi? Give a brief description of them, and include the time period and community being described by Oboler.

2. As you read about the Nandi, you may be surprised by some of their customs. Indicate which specific customs surprise you. Describe whether you think you are reacting simply because their customs are different from your customs, whether you are being ethnocentric, or if you prefer their customs.

3. Anthropologists have to learn not to judge behavior in another culture in terms of their own culture. Give an example from Regina Smith Oboler's fieldwork among the Nandi.

Photo Credits

Glossary

Acculturation The process of extensive borrowing of aspects of culture in the context of superordinate–subordinate relations between societies; usually occurs as the result of external pressure.

Adaptive customs Cultural traits that enhance survival and reproductive success in a particular environment.

Cultural relativism The attitude that a society's customs and ideas should be viewed within the context of that society's problems and opportunities.

Culture The set of learned behaviors, beliefs, attitudes, values, and ideals that are characteristic of a particular society or other social group.

Diffusion The borrowing by one society of a cultural trait belonging to another society as the result of contact between the two societies.

Ethnocentric Refers to judgment of other cultures solely in terms of one's own culture.

Ethnocentrism The attitude that other societies' customs and ideas can be judged in the context of one's own culture.

Ethnogenesis Creation of a new culture.

Globalization The ongoing spread of goods, people, information, and capital around the world.

Maladaptive customs Cultural traits that diminish the chances of survival and reproduction in a particular environment.

Norms Standards or rules about acceptable behavior in a society. The importance of a norm usually can be judged by how members of a society respond when the norm is violated.

Revolution A usually violent replacement of a society's rulers.

Society A group of people who occupy a particular territory and speak a common language not generally understood by neighboring peoples. By this definition, societies do not necessarily correspond to nations.

Subculture The shared customs of a subgroup within a society.

Notes

1. Linton 1945, 30.
2. Sapir 1938, cited by Pelto and Pelto 1975, 1.
3. Pelto and Pelto 1975, 14–15.
4. de Waal 2001, 269.
5. M. F. Brown 2008, 372.
6. Hewlett 2004.
7. Miner 1956, 504–05, reproduced by permission of the American Anthropological Association. Although Miner is not a foreign visitor, he wrote this description in a way that shows how these behaviors might be seen from an outside perspective.
8. Lee 1972.
9. Hatch 1997.
10. Durkheim 1938/1895, 3.
11. Asch 1956.
12. Bond and Smith 1996.
13. Berns et al. 2005.
14. Hall 1966, 159–60.
15. Ibid., 120.
16. R. Brown 1965, 549–609.
17. Chibnik 1981, 256–68.
18. Linton 1936, 306.
19. Ibid., 310–11.
20. Silver 1981.
21. Greenfield, Maynard, and Childs 2000.
22. Rogers 1983, 263–69.
23. Valente 1995, 21.
24. Linton 1936, 326–27.
25. G. M. Foster 1962, 26.
26. Bodley 1990: 7–11.
27. Pelto and Müller-Wille 1987, 207–43.
28. Aporta and Higgs 2005.
29. Bodley 1990: 38–41.
30. Schrauf 1999.
31. Roth 2001.
32. Boyd and Richerson 1996/1985, 106.
33. D. T. Campbell 1965. See also Boyd and Richerson 1996/1985; Durham 1991.
34. The historical information we refer to comes from a book by Nevins (1927). For how radical the American Revolution was, see G. Wood 1992.
35. Paige 1975.
36. Bestor 2001, 76.
37. Trouillot 2001, 128.
38. Durrenberger 2001a; see also Hannerz 1996.
39. Traphagan and Brown 2002.
40. Trouillot 2001, 128.
41. Bradsher 2002, 3.
42. Guest and Jones 2005.
43. Yergin 2002, A29.
44. G. Thompson 2002, A3.
45. Sengupta 2002, A3.
46. J. D. Hill 1996, 1.
47. Bilby 1996, 127–28, referring to Hoogbergen 1990, 23–51.
48. Bilby 1996, 128–37.
49. Kottak 1996, 136, 153.
50. Roosens 1989, 9.
51. Cashdan 2001.
52. C. R. Ember and Levinson 1991.

Bibliography

Aporta, Claudio, and Eric Higgs. 2005. Satellite culture: Global positioning systems, Inuit wayfinding, and the need for a new account of technology. *Current Anthropology* 46:729–46.

Asch, Solomon. 1956. Studies of independence and conformity: A minority of one against a unanimous majority. *Psychological Monographs* 70:1–70.

Berns, G., J. Chappelow, C. Zink, G. Pagnoni, M. Martin-Skurski, and J. Richards. 2005. Neurobiological correlates of social conformity and independence during mental rotation. *Biological Psychiatry* 58:245–53.

Bestor, Theodore C. 2001. Supply-side sushi: Commodity, market, and the global city. *American Anthropologist* 103:76–95.

Bilby, Kenneth. 1996. Ethnogenesis in the Guianas and Jamaica: Two Maroon cases. In *Ethnogenesis in the Americas,* ed. J. D. Hill, 119–41. Iowa City: University of Iowa Press.

Bodley, John H. 1990. *Victims of progress,* 3rd edition. Mountain View CA: Mayfield Publishing Company.

Bond, Rod, and Peter B. Smith. 1996. Culture and conformity: A meta-analysis of studies using Asch's (1952b, 1956) line judgment task. *Psychological Bulletin* 11:111–37.

Boyd, Robert, and Peter J. Richerson. 1996/1985. *Culture and the evolutionary process.* Chicago: University of Chicago Press.

Bradsher, Keith. 2002. Pakistanis fume as clothing sales to U.S. tumble. *New York Times,* June 23, p. 3.

Brown, Michael F. 2008. Cultural relativism 2.0. *Current Anthropology* 49:363–83.

Brown, Roger. 1965. *Social psychology.* New York: Free Press.

Campbell, Donald T. 1965. Variation and selective retention in socio-cultural evolution. In *Social change in developing areas,* eds. H. Barringer, G. Blankstein, and R. Mack. Cambridge, MA: Schenkman.

Cashdan, Elizabeth. 2001. Ethnic diversity and its environmental determinants: Effects of climate, pathogens, and habitat diversity. *American Anthropologist* 103:968–91.

Chibnik, Michael. 1981. The evolution of cultural rules. *Journal of Anthropological Research* 37:256–68.

Durham, William H. 1991. *Coevolution: Genes, culture and human diversity.* Stanford, CA: Stanford University Press.

de Waal, Frans. 2001. *The ape and the sushi master: Cultural reflections of a primatologist.* New York: Basic Books.

Durkheim, Émile. 1938/1895. *The rules of sociological method.* 8th ed. trans. Sarah A. Soloway and John H. Mueller. ed. George E. Catlin. New York: Free Press.

Durrenberger, E. Paul. 2001a. Anthropology and globalization. *American Anthropologist* 103:531–35.

Ember, Carol R., and David Levinson. 1991. The substantive contributions of worldwide cross-cultural studies using secondary data. *Behavior Science Research* [Special issue: Cross-cultural and comparative research: Theory and method], 25:79–140.

Foster, George M. 1962. *Traditional cultures and the impact of technological change.* New York: Harper & Row.

Greenfield, Patricia M., Ashley E. Maynard, and Carla P. Childs. 2000. History, culture, learning, and development. *Cross-Cultural Research* 34:351–74.

Guest, Greg, and Eric C. Jones. 2005. Globalization, health, and the environment: An introduction. In *Globalization, health, and the environment: An integrated perspective,* ed. Greg Guest, 3–26. Lanham, MD: Roman & Littlefield.

Hall, Edward T. 1966. *The hidden dimension.* Garden City, NY: Doubleday.

Hannerz, Ulf. 1996. *Transnational connections: Culture, people, places.* London: Routledge.

Hatch, Elvin. 1997. The good side of relativism. *Journal of Anthropological Research* 53:371–81.

Hewlett, Barry S. 2004. Diverse contexts of human infancy. In MyAnthroLibrary, eds. C. R. Ember, M. Ember, and P. N. Peregrine. MyAnthroLibrary.com. Pearson.

Hill, Jonathan D. 1996. Introduction: Ethnogenesis in the Americas, 1492–1992. In *Ethnogenesis in the Americas,* ed. J. D. Hill, 1–19. Iowa City: University of Iowa Press.

Hoogbergen, Wim. 1990. *The Boni Maroon Wars in Suriname.* Leiden: E. J. Brill.

Kottak, Conrad Phillip. 1996. The media, development, and social change. In *Transforming societies, transforming anthropology,* ed. E. F. Moran. Ann Arbor: University of Michigan Press.

Lee, Richard B. 1972. Population growth and the beginnings of sedentary life among the !Kung bushmen. In *Population growth,* ed. B. Spooner. Cambridge, MA: MIT Press.

Linton, Ralph. 1936. *The study of man.* New York: Appleton-Century-Crofts.

Linton, Ralph. 1945. *The cultural background of personality.* New York: Appleton-Century-Crofts.

Miner, Horace. 1956. Body rituals among the Nacirema. *American Anthropologist* 58:504–05.

Nevins, Allan. 1927. *The American states during and after the revolution.* New York: Macmillan.

Paige, Jeffery M. 1975. *Agrarian revolution: Social movements and export agriculture in the underdeveloped world.* New York: Free Press.

Pelto, Pertti J., and Ludger Müller-Wille. 1987. Snowmobiles: Technological revolution in the Arctic. In *Technology and social change.* 2nd ed. eds. H. R. Bernard and P. J. Pelto. Prospect Heights, IL: Waveland Press.

Pelto, Pertti J., and Gretel H. Pelto. 1975. Intra-cultural diversity: Some theoretical issues. *American Ethnologist* 2:1–18.

Rogers, Everett M. 1983. *Diffusion of innovations.* 3rd ed. New York: Free Press.

Roosens, Eugeen E. 1989. *Creating ethnicity: The process of ethnogenesis.* Newbury Park, CA: Sage.

Roth, Eric Abella. 2001. Demise of the sepaade tradition: Cultural and biological explanations. *American Anthropologist* 103:1014–23.

Sapir, Edward. 1938. Why cultural anthropology needs the psychiatrist. *Psychiatry* 1:7–12.

Schrauf, Robert W. 1999. Mother tongue maintenance among North American ethnic groups. *Cross-Cultural Research* 33:175–92.

Sengupta, Somini. 2002. Money from kin abroad helps Bengalis get by. *New York Times,* June 24, p. A3.

Silver, Harry R. 1981. Calculating risks: The socioeconomic foundations of aesthetic innovation in an Ashanti carving community. *Ethnology* 20:101–14.

Thompson, Ginger. 2002. Mexico is attracting a better class of factory in its south. *New York Times,* June 29, p. A3.

Traphagan, John W., and L. Keith Brown. 2002. Fast food and intergenerational commensality in Japan: New styles and old patterns. *Ethnology* 41:119–34.

Marriage, Family, and Kinship

From Chapter 8 of *Human Culture*, Second Edition. Carol R. Ember, Melvin Ember. Copyright © 2012 by Pearson Education, Inc. All rights reserved.

Marriage, Family, and Kinship

((•—[Listen to the Chapter Audio on myanthrolab.com   [📖•—[Read on myanthrolab.com

Nearly all societies known to anthropology have had the custom of marriage. Why marriage is customary in nearly every society we know of is a classic and perplexing question, and one we attempt to deal with here. The near universality of marriage customs does not mean that everyone in a society gets married, nor that marriage and family customs are the same in all societies. On the contrary, there is much variation from society to society in how one marries, whom one marries, and even how many people a person can be married to simultaneously.

Families are universal; all societies have parent–child groups, but the form and size of the family can vary from society to society. Some societies have large extended families with two or more related parent–child groups; others have smaller independent families. Today, marriage is not always the basis for family life. One-parent families are becoming increasingly common in our own and other societies. Marriage has not disappeared in these places—it is still customary to marry—but more individuals are choosing now to have children without being married.

As we will see, kin groups that include hundreds or even thousands of related people are found in many societies and structure economic, social-political, and religious functions. In noncommercial societies, kin groups were probably the most important aspect of social organization.

Marriage

When anthropologists speak of marriage, they do not mean to imply that couples everywhere must get marriage certificates or have wedding ceremonies, as in our own society. **Marriage** merely means a socially approved sexual and economic union, usually between a woman and a man. It is presumed, by both the couple and others, to be more or less permanent, and it subsumes reciprocal rights and obligations between the two spouses and between spouses and their future children.[1] Marriage to more than one spouse at a time is quite common in many societies, as we shall see.

It is a socially approved sexual union in that a married couple does not have to hide the sexual nature of their relationship. A woman might say, "I want you to meet my husband," but

The bride's relatives arrive at the groom's home bearing gifts and Piki bread from the bride's family at a traditional Hopi engagement ceremony in Arizona.

she could not say, "I want you to meet my lover" without causing some embarrassment in most societies. Although the union may ultimately be dissolved by divorce, couples in all societies begin marriage with some idea of permanence in mind. Implicit too in marriage are reciprocal rights and obligations. These may be more or less specific and formalized regarding matters of property, finances, and childrearing. Marriage entails both a sexual and an economic relationship, as George Peter Murdock noted: "Sexual relations can occur without economic cooperation, and there can be a division of labor between men and women without sex. But marriage unites the economic and the sexual."[2]

Why is Marriage Nearly Universal?

Because virtually all societies practice female–male marriage as we have defined it, we can assume that the custom is adaptive. Several interpretations have traditionally been offered to explain why all human societies have the custom of marriage. Each suggests that marriage solves problems found in all societies: how to share the products of a gender division of labor; how to care for infants, who are dependent for a long time; and how to minimize sexual competition. To evaluate the plausibility of these interpretations, we must ask whether marriage provides the best or the only reasonable solution to each problem. After all, we are trying to explain a custom that is virtually universal. The comparative study of other animals, some of which have something like marriage, may help us to evaluate these explanations.

Gender Division of Labor It is generally accepted that males and females in every society perform different economic activities. This gender division of labor has often been cited as a reason for marriage because society has to have some mechanism by which women and men share the products of their labor.[3] But it seems unlikely that marriage is the only possible solution. The hunter-gatherer rule of sharing could be extended to include all the products brought in by both women and men. Thus, although marriage may solve the problem of sharing the fruits of a division of labor, it clearly is not the only possible solution.

Prolonged Infant Dependency Humans exhibit the longest period of infant dependency of any primate. The child's prolonged dependence places the greatest burden on the mother, who is the main child caregiver in most societies. Prolonged child care by human females may limit the kinds of work they can do. Also, they may need the help of a man to do certain types of work, such as hunting, that are incompatible with child care. Because of this prolonged dependency, it has been suggested that marriage is necessary.[4] But here the argument becomes essentially the same as the division-of-labor argument, and it has the same logical weakness. It is not clear why a group of women and men, such as a hunter-gatherer band, could not cooperate in providing for dependent children without marriage.

Sexual Competition Unlike most other female primates, the human female may engage in intercourse at any time throughout the year. Some scholars have suggested that more or less continuous female sexuality may have created a serious problem: considerable sexual competition between males for females. It is argued that society had to prevent such competition to survive, that it had to develop some way of minimizing the rivalry among males for females to reduce the chance of lethal and destructive conflict.[5]

There are several problems with this argument. First, why should continuous female sexuality make for more sexual competition in the first place? One might argue the other way around.

There might be more competition over the scarcer resources that would be available if females were less frequently interested in sex. Second, males of many animal species, even some that have relatively frequent female sexuality (as do many of our close primate relatives), do not show much aggression over females. Third, why couldn't sexual competition, even if it existed, be regulated by cultural rules other than marriage? For instance, society might have adopted a rule whereby men and women circulated among all the opposite-sex members of the group, each person staying a specified length of time with each partner. Such a system presumably would solve the problem of sexual competition. On the other hand, such a system might not work particularly well if individuals came to prefer certain other individuals. Jealousies attending those attachments might give rise to even more competition.

Other Mammals and Birds: Postpartum Requirements None of the theories we have discussed explains convincingly why marriage is the only or the best solution to a particular problem. Also, we have some comparative evidence on mammals and birds that casts doubt on those theories.[6] How can evidence from other animals help us evaluate theories about human marriage? If we look at the animals that, like humans, have some sort of stable female–male mating, as compared with those that are completely promiscuous, we can perhaps see what sorts of factors may predict male–female bonding ("marriage") in the warm-blooded animal species. Most species of birds, and some mammals such as wolves and beavers, have male-female bonding. Among 40 mammal and bird species, none of the three factors discussed previously—division of labor, prolonged infant dependency, and greater female sexuality—predicts or is correlated strongly with male–female bonding. With respect to division of labor by sex, most other animals have nothing comparable to a humanlike division of labor, but many have stable female–male matings anyway. The two other supposed factors—prolonged infant dependency and female sexuality—predict just the opposite of what we might expect. Mammal and bird species that have longer dependency periods or more female sexuality are less likely to have stable matings.

Does anything predict male–female bonding? One factor does among mammals and birds, and it may also help explain human marriage. Animal species in which females can simultaneously feed themselves and their babies after birth (*postpartum*) tend not to have stable matings;

Most birds, like these Canadian geese, have male-female bonding. Shortly after hatching, it would be difficult for a mother alone to feed herself, her babies, and protect the young without help.

species in which postpartum mothers cannot feed themselves and their babies at the same time tend to have stable matings. Among the typical bird species, a mother would have difficulty feeding herself and her babies simultaneously. Because the young cannot fly for a while and must be protected in a nest, the mother risks losing them to other animals if she goes off to obtain food. But if she has a male bonded to her (as most bird species do), he can bring back food or take a turn watching the nest. Among animal species that have no postpartum feeding problem, babies are able to travel with the mother almost immediately after birth as she moves about to eat (as do grazers such as horses), or the mother can transport the babies as she moves about to eat (as do baboons and kangaroos). We think the human female has a postpartum feeding problem. When humans lost most of their body hair, babies could not readily travel with the mother by clinging to her fur. And when humans began to depend on certain kinds of food-getting that could be dangerous (such as hunting), mothers could not engage in such work with their infants along.[7]

Recent research on the Hadza foragers of Tanzania appears to support this view. Frank Marlowe found that the caloric contribution of mothers and fathers depends on whether or not they have a nursing infant. Hadza women may generally contribute more calories than men to the diet, but married women who are nursing contribute substantially less than other married women. The lower contribution of nursing mothers appears to be made up by the Hadza father. Fathers with nursing children contribute significantly more food to the household than fathers with older children.[8]

Even if we assume that human mothers have a postpartum feeding problem, we still have to ask if marriage is the most likely solution to the problem. We think so, because other conceivable solutions probably would not work as well. For example, if a mother took turns babysitting with another mother, neither might be able to collect enough food for both mothers and the two sets of children dependent on them. But a mother and father share the same set of children, and therefore it would be easier for them to feed themselves and their children adequately. Another possible solution is no pair bonding at all, just a promiscuous group of males and females. But in that kind of arrangement, we think, a particular mother probably would not always be able to count on some male to watch her baby when she had to go out for food or to bring her food when she had to watch her baby. Thus, it seems to us that the problem of postpartum feeding by itself helps to explain why some animals, including humans, have relatively stable male–female bonds.[9] Of course, there is still the question of whether research on other animals can be applied to human beings. We think it can, but not everybody will agree.

How Does One Marry?

When we say that marriage is a socially approved sexual and economic union, we mean that all societies have some way of marking the onset of a marriage, but the ways of doing so vary considerably. For reasons that we don't fully understand, some cultures mark marriages by elaborate rites and celebrations; others mark marriages in much more informal ways. And most societies have economic transactions before, during, or even after the onset of the marriages.

Economic Aspects of Marriage "It's not man that marries maid, but field marries field, vineyard marries vineyard, cattle marry cattle." In its down-to-earth way, this German peasant saying indicates that, in many societies, marriage involves economic considerations. In our culture, economic considerations may or may not be explicit. However, in about 75 percent of the societies known to anthropology,[10] one or more explicit economic transactions take place before or after the marriage.

Bride Price **Bride price** or **bride wealth** is a gift of money or goods from the groom or his kin to the bride's kin. Bride price is the most common form of transaction. In one cross-cultural sample, 44 percent of the societies with economic transactions at marriage practiced bride price; in almost all of those societies, the bride price was substantial.[11] Bride price occurs all over the world but is especially common in Africa and Oceania. Payment can be made in different currencies; livestock and food are two of the more common. With the increased importance of commercial exchange, money has increasingly become part of the bride price payments.

What kinds of societies are likely to have the custom of bride price? Cross-culturally, societies with bride price are likely to practice horticulture and lack social stratification. Bride price is also likely where women contribute a great deal to primary subsistence activities[12] and where they contribute more than men to all kinds of economic activities.[13] Although these findings might suggest that women are highly valued in such societies, recall that the status of women relative to men is not higher in societies in which women contribute a lot to primary subsistence activities. Indeed, bride price is likely to occur in societies in which men make most of the decisions in the household,[14] and decision making by men is one indicator of lower status for women.

Bride Service **Bride service**, which is the next most common type of economic transaction at marriage—occurring in about 19 percent of the societies with economic transactions—requires the groom to work for the bride's family, sometimes before the marriage begins, sometimes after. Bride service varies in duration. In some societies, it lasts for only a few months; in others, as long as several years. Native North and South American societies were likely to practice bride service, particularly if they were egalitarian food collectors.[15]

Exchange of Females Of the societies that have economic transactions at marriage, 6 percent have the custom whereby a sister or female relative of the groom is exchanged for the bride. These societies tend to be horticultural, egalitarian, and to have a relatively high contribution of women to primary subsistence.[16]

Gift Exchange Gift exchange, which involves the exchange of gifts of about equal value by the two kin groups about to be linked by marriage, occurs somewhat more often than the exchange of females (about 11 percent of those with economic transactions).[17] For example, among the Andaman Islanders, as soon as a boy and girl indicate their intention to marry, their respective sets of parents cease all communication and begin sending gifts of food and other objects to each other through a third party. This arrangement continues until the marriage is completed and the two kin groups are united.[18]

Dowry A **dowry** is usually a substantial transfer of goods or money from the bride's family to the bride, the groom, or the couple.[19] Unlike the types of transactions we have discussed so far, the dowry, which occurs in about 8 percent of the societies with economic transactions, is usually not a transaction between the kin of the bride and the kin of the groom. A family has to have wealth to give a dowry, but because the goods go to the new household, no wealth comes back to the family that gave the dowry. Payment of dowries was common in medieval and Renaissance Europe; the custom is still practiced in parts of eastern Europe and in sections of southern Italy and France, where land is often the major item the bride's family provides. Parts of India also practice the dowry. In contrast to societies with bride price, societies with dowry tend to be those in which women contribute relatively little to primary subsistence activities, there is a high

A young Iraqi couple in 2008 look at gold jewelry that will be part of her dowry. It is considered to be hers no matter what happens to the marriage.

degree of social stratification, and a man is not allowed to be married to more than one woman simultaneously.[20]

The dowry is provided by the bride's family to the bride, the groom, or the couple. But sometimes the payments to the bride originate from the groom's family. Because the goods are sometimes first given to the bride's father, who passes most if not all of them to her, this kind of transaction is called **indirect dowry**.[21] Indirect dowry occurs in about 12 percent of the societies in which marriage involves an economic transaction.

Whom Should One Marry or Not Marry?

Probably every child in our society knows the story of Cinderella—the poor, downtrodden, but lovely girl who accidentally meets, falls in love with, and eventually marries a prince. It is a charming tale, but it is misleading as a guide to mate choice in our society. All societies have rules restricting marriage with some other people, as well as preferences about which other people are the most desirable mates. Even in a modern, urbanized society such as ours, where theoretically mate choice is free, people tend to marry within their own class and geographic area.

Incest Taboo Perhaps the most rigid regulation, found in *all* cultures, is the **incest taboo**, which prohibits sexual intercourse or marriage between some categories of kin.

The most universal aspect of the incest taboo is the prohibition of sexual intercourse or marriage between mother and son, father and daughter, and brother and sister. No society in recent times has permitted either sexual intercourse or marriage between those pairs. A few societies in the past, however, did permit incest, mostly within the royal and aristocratic families, though generally it was forbidden to the rest of the population. For example, the Incan and Hawaiian royal families allowed marriage within the family. Probably the best-known example of allowed incest involved Cleopatra of Egypt who was married to two of her younger brothers at different times.[22] The reasons seem to have been partly religious—a member of the family of the pharaoh, who was considered a god, could not marry any "ordinary" human—and partly economic, for marriage within the family kept the royal property undivided. In Egypt, between 30 B.C. and A.D. 324, incest was allowed not just in the royal family; an estimated 8 percent of commoner marriages were brother–sister marriages.[23] But, despite these exceptions, the fact remains that no culture we know of today permits or accepts incest within the nuclear family.

Arranged Marriages In an appreciable number of societies, marriages are arranged; immediate families or go-betweens handle the negotiations. Sometimes betrothals are completed while the future partners are still children. This was formerly the custom in much of Hindu India, China, Japan, and eastern and southern Europe. Implicit in the arranged marriage is the conviction that the joining together of two kin groups to form new social and economic ties is too important to be left to free choice and romantic love.

Arranged marriages are becoming less common in many places, and couples are beginning to have more say about their marriage partners. But in 1960, marriages were still arranged on the Pacific island of Rotuma, and sometimes the bride and groom did not meet until the wedding day. Today, weddings are much the same, but couples are allowed to "go out" and have a say about whom they wish to marry.[24]

Exogamy and Endogamy Marriage partners often must be chosen from outside one's own kin group or community; this is known as a rule of **exogamy**. Exogamy can take many forms. It may mean marrying outside a particular group of kin or outside a particular village or group of villages. When there are rules of exogamy, violations are often believed to cause harm. On the islands of Yap in Micronesia, people who are related through women are referred to as "people of one belly." The elders say that if two people from the same kinship group married, they would not have any female children and the group would die out.[25]

A study of foragers and horticulturalists found a clear relationship between population density and the distance between the communities of the husband and wife—the lower the density, the greater the marriage distance. Because foragers generally have lower densities than horticulturalists, they generally have further to go to find mates. Among the San, for instance, the average husband and wife had lived 40 miles (65 kilometers) from each other before they were married.[26]

A rule of **endogamy** obliges a person to marry within some group. The caste groups of India traditionally have been endogamous. The higher castes believed that marriage with lower castes would "pollute" them, and such unions were forbidden. Caste endogamy is also found in some parts of Africa.

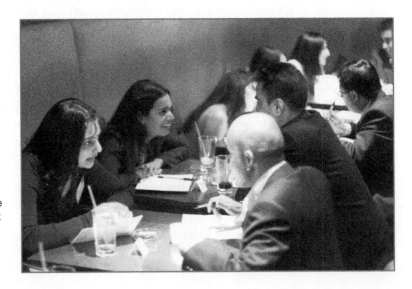

These young South Asian Hindus in Great Britain are "speed dating." They talk with potential spouses for three minutes each. Traditionally, parents arrange marriages.

Cousin Marriages Kinship terminology for most people in the United States does not differentiate between types of cousins. In some other societies, such distinctions may be important, particularly with regard to first cousins; the terms for the different kinds of first cousins may indicate which cousins are suitable marriage partners (sometimes even preferred mates) and which are not. Although most societies prohibit marriage with all types of first cousins,[27] some societies allow and even prefer particular kinds of cousin marriage.

Cross-cousins are children of siblings of the opposite sex; that is, a person's cross-cousins are the father's sisters' children and the mother's brothers' children. **Parallel cousins** are children of siblings of the same sex; a person's parallel cousins, then, are the father's brothers' children and the mother's sisters' children. The Chippewa Indians used to practice cross-cousin marriage, as well as cross-cousin joking. With his female cross-cousins, a Chippewa man was expected to exchange broad, risqué jokes, but he would not do so with his parallel cousins, with whom severe propriety was the rule. In general, in any society in which cross-cousin marriage is allowed but parallel cousin is not, there is a joking relationship between a man and his female cross-cousins. This attitude contrasts with the formal and very respectful relationship the man maintains with female parallel cousins. Apparently, the joking relationship signifies the possibility of marriage, whereas the respectful relationship signifies the extension of the incest taboo to parallel cousins.

Parallel-cousin marriage is fairly rare, but Muslim societies usually prefer such marriages, allowing other cousin marriages as well. The Kurds, who are mostly Sunni Muslims, prefer a young man to marry his father's brother's daughter (for the young woman, this would be her father's brother's son). The father and his brother usually live near each other, so the woman will stay close to home in such a marriage. The bride and groom are also in the same kin group, so marriage in this case also entails kin group endogamy.[28]

There is evidence from cross-cultural research that cousin marriages are most apt to be permitted in relatively large and densely populated societies. Perhaps this is because the likelihood of such marriages, and therefore the risks of inbreeding, are minimal in those societies.[29]

How Many Does One Marry?

We are accustomed to thinking of marriage as involving just one man and one woman at a time—**monogamy**—but most societies known to anthropology have allowed a man to be married to more than one woman at the same time—**polygyny**. At any given time, however, the majority of men in societies permitting polygyny are married monogamously; few or no societies have enough women to permit most men to have at least two wives. Polygyny's mirror image—one woman being married to more than one man at the same time, called **polyandry**—is practiced in very few societies. Polygyny and polyandry are the two types of **polygamy**, or plural spouse marriage. **Group marriage**, in which more than one man is married to more than one woman at the same time, sometimes occurs but is not customary in any known society.

Polygyny The Old Testament has many references to men with more than one wife simultaneously: King David and King Solomon are just two examples of men polygynously married. Polygyny in many societies is a mark of a man's great wealth or high status. In such societies, only the very wealthy can, and are expected to, support more than one wife. Some Muslim societies, especially Arabic-speaking ones, still view polygyny in this light. But a man does not always have to be wealthy to be polygynous; indeed, in some societies in which women are important

Polygyny is practiced by some in this country, even though it is prohibited by law.

contributors to the economy, it seems that men try to have more than one wife to become wealthier. For example, among the Siwai, a society in the South Pacific, status is achieved through feast giving. Pork is the main dish at these feasts, so the Siwai associate pig raising with prestige. This great interest in pigs sparks an interest in wives, because in Siwai society, women raise the food needed to raise pigs. Thus, although having many wives does not in itself confer status among the Siwai, the increase in pig herds that may result from polygyny is a source of prestige for the owner.[30]

Polygynously married Siwai men do seem to have greater prestige, but they complain that a household with multiple wives is difficult. Sinu, a Siwai, described his plight:

> There is never peace for a long time in a polygynous family. If the husband sleeps in the house of one wife, the other one sulks all the next day. If the man is so stupid as to sleep two consecutive nights in the house of one wife, the other one will refuse to cook for him, saying, "So-and-so is your wife; go to her for food. Since I am not good enough for you to sleep with, then my food is not good enough for you to eat."[31]

Co-wife conflict seems not to be present in some societies. For example, Margaret Mead reported that married life among the Arapesh of New Guinea, even in the polygynous marriages, was "so even and contented that there is nothing to relate of it at all."[32] Why might there be little or no obvious jealousy between co-wives in a society? One possible reason is that a man is married to two or more sisters—**sororal polygyny**; it seems that sisters, having grown up together, are more likely to get along and cooperate as co-wives than are co-wives who are not also sisters—**nonsororal polygyny**. Indeed, a recent cross-cultural study confirms that endemic conflict and persistent resentment were virtually ubiquitous in societies with nonsororal polygyny.[33] The most commonly reported reason for the conflict and resentment was insufficient access to the husband for sex and emotional support. Perhaps because conflict is so common, polygynous societies have invented customs to try to lessen conflict and jealousy in co-wives:

1. Co-wives who are not sisters tend to have separate living quarters; sororal co-wives almost always live together.

2. Co-wives have clearly defined equal rights in matters of sex, economics, and personal possessions.

3. Senior wives often have special prestige, which may compensate the first wife for her loss of physical attractiveness.[34]

We must remember that, although jealousy and conflict are commonly mentioned in polygynous marriages, they are not always present. People who practice polygyny may think it has considerable advantages. In a study conducted by Philip and Janet Kilbride in Kenya, female as well as male married people agreed that polygyny had economic and political advantages. Polygynous families provide plenty of farm labor and extra food that can be marketed. They also tend to be influential in their communities and are likely to produce individuals who become government officials.[35] And in South Africa, Connie Anderson found that women choose to be married to a man with other wives because the other wives could help with child care and household work, provide companionship, and allow more freedom to come and go. Some women said they chose polygynous marriages because there was a shortage of marriageable males.[36]

How can we account for the fact that polygyny is allowed and often preferred in most of the societies known to anthropology? One theory is that polygyny will be permitted in societies that have a long **postpartum sex taboo**.[37] Recall that John Whiting suggested that couples, particularly in societies where staple foods have little protein, abstain from sexual intercourse for a long time to protect their child from *kwashiorkor*. If a child gets protein from mother's milk during its first few years, the likelihood of contracting kwashiorkor may be greatly reduced. Societies with long postpartum sex taboos also tend to be polygynous. Perhaps, then, a man's having more than one wife is a cultural adjustment to the taboo since men may seek other sexual relationships during the period of a long post-partum sex taboo. However, it is not clear why polygyny is the only possible solution to the problem. After all, it is conceivable that all of a man's wives might be subject to the postpartum sex taboo at the same time. Furthermore, there may be sexual outlets outside marriage.

Another explanation of polygyny is that it is a response to an excess of women over men, due largely to the prevalence of warfare in a society. Because men and not women are generally the warriors, warfare almost always takes a greater toll of men's lives. Given that almost all adults in noncommercial societies are married, polygyny may be a way of providing spouses for surplus women. Indeed, there is evidence that societies with imbalanced sex ratios in favor of women tend to have both polygyny and high male mortality in warfare. Conversely, societies with balanced sex ratios tend to have both monogamy and low male mortality in warfare.[38]

A third explanation is that a society will allow polygyny when men marry at an older age than women. The argument is similar to the sex ratio interpretation. Delaying the age of marriage for men would produce an artificial, though not an actual, excess of marriageable women. Why marriage for men is delayed is not clear, but the delay does predict polygyny.[39]

Is one of these explanations better than the others, or are all three factors—long postpartum sex taboo, an imbalanced sex ratio in favor of women, and delayed age of marriage for men— important in explaining polygyny? One way of trying to decide among alternative explanations is to do what is called a *statistical-control analysis,* which allows us to see if a particular factor still predicts when the effects of other possible factors are removed. In this case, when the possible effect of sex ratio is removed, a long postpartum sex taboo no longer predicts polygyny and hence is probably not a cause of polygyny.[40] But both an actual excess of women and a late age of marriage for men seem to be strong predictors of polygyny. Added together, these two factors predict even more strongly.[41]

Behavioral ecologists have also suggested ecological reasons why both men and women might prefer polygynous marriages. If there are enough resources, men might prefer polygyny because they can have more children if they have more than one wife. If resources are highly variable and men control resources, women might find it advantageous to marry a man with many resources even if she is a second wife. A recent study of foragers suggests that foraging societies in which men control hunting or fishing territories are more likely to be polygynous. The main problem with the theory of variable resources and their marital consequences is that many societies, particularly in the "modern" world, have great variability in wealth, but little polygyny. So behavioral ecologists have had to argue that polygyny is lacking because of socially imposed constraints. Degree of disease in the environment may also be a factor. Bobbi Low has suggested that a high incidence of disease may reduce the prevalence of "healthy" men. In such cases, it may be to a woman's advantage to marry a "healthy" man even if he is already married, and it may be to a man's advantage to marry several unrelated women to maximize genetic variation (and disease resistance) among his children. Indeed, societies with many pathogens are more likely to have polygyny.[42] A recent cross-cultural study compared the degree of disease explanation of polygyny with the imbalanced sex-ratio explanation. Both were supported. The number of pathogens predicted particularly well in more densely populated complex societies, where pathogen load is presumably greater. The sex-ratio explanation predicted particularly well in sparser, nonstate societies.[43] An excess of females and pathogen stress predicted polygyny in modern nations too.[44]

Polyandry George Peter Murdock's "World Ethnographic Sample" included only four societies (less than 1 percent of the total) in which polyandry, or the marriage of several men to one woman, was practiced.[45] When the husbands are brothers we call it **fraternal polyandry**; if they are not brothers, it is **nonfraternal polyandry**. Some Tibetans, the Toda of India, and the Sinhalese of Sri Lanka have practiced fraternal polyandry. Among some Tibetans who practice fraternal polyandry, biological paternity seems to be of no particular concern; there is no attempt to link children biologically to a particular brother, and all children are treated the same.[46]

One possible explanation for the practice of polyandry is a shortage of women. The Toda practiced female infanticide[47]; the Sinhalese had a shortage of women but denied the practice of female infanticide.[48] A correlation between shortage of women and polyandry would account for why polyandry is so rare in the ethnographic record; an excess of men is rare cross-culturally.

Another possible explanation is that polyandry is an adaptive response to severely limited resources. Melvyn Goldstein studied Tibetans who live in the northwestern corner of Nepal, above 12,000 feet in elevation. Cultivable land is extremely scarce there, with most families having less than an acre. The people say they practice fraternal polyandry to prevent the division of a family's farm and animals. Instead of dividing up their land among them and each taking a wife, brothers preserve the family farm by sharing a wife. Although not recognized by the Tibetans, their practice of polyandry minimizes population growth. There are as many women as men of marriageable age. But about 30 percent of the women do not marry, and, although these women do have some children, they have far fewer than married women. Thus, the practice of polyandry minimizes the number of mouths to feed and therefore maximizes the standard of living of the polyandrous family.[49]

Family

All societies have families. A **family** is a social and economic unit consisting minimally of one or more parents (or parent substitute) and their children. Members of a family always have certain reciprocal rights and obligations, particularly economic ones. Family members usually live in one household, but common residence is not a defining feature of families. In simpler societies, the family and the household tend to be indistinguishable; only in more complex societies, and in societies becoming dependent on commercial exchange, may some members of a family live elsewhere.[50]

Variation in Family Form

The minimal family has one parent (or parent substitute). Single-parent families, usually headed by the mother, are common in some societies, but most societies typically have larger families. These larger family units usually include at least one **nuclear family** (a married couple and their children), but there is often polygamy, so there may be more than one spouse with more than one set of children. If a single-parent family, nuclear family, polygynous, or polyandrous family lives alone, each is an **independent family**. However, the **extended family** is the prevailing form of family in more than half the societies known to anthropology.[51] It may consist of two or more single-parent, monogamous, polygynous, or polyandrous families linked by a blood tie. Most commonly, the extended family consists of a married couple and one or more of the married children, all living in the same house or household. The constituent nuclear families are normally linked through the parent–child tie. An extended family, however, is sometimes composed of families linked through a sibling tie. Such a family might consist of two married brothers, their wives, and their children. Extended families may be very large, containing many relatives and including three or four generations. A diagram of these different types of family can be found in Figure 1.

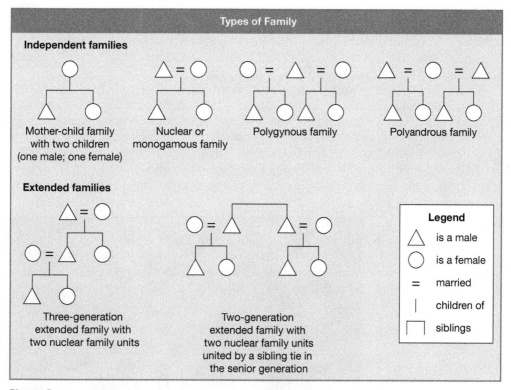

Figure 1

Anthropologists commonly use diagrams to represent family structures. At the top are four types of independent family assuming only two children (one male, one female) and only two spouses where multiple spouses are allowed. At the bottom are two types of extended family. These diagrams show only small extended families, but extended families can have many constituent family units if there are many children as well as plural marriages.

Extended-Family Households

In a society composed of extended-family households, marriage does not bring as pronounced a change in lifestyle as it does in our culture, where the couple typically moves to a new residence and forms a new, and basically independent, family unit. In extended families, the newlyweds are assimilated into an existing family unit. Margaret Mead described such a situation in Samoa:

> . . . the young couple live in the main household, simply receiving a bamboo pillow, a mosquito net and a pile of mats for their bed. . . . The wife works with all the women of the household and waits on all the men. The husband shares the enterprises of the other men and boys. Neither in personal service given or received are the two marked off as a unit.[52]

A young couple in Samoa, as in other societies with extended families, generally has little decision-making power over the governing of the household. Often the responsibility of running the household rests with the senior male. Nor can the new family accumulate its own property and become independent; it is a part of the larger corporate structure. Eventually the young people will have authority when the parents die.

Possible Reasons for Extended-Family Households

Why do most societies known to anthropology commonly have extended-family households? Extended-family households are found most frequently in societies with sedentary agricultural economies. M. F. Nimkoff and Russell Middleton suggested that the extended family may be a social mechanism that prevents the economically ruinous division of family property in societies in which property such as cultivated land is important.[53]

But agriculture is only a weak predictor of extended-family households. Many agriculturalists lack them, and many nonagricultural societies have them. A different theory is that extended-family households come to prevail in societies that have incompatible activity requirements—that is, requirements that cannot be met by a mother or a father in a one-family household. In other words, extended-family households are generally favored when the work a mother has to do outside the home (cultivating fields or gathering foods far away) makes it difficult for her to also care for her children and do other household tasks. Similarly, extended families may be favored when

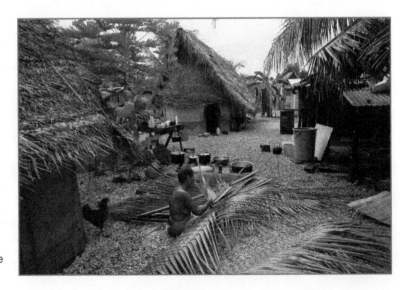

The traditional houses of an extended family on Satawal Island in the Carolines, Micronesia.

the required outside activities of a father (warfare, trading trips, or wage labor far away) make it difficult for him to do the subsistence work required of males. There is cross-cultural evidence that societies with such incompatible activity requirements are more likely to have extended-family households than societies with compatible activity requirements, regardless of whether or not the society is agricultural. Even though they have incompatible activity requirements, however, societies with commercial or monetary exchange may not have extended-family households perhaps because a family may obtain the necessary help by "buying" the required services.[54]

In many societies, there are kin groups even larger than extended families. The rest of this text discusses the varieties of such groupings.

Marital Residence and Kinship

In the United States and Canada, as well as in many other industrial societies, a young man and woman usually establish a place of residence apart from their parents or other relatives when they marry, if they have not already moved away before that. Our society is so oriented toward this pattern of marital residence—*neolocal (new-place) residence*—that it seems to be the obvious and natural one to follow. Young adults may learn to live away from home most of the year if they join the armed forces or attend an out-of-town college. In any case, when young people marry, they generally live apart from family.

So familiar is neolocal residence to us that we tend to assume that all societies must practice the same pattern. On the contrary, of the 565 societies in George Peter Murdock's "World Ethnographic Sample," only about 5 percent followed this practice.[55] About 95 percent of the world's societies have had some other pattern of residence whereby a new couple settles within, or very close to, the household of the parents or some other close relative of either the groom or the bride. Marital residence largely predicts the types of kin groups found in a society, as well as how people refer to and classify their various relatives.

Patterns of Marital Residence

In societies in which newly married couples customarily live with or close to their kin, the pattern of residence varies. Children in all societies are required to marry outside the nuclear family because of the incest taboo and, with few exceptions, couples in almost all societies live together after they are married. Therefore, some children have to leave home when they marry. But which married children remain at home and which reside elsewhere? Societies vary in the way they deal with this question, but there are not many different patterns. The prevailing one could be one of the following (the percentages of each in the ethnographic record do not sum to 100 because of rounding):

1. **Patrilocal residence.** The son stays and the daughter leaves, so that the married couple lives with or near the husband's parents (67 percent of all societies).

2. **Matrilocal residence.** The daughter stays and the son leaves, so that the married couple lives with or near the wife's parents (15 percent of all societies).

3. **Bilocal residence.** Either the son or the daughter leaves, so that the married couple lives with or near either the wife's or the husband's parents (7 percent of all societies).

4. **Avunculocal residence.** Both son and daughter normally leave, but the son and his wife settle with or near his mother's brother (4 percent of all societies).[56]

In these definitions, we use the phrase "the married couple lives *with or near*" a particular set of in-laws. When couples live with or near the kin of a spouse, the couple may live in the same

In many societies known to anthropology, the bride goes to live with or near the husband's family. In a reenactment of a traditional Korean wedding ceremony, a bride is carried to the home of the groom.

household with those kin, creating an *extended-family* household, or they may live separately in an *independent-family* household, but nearby. (Because matrilocal, patrilocal, and avunculocal residence specify just one pattern, they are often called nonoptional or **unilocal residence** patterns.) A fifth pattern of residence is neolocal, in which the newly married couple does not live with or near kin.

5. **Neolocal residence.** Both son and daughter leave; married couples live apart from the relatives of both spouses (5 percent of all societies).

How does place of residence affect the social life of the couple? Because the pattern of residence governs with or near whom individuals live, it largely determines which people those individuals interact with and have to depend on. If the kin of the husband surrounds a married couple, for example, the chances are that those relatives will figure importantly in the couple's future. Whether the couple lives with or near the husband's or the wife's kin can also be expected to have important consequences for the status of the husband or wife. If married couples live patrilocally, as occurs in most societies, the wife may be far from her own kin. In any case, she will be an outsider among a group of male relatives who have grown up together. The feeling of being an outsider is particularly strong when the wife has moved into a patrilocal extended-family household.

Among the Tiv of central Nigeria,[57] the patrilocal extended family consists of the "great father," who is the head of the household, and his younger brothers, his sons, and his younger brothers' sons. Also included are the in-marrying wives and all unmarried children. (The sisters and daughters of the household head who have married would have gone to live where their husbands lived.) Authority is strongly vested in the male line, particularly the oldest of the household, who has authority over bride price, disputes, punishment, and plans for new buildings.

A somewhat different situation exists if the husband comes to live with or near his wife's parents. In this case, the wife and her kin take on somewhat greater importance, and the husband is the outsider. As we shall see, however, the matrilocal situation is not quite the mirror image of the patrilocal because the husband's kin in matrilocal societies often are not far away. Moreover, even though residence is matrilocal, women often do not have as much to say in decision making as their brothers do.

If the married couple does not live with or near the parents or close kin of either spouse, the situation is again quite different. It should not be surprising that relatives and kinship connections do not figure very largely in everyday life in neolocal residence situations. Toward the end of this text, we consider the factors that may explain residential variation; these same factors may also help explain the types of kinship groups that develop.

The Structure of Kinship

In noncommercial societies, kinship connections structure many areas of social life—from the kind of access an individual has to productive resources to the kind of political alliances formed between communities and larger territorial groups. In some societies, in fact, kinship connections have an important bearing on matters of life and death. In societies with feuding, any member of a kin group may be considered a suitable target to revenge a previous death. It is no wonder that anthropologists often speak of the web of kinship as providing the main structure of social action in noncommercial societies.

If kinship is important, there is still the question of which set of kin a person affiliates with and depends on. After all, if every single relative were counted as equally important, there would be an unmanageably large number of people in each person's kinship network. Consequently, in most societies in which kinship connections are important, rules allocate each person to a particular and definable set of kin.

Types of Affiliation with Kin We distinguish three main types of affiliation with kin: *unilineal descent, ambilineal descent,* and *bilateral kinship.* The first two types (unilineal descent and ambilineal descent) are based on **rules of descent**, which are rules that connect individuals with particular sets of kin because of known or presumed common ancestry.

Unilineal descent refers to the fact that a person is affiliated with a group of kin through descent links of one sex only—either males only or females only. Thus, unilineal descent can be either patrilineal or matrilineal.

1. **Patrilineal descent** affiliates individuals with kin of both sexes related to them *through men only.* As Figure 2 indicates, the children in patrilineal systems in each generation belong

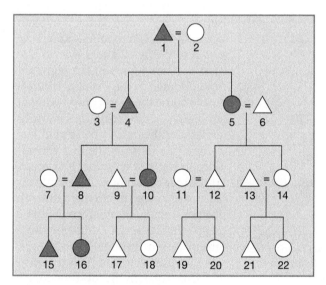

Note: A triangle represents a male; a circle represents a female; an equal sign (=) represents a marriage; vertical lines show descent; horizontal lines indicate siblings.

Figure 2 Patrilineal Descent
Individuals 4 and 5, who are the children of 1 and 2, affiliate with their father's patrilineal kin group, represented by the color blue. In the next generation, the children of 3 and 4 also belong to the blue kin group because they take their descent from their father, who is a member of that group. However, the children of 5 and 6 do not belong to this patrilineal group because they take their descent from their father, who is a member of a different group. That is, although the mother of 12 and 14 belongs to the blue patrilineal group, she cannot pass on her descent affiliation to her children, and because her husband (6) does not belong to her patrilineage, her children (12 and 14) belong to their father's group. In the fourth generation, only 15 and 16 belong to the blue patrilineal group because their father is the only male member of the preceding generation who belongs to the blue patrilineal group. In this diagram, then, 1, 4, 5, 8, 10, 15, and 16 are affiliated by the patrilineal descent; all the other individuals belong to other patrilineal groups.

to the kin group of their father; their father, in turn, belongs to the group of his father; and so on. Although a man's sons and daughters are all members of the same descent group, affiliation with that group is transmitted only by the sons to their children. Just as patrilocal residence is much more common than matrilocal residence, patrilineal descent is more common than matrilineal descent.

2. **Matrilineal descent** affiliates individuals with kin of both sexes related to them *through women only.* In each generation, then, children belong to the kin group of their mother (see Figure 3). Although a woman's sons and daughters are all members of the same descent group, only her daughters can pass on their descent affiliation to their children.

Unilineal rules of descent affiliate an individual with a line of kin extending back in time and into the future. By virtue of this line of descent, whether it extends through males or females, some very close relatives are excluded. For example, in a patrilineal system, your mother and your mother's parents do not belong to your patrilineal group, but your father and his father (and their sisters) do. In your own generation in a matrilineal or patrilineal system, some cousins are excluded, and in your children's generation, some of your nieces and nephews are excluded.

Unilineal rules of descent can form clear-cut, and hence unambiguous, groups of kin, which can act as separate units even after the death of individual members. Referring again to Figures 2 and 3, we can see that the individuals in the highlight color belong to the same patrilineal or matrilineal descent group without ambiguity; individuals in the fourth generation belong to the group just as much as those in the first generation. In contrast to unilineal descent, **ambilineal descent** affiliates individuals with kin related to them through men *or* women. In other words, some people in the society affiliate with a group of kin through their fathers; others affiliate through their mothers. Consequently, the descent groups show both female and male genealogical links and they often if not usually overlap in membership.

These three rules of descent (patrilineal, matrilineal, and ambilineal) are usually, but not always, mutually exclusive. Most societies can be characterized as having only one rule of descent, but two principles are

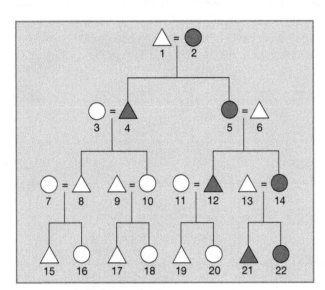

Figure 3 Matrilineal Descent
Individuals 4 and 5, who are the children of 1 and 2, affiliate with their mother's kin group, represented by the color blue. In the next generation, the children of 5 and 6 also belong to the blue kin group because they take their descent from their mother, who is a member of that group. However, the children of 3 and 4 do not belong to this matrilineal group because they take their descent from their mother, who is a member of a different group; their father, although a member of the blue matrilineal group, cannot pass his affiliation on to them under the rule of matrilineal descent. In the fourth generation, only 21 and 22 belong to the blue matrilineal group because their mother is the only female member of the preceding generation who belongs. Thus, individuals 2, 4, 5, 12, 14, 21, and 22 belong to the same matrilineal group.

Marriage, Family, and Kinship

sometimes used to affiliate individuals with different sets of kin for different purposes. Some societies have, then, what is called **double descent** or **double unilineal descent**, whereby individuals affiliate for some purposes with a group of matrilineal kin and for other purposes with a group of patrilineal kin.

Many societies, including our own, do not have lineal (matrilineal, patrilineal, or ambilineal) descent groups—sets of kin who believe they descend from a common ancestor. These are societies with **bilateral kinship**. *Bilateral* means "two-sided," and in this case, it refers to the fact that one's relatives on both the mother's and father's sides are equal in importance or, more usually, in unimportance. Kinship reckoning in bilateral societies does not refer to common descent but rather is horizontal, moving outward from close to more distant relatives rather than upward to common ancestors (see Figure 4).

The term **kindred** describes a person's bilateral set of relatives who may be called upon for some purpose. Most bilateral societies have kindreds that overlap in membership. In North America, we think of the kindred as including the people we might invite to weddings, funerals, or some other ceremonial occasion; a kindred, however, is not usually a definite group. As anyone who has been involved in creating a wedding invitation list knows, a great deal of time may be spent deciding which relatives ought to be invited and which ones can legitimately be excluded. Societies with bilateral kinship differ in precisely how distant relatives have to be before they are lost track of or before they are not included in ceremonial activities.

The distinctive feature of bilateral kinship is that, aside from brothers and sisters, no two people belong to exactly the same kin group. Your kindred contains close relatives spreading out on both your mother's and father's sides, but the members of your kindred are affiliated only by way of their connection to you (**ego**, or the focus). Thus, the kindred is an *ego-centered* group of kin. Because different people (except for brothers and sisters) have different mothers and fathers,

Figure 4 Bilateral Kinship
In a bilateral system, the kindred is ego-centered; hence, it varies with different points of reference (except for brothers and sisters). In any bilateral society, the kindred minimally includes parents, grandparents, aunts, uncles, and first cousins. So, if we look at the close kindred of the brother and sister 20 and 21 (enclosed by the solid line), it would include their parents (9 and 10), their aunts and uncles (7, 8, 11, 12), their grandparents (1, 2, 3, 4), and their first cousins (16–19, 22–25). But the kindred of the brother and sister 24 and 25 (shown by the dashed line) includes only some of the same people (3, 4, 10–12, 20–23); in addition, the kindred of 24 and 25 includes people not in the kindred of 20 and 21 (5, 6, 13–15, 26–29).

your first cousins will have different kindreds, and even your own children will have different kindred from yours. The ego-centered nature of the kindred makes it difficult for it to serve as a permanent or persistent group. The only thing the people in a kindred have in common is the ego or focal person who brings them together. A kindred usually has no name, no common purpose, and only temporary meetings centered around the ego.[58] Because everyone belongs to many different and overlapping kindreds, the society is not divided into clear-cut groups. This does not mean that the kindred cannot be turned to for help. Among the Chipewyan of sub-arctic Canada, for example, people would borrow a fishing net from a kindred member, or ask a kindred member to provide child care for a young person whose parent was ill. But recently, with the national and provincial governments providing resources such as housing and medical assistance, and with the increase in opportunities for wage labor, the kindred has ceased to be the main source of help for people in need. Aid from the state is making kinship less useful.[59]

Variation in Unilineal Descent Systems

In a society with unilineal descent, people usually refer to themselves as belonging to a particular unilineal group or set of groups because they believe they share common descent in either the male (patrilineal) or female (matrilineal) line. Anthropologists distinguish several types of unilineal descent groups: lineages, clans, phratries, and moieties.

Lineages   A **lineage** is a set of kin whose members trace descent from a common ancestor through known links. There may be **patrilineages** or **matrilineages**, depending on whether the links are traced through males only or through females only. Lineages are often designated by the name of the common male or female ancestor. In some societies, people belong to a hierarchy of lineages. That is, they first trace their descent back to the ancestor of a minor lineage, then to the ancestor of a larger and more inclusive major lineage, and so on.

Totem poles often symbolize the history of a descent group. A totem pole in Ketchikan, Alaska.

Clans   A **clan** (also sometimes called a **sib**) is a set of kin whose members believe themselves to be descended from a common ancestor, but the links back to that ancestor are not specified. In fact, the common ancestor may not even be known. Clans with patrilineal descent are called **patriclans**; clans with matrilineal descent are called **matriclans**. Clans often are designated by an animal name (Bear, Wolf), called a **totem**, which may have some special significance for the group and, at the very least, is a means of group identification. The word *totem* comes from the Ojibwa Indian word *ototeman,* "a relative of mine." In some societies, people have to observe taboos relating to their clan totem animal, such as being forbidden to kill or eat their totem.

Phratries   A **phratry** is a unilineal descent group composed of supposedly related clans or sibs. As with clans, the descent links in phratries are unspecified.

Moieties   When a whole society is divided into two unilineal descent groups, we call each group a **moiety**. (The word *moiety* comes from a French word meaning "half.") The people in each moiety believe themselves to be descended from a common ancestor, although they cannot specify how. Societies with moiety systems usually have relatively small populations (fewer than 9,000 people). Societies with phratries and clans tend to be larger.[60]

Combinations   Many societies have two or more types in various combinations. For example, some societies have lineages and clans; others may have clans and phratries but no lineages; and still others may have clans and moieties but neither phratries nor lineages. Even if societies have more than one type of unilineal kin group—for example, lineages and clans—there is no ambiguity about membership. Small groups are simply subsets of larger units; the larger units include people who say they are unilineally related further back in time.

Patrilineal Organization   Patrilineal organization is the most frequent type of descent system. The Kapauku Papuans, a people living in the central highlands of western New Guinea, are an example of a patrilineal society with various types of descent groups.[61] The male members of a patrilineage—all the living males who can trace their actual relationship through males to a common ancestor—constitute the male population of a single village or, more likely, a series of adjoining villages. The male members of the lineage live together by virtue of a patrilocal rule of residence and a fairly stable settlement pattern. A son stays near his parents and brings his wife to live in or near his father's house; the daughters leave home and go to live with their husbands. If the group lives in one place over a long period, the male descendants of one man will live in the same territory.

The members of the same patrilineage address each other affectionately and, within this group, a headman maintains law and order. Killing within the lineage is considered a serious offense, and any fighting that takes place is done with sticks rather than lethal weapons such as spears. The Kapauku also belong to larger and more inclusive patrilineal descent groups—clans and phratries. If a member of the patriclan eats the clan's plant or animal totem, it is believed that the person will become deaf. Kapauku are also forbidden to marry anyone from their clan. In other words, the clan is exogamous. Unlike the members of the patrilineage, the male members of the patriclan do not all live together. The lineage is also the largest group of kinsmen that acts together politically. Among clan members, there is no mechanism for resolving disputes, and members of the same patriclan (who belong to different lineages) may even go to war with one another.

The most inclusive patrilineal descent group among the Kapauku is the phratry, each of which is composed of two or more clans. The members of a phratry observe all the totemic taboos of the clans that belong to that phratry. Intermarriage of members of the same clan is forbidden, but members of the same phratry, if they belong to different clans, may marry.

Matrilineal Organization   Although societies with matrilineal descent seem in many respects like mirror images of their patrilineal counterparts, they differ in one important way. That difference has to do with who exercises authority. In patrilineal systems, descent affiliation is transmitted through males, and it is also the males who exercise authority. Consequently, in the patrilineal system, lines of descent and of authority converge. In a matrilineal system, however, although the line of descent passes through females, females rarely exercise authority in their kin groups. Usually males do. Thus, the lines of authority and descent do not converge.[62] Because males exercise authority in the kin group, an individual's mother's brother becomes an important authority figure because he is the individual's closest male matrilineal relative in the parental generation.

The individual's father does not belong to the individual's own matrilineal kin group and thus has no say in kin group matters.

The divergence of authority and descent in a matrilineal system has some effect on community organization and marriage. Most matrilineal societies practice matrilocal residence. Daughters stay at home after marriage and bring their husbands to live with them; sons leave home to join their wives. But the sons who are required to leave will be the ones who eventually exercise authority in their kin groups. This situation presents a problem. The solution that seems to have been realized in most matrilineal societies is that, although the males move away to live with their wives, they usually do not move too far away; indeed, they often marry women who live in the same village. Thus, matrilineal societies tend not to be locally exogamous—that is, members often marry people from inside the village—whereas patrilineal societies are often locally exogamous.[63]

NEW PERSPECTIVES ON GENDER

Variation in Residence and Kinship: What Difference Does It Make to Women?

When we say that residence and kinship have profound effects on people's lives, what exactly do we mean? We may imagine that it is hard for a woman in a patrilocal society to move at marriage into another village where her husband has plenty of relatives and she has few. But do we have evidence of that? Most ethnographies usually do not give details about people's feelings, but some do. For example, Leigh Minturn gives us the text of a letter that one new Rajput bride (who grew up in the village of Khalapur, India) sent to her mother shortly after she married into her husband's village. The letter was written when the bride had been gone 6 weeks, but she repeatedly asked if her mother, her father, and her aunts had forgotten her. She begged to be called home and said her bags were packed. She described herself as "a parrot in a cage" and complained about her in-laws. The bride's mother was not alarmed; she knew that such complaints were normal, reflections of her daughter's separation anxiety. Seven years later, when Minturn returned to India, the mother reported the daughter to be happy. Still, a few other brides did have more serious symptoms: ghost possession, 24- to 36-hour comas, serious depression, or suicide. What research has not told us is whether these serious symptoms are present more often in patrilocal, patrilineal societies than in other societies, particularly matrilocal, matrilineal societies.

Conversely, do men have some symptoms in matrilocal, matrilineal societies that they do not have in patrilocal societies? We do not know.

What about the status of women? Some research suggests that matrilocality and matrilineality enhance some aspects of women's status, but perhaps not as much as we might think. Even in matrilineal societies, men are usually the political leaders. The main effect of matrilocality and matrilineality appears to be that women control property, but they also tend to have more domestic authority in the home, more equal sexual restrictions, and more value placed on their lives. Alice Schlegel pointed out that women's status is not always relatively high in matrilineal societies, because they can be dominated by the husband or by brothers (because brothers play important roles in their kin groups). Only when neither the husband nor the brother dominates may women have considerable control over their own lives. Certainly the combination of matrilocality and matrilineality is better for women's status than patrilocality and patrilineality. Matrilocality and matrilineality might not enhance women's status because of the dominance of male matrilineal kin, but patrilocality and patrilineality are very likely to detract from women's status. Norma Diamond stated that, even after the Chinese Communist revolution, which abolished the landholding estates of patrilineages and gave women

Marriage, Family, and Kinship

The matrilineal organization on Chuuk, a group of small islands in the Pacific, illustrates the general pattern of authority in matrilineal systems.[64] The Chuukese have both matrilineages and matriclans. The matrilineage is a property-owning group whose members trace descent from a known common ancestor in the female line. The female lineage members and their husbands occupy a cluster of houses on the matrilineage's land. The property of the lineage group is administered by the oldest brother of the group, who allocates the productive property of his matrilineage and directs the work of the members. He also represents the group in dealings with the district chief and all outsiders, and he must be consulted on any matter that affects the group. There is also a senior woman of the lineage who exercises some authority, but only insofar as the activities of the women are concerned. She may supervise the women's cooperative work (they usually work separately from the men) and manage the household.

access to education as well as jobs outside the home, male dominance continued. The mode of production and labor changed, but patrilocality did not. Women were still usually the in-marrying strangers, and members of the patrilineage became a work team on the collective farm. Diamond pointed out that those few women who became local leaders were likely to have atypical marriages that allowed them to live in the villages of their birth.

Residence and descent also predict societal attempts to control reproduction. According to Suzanne Frayser, patrilineal societies have several sexual and reproductive dilemmas. One dilemma is the contradiction between the importance of males in kinship and women's role in reproduction. If patrilineal societies denigrate women too much, women may try to decrease their reproduction. If patrilineal societies exalt women too much, that exaltation may detract from the value of men. A second dilemma has to do with paternity, which is essential for patrilineal descent but harder than maternity to be certain of. Frayser argued that, because kin group links are traced through males in patrilineal societies, they will do more to ensure that the man a woman marries is the father. Frayser suggested that patrilineal societies therefore will be more restrictive about a woman's sexuality. Indeed, the results of her cross-cultural study indicate that patrilineal societies are more likely than other societies to prohibit premarital and extramarital sex for women, and they are more likely to make it very difficult for a woman to divorce her husband.

Of course, we have to remember that there is considerable variation within patrilocal/patrilineal societies and matrilocal/matrilineal societies. In the patrilineal society that Audrey Smedley studied—the Birom of the Jos Plateau in Nigeria—women were formally barred from owning property, from holding political offices, and from major decision making. Yet, her fieldwork revealed that they had considerable autonomy in their personal lives in everyday life, including the legal right to take on lovers. Indeed, they had considerable indirect influence on decision making and were strong supporters of the patrilineal system. Smedley speculates that women support patrilineality in some environmental circumstances because it serves their interests and those of their children too. For example, male crops are highly valued, but such crops are grown on the more dangerous plains where men risked death at the hands of raiders from other groups. Food was scarce, so it may have been adaptive for everyone, including women, to give special status to men for growing crops in dangerous places.

Sources: N. Diamond 1975; Frayser 1985, 338–47; Minturn 1993, 54–71; Schlegel 2009; Smedley 2004; M. K. Whyte 1978b, 132–34.

Within the nuclear family, the father and mother have the primary responsibility for raising and disciplining their children. When a child reaches puberty, however, the father's right to discipline or exercise authority over the child ceases. The mother continues to exercise her right of discipline, but her brother may interfere. A woman's brother rarely interferes with his sister's child before puberty, but he may exercise some authority after puberty, especially because he is an elder in the child's own matrilineage. On Chuuk, men rarely move far from their birthplace. As Ward Goodenough pointed out, "Since matrilocal residence takes the men away from their home lineages, most of them marry women whose lineage houses are within a few minutes walk of their own."[65]

Functions of Unilineal Descent Groups

Unilineal descent groups exist in societies at all levels of cultural complexity.[66] Apparently, however, they are most common in noncommercial food-producing, as opposed to food-collecting, societies.[67] Unilineal descent groups often have important functions in the social, economic, political, and religious realms of life:

1. **Regulating Marriage.** In unilineal societies, individuals are not usually permitted to marry within their own unilineal descent groups. In general, the incest taboo in unilineal societies is extended to all presumed unilineal relatives.

2. **Economic Functions.** Members of a person's lineage or clan are often required to side with that person in any quarrel or lawsuit, to help him or her get established economically, to contribute to a bride price or fine, and to support the person in life crises. Mutual aid often extends to economic cooperation on a regular basis. The unilineal descent group may act as a corporate unit in landownership.

    The descent group sometimes views money earned—either by harvesting a cash crop or by leaving the community for a time to work for cash wages—as belonging to all. In recent times, however, young people in some places have shown an unwillingness to part with their money, viewing it as different from other kinds of economic assistance.

3. **Political Functions.** Headmen or elders may also have the right to settle disputes between two members within a lineage, although they generally lack power to force a settlement. And they may act as intermediaries in disputes between a member of their own clan and a member of an opposing kin group. One of the most important political functions of unilineal descent groups is their role in warfare—the attempt to resolve disputes within and outside the society by violent action. In societies without towns or cities, the organization of such fighting is often in the hands of descent groups.

4. **Religious Functions.** A clan or lineage may have its own religious beliefs and practices, worshiping its own gods or goddesses and ancestral spirits.

Ambilineal Systems

Societies with ambilineal descent groups are far less numerous than unilineal or even bilateral societies. Ambilineal societies, however, resemble unilineal ones in many ways. For instance, the members of an ambilineal descent group believe that they are descended from a common ancestor, although frequently they cannot specify all the genealogical links. The descent group is commonly named and may have an identifying emblem or even a totem; the descent group may own land and other productive resources; and myths and religious practices are often associated with the group. Marriage is often regulated by group membership, just as in unilineal systems, although kin group exogamy is not nearly as common as in unilineal systems. Moreover, ambilineal societies resemble unilineal ones in having various levels or types of descent groups. They may have lineages and higher orders of descent groups, distinguished (as in unilineal systems) by whether or not all the genealogical links to the supposed common ancestors are specified.[68]

Explaining Variation in Residence

If married couples in most societies live with or near kin, as in patrilocal, matrilocal, bilocal, and avunculocal patterns of residence, then why do couples in some societies, such as our own, typically live apart from kin? And, among the societies in which couples live with or near kin, why do most choose the husband's side (patrilocal residence), but some the wife's side (matrilocal residence)? Why do some non-neolocal societies allow a married couple to go to either the wife's or the husband's kin (bilocal residence), whereas most others do not allow a choice?

Neolocal Residence Many anthropologists have suggested that neolocal residence is related to the presence of a money or commercial economy. They argue that, when people can sell their labor or their products for money, they can buy what they need to live, without having to depend on kin. Indeed, neolocal residence tends to occur in societies with monetary or commercial exchange, whereas societies without money tend to have patterns of residence that locate a couple near or with kin.[69] The presence of money, then, partially accounts for neolocal residence: Money seems to allow couples to live on their own. Still, this fact does not quite explain why they choose to do so. One reason may be that couples in commercial societies do better on their own because the jobs available require physical or social mobility. Or perhaps couples prefer to live apart from kin because they want to avoid some of the interpersonal tensions and demands that may be generated by living with or near kin.

Matrilocal versus Patrilocal Residence It is traditionally assumed that, in societies in which married children live near or with kin, the pattern of residence will tend to be patrilocal if males contribute more to the economy and matrilocal if women contribute more. However plausible that assumption may seem, the cross-cultural evidence does not support it. Where men do most of the primary subsistence work, residence is patrilocal no more often than would be expected by chance. Conversely, where women do an equal amount or more of the subsistence work, residence is no more likely to be matrilocal than patrilocal.[70] And if we counted all work inside and outside the home, most societies should be matrilocal because women usually do more. But that is not true either; most societies are not matrilocal.

We can predict whether residence will be matrilocal or patrilocal, however, from the type of warfare practiced in the society. In most societies known to anthropology, neighboring

The Iroquois longhouses could house over 80 people. The female members of a matrilineage with their in-marrying husbands traditionally lived in one longhouse.

communities or districts are enemies. The type of warfare that breaks out periodically between such groups is called *internal* because the fighting occurs between groups that speak the same language. In other societies, the warfare is never within the same society but only with other language groups. This pattern of warfare is referred to as purely *external*. Cross-cultural evidence suggests that, in societies where warfare is at least sometimes internal, residence is almost always patrilocal rather than matrilocal. In contrast, residence is usually matrilocal when warfare is purely external.[71]

How can we explain this relationship between type of warfare and matrilocal versus patrilocal residence? One theory is that patrilocal residence tends to occur with internal warfare because there may be concern over keeping sons close to home to help with defense. Because women do not usually constitute the fighting force in any society, having sons reside at home after marriage might be favored as a means of maintaining a loyal and quickly mobilized fighting force in case of surprise attack from nearby. If warfare is purely external, however, people may not be so concerned about keeping their sons at home because families need not fear attack from neighboring communities or districts.[72]

With purely external warfare, then, the pattern of residence may be determined by other considerations, especially economic ones. If the women do most of the primary subsistence work in societies with purely external warfare, families might want their daughters to remain at home after marriage, so the pattern of residence might become matrilocal. If warfare is purely external but men still do more of the primary subsistence work, residence should still be patrilocal. Thus, the need to keep sons at home after marriage when there is internal warfare may take precedence over any considerations based on division of labor. Perhaps only when internal warfare is nonexistent may a female-dominant division of labor give rise to matrilocal residence.

The frequent absence of men because of long-distance trade or wage labor in distant places may also provide an impetus for matrilocal residence even after warfare ceases. For example, among the Miskito of eastern Central America, matrilocality allowed domestic and village life to continue without interruption when men were away from home for long periods of time, working as lumberers, miners, river transporters, and more recently as deep-sea divers for lobster, for which there is a lot of demand in the international economy. Even though some men would always be away from home, the Miskito continued to get food in their traditional ways, from farming (done mostly by the women) and from hunting and fishing (which was mostly men's work).[73]

Bilocal Residence In societies that practice bilocal residence, a married couple goes to live with or near either the husband's or the wife's parents. Although this pattern seems to involve a choice for the married couple, theory and research suggest that bilocal residence may occur out of necessity instead. Elman Service suggested that bilocal residence is likely to occur in societies that have recently suffered a severe and drastic loss of population because of the introduction of new infectious diseases.[74] Over the last 400 years, contact with Europeans in many parts of the world has resulted in severe population losses among non-European societies that lacked resistance to the Europeans' diseases. If couples need to live with some set of kin to make a living in noncommercial societies, it seems likely that couples in depopulated, noncommercial societies might have to live with whichever spouse's parents and other relatives are still alive. This interpretation is supported by cross-cultural evidence. Recently depopulated societies tend to have bilocal residence or frequent departures from unilocality, whereas societies that are not recently depopulated tend to have one pattern or another of unilocal residence.[75]

In hunter-gatherer societies, a few other circumstances may also favor bilocal residence. Bilocality tends to be found among those hunter-gatherers who have very small bands or unpredictable and low rainfall. Residential "choice" in these cases may be a question of adjusting marital residence to where the couple will have the best chance to survive or to find close relatives with whom to live and work.[76]

Avunculocal Residence Now that we have learned about matrilineal systems, the avunculocal pattern of residence, whereby married couples live with or near the husband's mother's brother, may become clearer. Although avunculocal residence is relatively rare, just about all avunculocal societies are matrilineal. As we have seen, the mother's brother plays an important role in decision making in most matrilineal societies. Aside from his brothers, who is a boy's closest male matrilineal relative? His mother's brother. Going to live with the mother's brother, then, provides a way of localizing male *matrilineal* relatives. But why should some matrilineal societies practice that form of residence? The answer may involve the prevailing type of warfare.

Avunculocal societies, in contrast with matrilocal societies, fight internally. Just as patrilocality may be a response to keep patrilineally related men home after marriage, avunculocality may also be a way of keeping related—in this case, matrilineally related—men together after marriage to provide for quick mobilization in case of surprise attack from nearby. Societies that already have strong, functioning matrilineal descent groups may choose initially, when faced with the emergence of fighting close to home, to switch to avunculocality rather than patrilocality. This is assuming that the close warfare results in high male mortality, which might make it more difficult to trace descent patrilineally than matrilineally. So such a society might begin to practice avunculocality rather than switch to patrilocality. Avunculocal residence would keep a higher number of related men together after marriage, compared with patrilocality, because there would be more possible links through women than through men if many men were dying relatively young in warfare.[77]

The Emergence of Unilineal Systems

Unilineal kin groups play very important roles in the organization of many societies. But not all societies have such groups. In societies that have complex systems of political organization, officials and agencies take over many of the functions that kin groups might perform, such as organizing work and warfare and allocating land. But not all societies that lack complex political organization have unilineal descent systems. Why, then, do some societies have unilineal descent systems, but others do not?

It is generally assumed that unilocal residence, patrilocal or matrilocal, is necessary for the development of unilineal descent. Patrilocal residence, if practiced for some time in a society, will generate a set of patrilineally related males who live in the same territory. Matrilocal residence over time will similarly generate a localized set of matrilineally related females. It is no wonder, then, that matrilocal and patrilocal residence are cross-culturally associated with matrilineal and patrilineal descent, respectively.[78]

But, although unilocal residence might be necessary for the formation of unilineal descent groups, it is apparently not the only condition required. For one thing, many societies with unilocal residence lack unilineal descent groups. For another, merely because related males or related females live together by virtue of a patrilocal or matrilocal rule of residence, it does not necessarily follow that the related people will actually view themselves as a descent group and function as such. Thus, it appears that other conditions are needed to supply the impetus for the formation of unilineal descent groups.

There is evidence that unilocal societies that engage in warfare are more apt to have unilineal descent groups than unilocal societies without warfare.[79] It may be, then, that the presence of fighting in societies lacking complex systems of political organization provides an impetus to the formation of unilineal descent groups. Unilineal descent groups provide individuals with unambiguous groups of people who can fight or form alliances as discrete units.[80] There is no ambiguity about an individual's membership. It is perfectly clear whether someone belongs to a particular clan, phratry, or moiety. This feature of unilineal descent groups enables them to act as separate and distinct units—mostly, perhaps, in warfare.

✓●—Study and Review on myanthrolab.com

Summary

1. All societies known today have the custom of marriage. Marriage is a socially approved sexual and economic union usually between a man and a woman that is presumed to be more or less permanent and that subsumes reciprocal rights and obligations between the two spouses and between the spouses and their children.

2. Marriage arrangements often include an economic element, including bride price (the most common form of economic transaction), bride service, female exchange, dowry, and indirect dowry.

3. Every society tells people whom they cannot marry, whom they can marry, and sometimes even whom they should marry. No society in recent times has allowed sex or marriage between brothers and sisters, mothers and sons, or fathers and daughters. In quite a few societies, marriages are arranged by the couple's kin. Some societies have rules of exogamy, which require marriage outside one's own kin group or community; others have rules of endogamy, requiring marriage within one's group. Although most societies prohibit all first-cousin marriages, some permit or prefer marriage with cross-cousins (children of siblings of the opposite sex) and parallel cousins (children of siblings of the same sex).

4. Most societies allow a man to be married to more than one woman at a time (polygyny). Polyandry, the marriage of one woman to several husbands, is rare.

5. The prevailing form of family in most societies is the extended family. It consists of two or more single-parent, monogamous (nuclear), polygynous, or polyandrous families linked by blood ties.

6. In our society, and in many other industrial societies, a newly married couple usually establishes a place of residence apart from parents or relatives (neolocal residence). But about 95 percent of the world's societies have some pattern of residence whereby the new couple settles within or very close to the household of the parents or some other close relative of the groom or bride. The four major patterns in which married couples live with or near kinsmen are the following: patrilocal residence (the most common), matrilocal residence, bilocal residence, and avunculocal residence.

7. In most societies where kinship is important, rules of affiliation allocate each person to a particular and definable set of kin. The three main types of affiliation with kin are: *unilineal descent* (patrilineal or matrilineal), *ambilineal descent,* and *bilateral kinship.*

8. With unilineal descent, people usually refer to themselves as belonging to a particular unilineal group or set of groups because they believe they share common descent in either the male or the female line. These people form what is called a unilineal descent group. There are several types, and a society may have more than one type: lineages, clans, phratries, and moieties.

Marriage, Family, and Kinship

Glossary Terms

ambilineal descent

avunculocal
  residence

bilateral kinship

bilocal residence

bride price (or bride
  wealth)

bride service

clan (or sib)

cross-cousins

double descent
  (or double unilineal
  descent)

dowry

ego

endogamy

exogamy

extended family

family

fraternal polyandry

group marriage

incest taboo

independent family

indirect dowry

kindred

lineage

marriage

matriclans

matrilineage

matrilineal descent

matrilocal residence

moiety

monogamy

neolocal residence

nonfraternal
  polyandry

nonsororal polygyny

nuclear family

parallel cousins

patriclans

patrilineage

patrilineal descent

patrilocal residence

phratry

polyandry

polygamy

polygyny

postpartum sex
  taboo

rules of descent

sororal polygyny

totem

unilineal descent

unilocal residence

Critical Questions

1. Will it remain customary in our society to marry? Why do you think it will or will not?

2. Why is polyandry so much less common than polygyny?

3. What other things about our society would change if we practiced other than neolocal residence?

4. Why might it be important for unilineal descent groups to be nonoverlapping in membership?

▶ Read the Original Source on myanthrolab.com

Read Alan Howard and Jan Rensel's "Rotuma: Interpreting a Wedding" on MyAnthroLab and answer the following questions.

1. Howard and Rensel suggest that weddings among the Rotuma express their core values. What core values are expressed in their weddings?

2. How has courtship and marriage changed?

3. Compare the essential features of weddings in your culture (make sure to mention the name of your culture) with those described for the Rotuma.

Photo Credits

Glossary

Ambilineal descent The rule of descent that affiliates individuals with groups of kin related to them through men or women.

Avunculocal residence A pattern of residence in which a married couple settles with or near the husband's mother's brother.

Bilateral kinship The type of kinship system in which individuals affiliate more or less equally with their mother's and father's relatives; descent groups are absent.

Bilocal residence A pattern of residence in which a married couple lives with or near either the husband's parents or the wife's parents.

Bride price A substantial gift of goods or money given to the bride's kin by the groom or his kin at or before the marriage. Also called *bride wealth*.

Bride service Work performed by the groom for his bride's family for a variable length of time either before or after the marriage.

Clan A set of kin whose members believe themselves to be descended from a common ancestor or ances-tress but cannot specify the links back to that founder; often designated by a totem. Also called a *sib*.

Cross-cousins Children of siblings of the opposite sex. One's cross-cousins are the father's sisters' children and mother's brothers' children.

Double descent or double unilineal descent A system that affiliates individuals with a group of matri-lineal kin for some purposes and with a group of patrilineal kin for other purposes.

Dowry A substantial transfer of goods or money from the bride's family to the bride.

Ego In the reckoning of kinship, the reference point or focal person.

Endogamy The rule specifying marriage to a person within one's own group (kin, caste, community).

Exogamy The rule specifying marriage to a person from outside one's own group (kin or community).

Extended family A family consisting of two or more single-parent, monogamous, polygynous, or poly-androus families linked by a blood tie.

Family A social and economic unit consisting minimally of a parent and a child.

Fraternal polyandry The marriage of a woman to two or more brothers at the same time.

Group marriage Marriage in which more than one man is married to more than one woman at the same time; not customary in any known human society.

Incest taboo Prohibition of sexual intercourse or marriage between mother and son, father and daughter, and brother and sister; often extends to other relatives.

Marriage, Family, and Kinship

Independent family A family unit consisting of one monogamous (nuclear) family, or one polygynous or one polyandrous family.

Indirect dowry Goods given by the groom's kin to the bride (or her father, who passes most of them to her) at or before her marriage.

Kindred A bilateral set of close relatives.

Lineage A set of kin whose members trace descent from a common ancestor through known links.

Marriage A socially approved sexual and economic union, usually between a man and a woman, that is presumed, both by the couple and by others, to be more or less permanent, and that subsumes reciprocal rights and obligations between the two spouses and their future children.

Matriclan A clan tracing descent through the female line.

Matrilineage A kin group whose members trace descent through known links in the female line from a common female ancestor.

Matrilineal descent The rule of descent that affiliates individuals with kin of both sexes related to them through women only.

Matrilocal residence A pattern of residence in which a married couple lives with or near the wife's parents.

Moiety A unilineal descent group in a society that is divided into two such maximal groups; there may be smaller unilineal descent groups as well.

Monogamy Marriage between only one man and only one woman at a time.

Neolocal residence A pattern of residence whereby a married couple lives separately, and usually at some distance, from the kin of both spouses.

Nonfraternal polyandry Marriage of a woman to two or more men who are not brothers.

Nonsororal polygyny Marriage of a man to two or more women who are not sisters.

Nuclear family A family consisting of a married couple and their young children.

Parallel cousins Children of siblings of the same sex. One's parallel cousins are the father's brothers' children and the mother's sisters' children.

Patriclan A clan tracing descent through the male line.

Patrilineage A kin group whose members trace descent through known links in the male line from a common male ancestor.

Patrilineal descent The rule of descent that affiliates individuals with kin of both sexes related to them through men only.

Patrilocal residence A pattern of residence in which a married couple lives with or near the husband's parents.

Phratry A unilineal descent group composed of a number of supposedly related clans (sibs).

Polyandry The marriage of one woman to more than one man at a time.

Polygamy Plural marriage; one individual is married to more than one spouse simultaneously. **Polygyny** and **polyandry** are types of polygamy.

Polygyny The marriage of one man to more than one woman at a time.

Postpartum sex taboo Prohibition of sexual intercourse between a couple for a period of time after the birth of their child.

Rules of descent Rules that connect individuals with particular sets of kin because of known or presumed common ancestry.

Sororal polygyny The marriage of a man to two or more sisters at the same time.

Totem A plant or animal associated with a clan (sib) as a means of group identification; may have other special significance for the group.

Unilineal descent Affiliation with a group of kin through descent links of one sex only.

Unilocal residence A pattern of residence (patrilocal, matrilocal, or avunculocal) that specifies just one set of relatives that the married couple lives with or near.

Notes

1. Stephens 1963, 5.
2. Murdock 1949, 8.
3. Murdock 1949, 7–8.
4. Ibid., 9–10.
5. See, for example, Linton 1936, 135–36.
6. M. Ember and C. R. Ember 1979.
7. Ibid.
8. Marlowe 2003, 221–23.
9. M. Ember and C. R. Ember 1979.
10. Schlegel and Eloul 1987, 119.
11. Schlegel and Eloul 1988, 295, Table 1. We used the data to calculate the frequency of various types of economic transactions in a worldwide sample of 186 societies.
12. Schlegel and Eloul 1988, 298–99.
13. Pryor 1977, 363–64.
14. Ibid.
15. Schlegel and Eloul 1988, 296–97.
16. Ibid.
17. Ibid.
18. Radcliffe-Brown 1922, 73.
19. Goody 1973, 17–21; Murdock 1967.
20. Pryor 1977, 363–65; Schlegel and Eloul 1988, 296–99.
21. Schlegel and Eloul 1988, following Goody 1973, 20.
22. R. Middleton 1962, 606.
23. Durham 1991, 293–94, citing research by Hopkins 1980.
24. Howard and Rensel 2009.
25. Lingenfelter 2009.
26. Macdonald and Hewlett 1999, 504–06.
27. M. Ember 1975, 262, Table 3.
28. Busby 2009.
29. M. Ember 1975, 260–69; see also Durham 1991, 341–57.
30. Oliver 1955, 352–53.
31. Ibid., 223–24, quoted in W. Stephens 1963, 58.
32. Mead 1950/1935, 101.
33. Jankowiak, Sudakov, and Wilreker 2005.
34. The discussion of these customs is based on W. Stephens 1963, 63–67.
35. Kilbride and Kilbride 1990, 202–06.
36. C. Anderson 2000, 102–03.
37. J. W. M. Whiting 1964.
38. M. Ember 1974b.
39. M. Ember 1984–1985. The statistical relationship between late age of marriage for men and polygyny was first reported by Witkowski 1975.
40. M. Ember 1974b, 202–05.
41. M. Ember 1984–1985. For other predictors of polygyny, see D. R. White and Burton 1988.
42. Low 1990.
43. M. Ember, C. R. Ember, and Low 2007.
44. Barber 2008.
45. Coult and Habenstein 1965; Murdock 1957.
46. M. C. Goldstein 1987, 39.

47. Stephens 1963, 45.
48. Hiatt 1980.
49. M. Goldstein 1987. Formerly, in feudal Tibet, a class of serfs who owned small parcels of land also practiced polyandry. Goldstein suggests that a shortage of land would explain their polyandry too. See M. C. Goldstein 1971.
50. Pasternak 1976, 96.
51. Coult and Habenstein 1965.
52. Mead 1961/1928, quoted in Stephens 1963, 134–35.
53. Nimkoff and Middleton 1960.
54. Pasternak, C. R. Ember, and M. Ember 1976, 109–23.
55. Coult and Habenstein 1965; Murdock 1957.
56. Percentages calculated from Coult and Habenstein 1965.
57. L. Bohannan and P. Bohannan 1953.
58. J. D. Freeman 1961.
59. Jarvenpa 2004.
60. C. R. Ember, M. Ember, and Pasternak 1974, 84–89.
61. Pospisil 1963.
62. Schneider 1961a.
63. M. Ember and C. R. Ember 1971, 581.
64. Schneider 1961b.
65. Goodenough 1951, 145.
66. Coult and Habenstein 1965.
67. Data from Textor 1967.
68. Davenport 1959.
69. M. Ember 1967.
70. M. Ember and C. R. Ember 1971. See also Divale 1974.
71. Divale 1974; M. Ember and Ember 1971, 583–85.
72. M. Ember and Ember 1971. For a different theory—that matrilocal residence precedes, rather than follows, the development of purely external warfare—see Divale 1974.
73. Helms 2009; Herlihy 2007; see also M. Ember and Ember 1971.
74. Service 1962, 137.
75. C. R. Ember and M. Ember 1972.
76. C. R. Ember 1975.
77. M. Ember 1974a.
78. Data from Textor 1967.
79. C. R. Ember et al. 1974.
80. The importance of warfare and competition as factors in the formation of unilineal descent groups is also suggested by Sahlins 1961, 332–45 and Service 1962.

Bibliography

Anderson, Connie M. 2000. The persistence of polygyny as an adaptive response to poverty and oppression in apartheid South Africa. *Cross-Cultural Research* 34:99–112.

Barber, Nigel. 2008. Explaining cross-national differences in polygyny intensity: Resource-defense, sex-ratio, and infectious diseases. *Cross-Cultural Research* 42:103–17.

Bohannan, Laura, and Paul Bohannan. 1953. *The Tiv of central Nigeria.* London: International African Institute.

Busby, Annette. 2009. Kurds: A culture straddling national borders. In MyAnthroLibrary, eds. C. R. Ember, M. Ember, and P. N. Peregrine. MyAnthroLibrary.com. Pearson.

Coult, Allan D., and Robert W. Habenstein. 1965. *Cross tabulations of Murdock's "World ethnographic sample."* Columbia: University of Missouri Press.

Davenport, William. 1959. Nonunilinear descent and descent groups. *American Anthropologist* 61:557–72.

Divale, William T. 1974. Migration, external warfare, and matrilocal residence. *Behavior Science Research* 9:75–133.

Durham, William H. 1991. *Coevolution: Genes, culture and human diversity.* Stanford, CA: Stanford University Press.

Ember, Carol R. 1975. Residential variation among hunter-gatherers. *Behavior Science Research* 9:135–49.

Ember, Carol R., and Melvin Ember. 1972. The conditions favoring multilocal residence. *Southwestern Journal of Anthropology* 28:382–400.

Ember, Carol R., Melvin Ember, and Burton Pasternak. 1974. On the development of unilineal descent. *Journal of Anthropological Research* 30:69–94.

Ember, Melvin. 1967. The emergence of neolocal residence. *Transactions of the New York Academy of Sciences* 30:291–302.

Ember, Melvin, and Carol R. Ember. 1971. The conditions favoring matrilocal versus patrilocal residence. *American Anthropologist* 73:571–94.

Ember, Melvin. 1974a. The conditions that may favor avunculocal residence. *Behavior Science Research* 9:203–09.

Ember, Melvin. 1974b. Warfare, sex ratio, and polygyny. *Ethnology* 13:197–206.

Marriage, Family, and Kinship

Ember, Melvin. 1975. On the origin and extension of the incest taboo. *Behavior Science Research* 10:249–81.

Ember, Melvin. 1984–1985. Alternative predictors of polygyny. *Behavior Science Research* 19:1–23.

Ember, Melvin, and Carol R. Ember. 1979. Male-Female bonding: A cross-species study of mammals and birds. *Behavior Science Research* 14:37–56.

Ember, Melvin, Carol R. Ember, and Bobbi S. Low. 2007. Comparing explanations of polygyny. *Cross-Cultural Research* 41:428–40.

Freeman, J. D. 1961. On the concept of the kindred. *Journal of the Royal Anthropological Institute* 91:192–220.

Goldstein, Melvyn C. 1971. Stratification, polyandry, and family structure in central Tibet. *Southwestern Journal of Anthropology* 27:65–74.

Goldstein, Melvyn C. 1987. When brothers share a wife. *Natural History* (March):39–48.

Goodenough, Ward H. 1951. *Property, kin, and community on Truk.* New Haven, CT: Yale University Press.

Goody, Jack. 1973. Bridewealth and dowry in Africa and Eurasia. In *Bridewealth and dowry,* eds. J. Goody and S. H. Tambiah. Cambridge, UK: Cambridge University Press.

Helms, Mary W. 2009. Miskito: Adaptations to colonial empires, past and present. In MyAnthroLibrary, eds. C. R. Ember, M. Ember, and P. N. Peregrine. MyAnthroLibrary.com. Pearson.

Herlihy, Laura Hobson. 2007. Matrifocality and women's power on the Miskito Coast. *Ethnology* 46:133–49.

Hiatt, Lester R. 1980. Polyandry in Sri Lanka: A test case for parental investment theory. *Man* 15:583–98.

Hopkins, Keith. 1980. Brother-sister marriage in Roman Egypt. *Comparative Studies in Society and History* 22:303–54.

Howard, Alan, and Jan Rensel. 2009. Rotuma: Interpreting a wedding. In MyAnthroLibrary, eds. C. R. Ember, M. Ember, and P. N. Peregrine. MyAnthroLibrary.com. Pearson.

Jankowiak, William, Monica Sudakov, and Benjamin C. Wilreker. 2005. Co-wife conflict and co-operation. *Ethnology* 44:81–98.

Jarvenpa, Robert. 2004. *Silot'ine:* An insurance perspective on Northern Dene kinship networks in recent history. *Journal of Anthropological Research* 60:153–78.

Kilbride, Philip L., and Janet C. Kilbride. 1990. Polygyny: A modern contradiction? In P. L. Kilbride and J. C. Kilbride, *Changing family life in East Africa: Women and children at risk.* University Park: Pennsylvania State University Press.

Lingenfelter, Sherwood G. 2009. Yap: Changing roles of men and women. In MyAnthroLibrary, eds. C. R. Ember, M. Ember, and P. N. Peregrine. MyAnthroLibrary.com. Pearson.

Linton, Ralph. 1936. *The study of man.* New York: Appleton-Century-Crofts.

Low, Bobbi. 1990. Marriage systems and pathogen stress in human societies. *American Zoologist* 30:325–39.

Macdonald, Douglas H., and Barry S. Hewlett. 1999. Reproductive interests and forager mobility. *Current Anthropology* 40:501–23.

Marlowe, Frank W. 2003. A critical period for provisioning by Hadza men: Implications for pair bonding. *Evolution and Human Behavior* 24:217–29.

Mead, Margaret. 1950/1935. *Sex and temperament in three primitive societies.* New York: Mentor.

Mead, Margaret. 1961/1928. *Coming of age in Samoa.* 3rd ed. New York: Morrow.

Middleton, Russell. 1962. Brother-sister and father-daughter marriage in ancient Egypt. *American Sociological Review* 27:603–11.

Murdock, George P. 1949. *Social structure.* New York: Macmillan.

Murdock, George P. 1957. World ethnographic sample. *American Anthropologist* 59:664–87.

Murdock, George P. 1967. Ethnographic atlas: A summary. *Ethnology* 6:109–236.

Nimkoff, Meyer F., and Russell Middleton. 1960. Types of family and types of economy. *American Journal of Sociology* 66:215–25.

Oliver, Douglas L. 1955. *A Solomon Island society.* Cambridge, MA: Harvard University Press.

Pasternak, Burton. 1976. *Introduction to kinship and social organization.* Upper Saddle River, NJ: Prentice Hall.

Pasternak, Burton, Carol R. Ember, and Melvin Ember. 1976. On the conditions favoring extended family households. *Journal of Anthropological Research* 32:109–23.

Pospisil, Leopold. 1963. *The Kapauku Papuans of West New Guinea.* New York: Holt, Rinehart & Winston.

Pryor, Frederic L. 1977. *The origins of the economy: A comparative study of distribution in primitive and peasant economies.* New York: Academic Press.

Radcliffe-Brown, Alfred R. 1922. *The Andaman Islanders: A study in social anthropology.* Cambridge, UK: Cambridge University Press.

Sahlins, Marshall D. 1961. The segmentary lineage: An organization of predatory expansion. *American Anthropologist* 63:332–45.

Schlegel, Alice, and Rohn Eloul. 1987. A new coding of marriage transactions. *Behavior Science Research* 21:118–40.

Schlegel, Alice, and Rohn Eloul. 1988. Marriage transactions: Labor, property, and status. *American Anthropologist* 90:291–309.

Schneider, David M. 1961a. Introduction: The distinctive features of matrilineal descent groups. In *Matrilineal kinship,* eds. D. M. Schneider and K. Gough, 1–29. Berkeley: University of California Press.

Schneider, David M. 1961b. Truk. In *Matrilineal kinship,* eds. D. M. Schneider and K. Gough, 202–33. Berkeley: University of California Press.

Service, Elman R. 1962. *Primitive social organization: An evolutionary perspective.* New York: Random House.

Stephens, William N. 1963. *The family in cross-cultural perspective.* New York: Holt, Rinehart & Winston.

Textor, Robert B., comp. 1967. *A cross-cultural summary.* New Haven, CT: HRAF Press.

White, Douglas R., and Michael L. Burton. 1988. Causes of polygyny: Ecology, economy, kinship, and warfare. *American Anthropologist* 90:871–87.

Whiting, John W. M. 1964. Effects of climate on certain cultural practices. In *Explorations in cultural anthropology,* ed. W. Goodenough. New York: McGraw-Hill.

Witkowski, Stanley R. 1975. *Polygyny, age of marriage, and female status.* Paper presented at the annual meeting of the American Anthropological Association, San Francisco.

Sex and Gender

From Chapter 7 of *Human Culture*, Second Edition. Carol R. Ember, Melvin Ember. Copyright © 2012 by Pearson Education, Inc. All rights reserved.

Sex and Gender

((•—[Listen to the Chapter Audio on myanthrolab.com   [◻•—[Read on myanthrolab.com

Humans come in two major varieties or sexes: female and male. Each has different reproductive organs. The contrast between them is one of the facts of life shared with most animal species. But having different organs of reproduction does not explain why males and females may also differ in other physical ways. There are some animal species—such as pigeons, gulls, and laboratory rats—in which the two sexes differ little in appearance.[1] The fact that we are a species with two sexes does not explain why human females and males typically look different, nor why human males and females should differ in behavior or be treated differently by society. Yet, no society we know of treats females and males in exactly the same way; indeed, females usually have fewer advantages than males. That is why we are careful to say that egalitarian societies have no *social groups* with unequal access to resources, power, and prestige. But within social groups (e.g., families), even egalitarian societies usually allow males greater access to economic resources, power, and prestige.

Because many of the differences between females and males may reflect cultural expectations and experiences, many researchers now prefer to speak of those as **gender differences**, reserving the term **sex differences** for purely biological differences.[2] Unfortunately, biological and cultural influences are not always clearly separable, so it is sometimes hard to know which term to use. As long as societies treat males and females differently, we may not be able to separate the effects of biology from the effects of culture, and both may be present. As we discuss differences and similarities between females and males, keep in mind that not all cultures conceive of gender as including just two categories. Sometimes "maleness" and "femaleness" are thought of as opposite ends of a continuum, or there might be three or more categories of gender, such as "female," "male," and "other."[3]

Here, we discuss what we know cross-culturally about how and why females and males may differ physically, in gender roles, and in personality. We also discuss how and why sexual behavior and attitudes about sex vary from culture to culture. First, we focus on how concepts about gender vary cross-culturally.

Gender Concepts

In the United States and many Western societies, there are only two genders: female or male. Your gender is assigned at birth based on external biological attributes. However, not all individuals feel comfortable with their gender assignment. The term *transgender* is now used to describe people who don't feel that their assigned gender fits them well.

The division into just two genders—male/female—is very common cross-culturally. But a strict dichotomy is far from universal. Some societies, like the Cheyenne Native Americans of the Great Plains, recognized male, female, and a third gender, referred to by the Cheyennes as "two-spirits." "Two-spirit" people were usually biological males. The gender status of "two-spirit" was often recognized after a boy finished his vision quest, usually in his preadolescent years. A two-spirit person would wear women's dress and take on many of the activities of women. A two-spirit might even be taken as a second wife by a man, but whether the man and the two spirit person engaged in sex is unknown. The role of a "two-spirit" person was not equivalent to becoming a woman, because two-spirits played special roles at weddings and childbirth. Europeans referred to a two-spirit individual as a *berdache*.[4] Accounts of "two-spirit" biological females who take on the role of men are relatively rare, but they do occur in a number of native North American societies, such as the Kaska of Yukon Territory, the Klamath of southern Oregon, and the Mohave of the Colorado River area in the southwestern United States. These biological female "two-spirits" could marry women, and such relationships were known to be lesbian relationships.[5]

In Oman, there is a third gender role called *xanith*. Anatomically male, *xaniths* speak of themselves as "women." However, *xaniths* have their own distinctive dress—they wear clothes that are neither male nor female. In fact, their clothes and dress seem in-between. Men wear white clothes, women bright patterns, and *xaniths* wear unpatterned pastels. Men have short hair, women long, and *xaniths* are medium-length. Women are generally secluded in their houses and can only go out with permission from their husbands, but the *xanith* is free to come and go and works as a servant and/or a homosexual prostitute. But the *xanith* gender role is not necessarily forever. A *xanith* may decide to marry, and if he is able to have intercourse with his bride, he becomes a "man." An older *xanith* who is no longer attractive may decide to become an "old man."[6]

Physique and Physiology

As we noted earlier, males and females cannot readily be distinguished in some animal species. Although they differ in chromosome makeup and in their external and internal organs of reproduction, they do not differ otherwise. In contrast, humans are *sexually dimorphic*—that is, the two sexes of our species are generally different in size and appearance. Females have proportionately wider pelvises. Males typically are taller and have heavier skeletons. Females have a larger proportion of their body weight in fat; males have a larger proportion of body weight in muscle. Males typically have greater grip strength, proportionately larger hearts and lungs, and greater aerobic capacity (greater intake of oxygen during strenuous activity).

North American culture tends to view "taller" and "more muscled" as better, which may reflect a bias toward males. But how did these differences come about? Natural selection may have favored these traits in males but selected against them in females. Because females bear children, selection may have favored earlier cessation of growth, and therefore less ultimate height so that the nutritional needs of a fetus would not compete with a growing mother's needs.[7] (Females achieve their ultimate height shortly after puberty, but boys continue to grow for years after puberty.) Similarly, there is some evidence that females are less affected than males by nutritional shortages, presumably because they tend to be shorter and have proportionately more fat.[8] Natural selection may have favored more proportionate "fatness" in females because that resulted in greater reproductive success.

Athletes can build up their muscle strength and increase their aerobic work capacity through training. Given that fact, cultural factors, such as how much a society expects and allows males and females to engage in muscular activity, could influence the degree to which females and males differ muscularly and in aerobic capacity. Similar training may account for the recent trend toward decreasing differences between females and males in certain athletic events, such as marathons and swim meets. Even when it comes to female and male physique and physiology, then, what we see may be the result of both culture and genes.[9]

Gender Roles

Productive and Domestic Activities

We understand that all societies assign or divide labor somewhat differently between females and males. Because role assignments have a clear cultural component, we speak of them as **gender roles**. What is of particular interest here about the gender division of labor is not so much that every society has different work for males and females but rather that so many societies divide up work in similar ways. The question, then, is: Why are there universal or near-universal patterns in such assignments?

Table 1 summarizes the worldwide patterns indicating which activities are performed by one gender in all or almost all societies, which activities are usually performed by one gender, and which activities are commonly assigned to either gender or both. Do the other distributions of activities in the table suggest why females and males generally do different things? Scholars have suggested four explanations or theories that we label: *strength theory, compatibility-with-child-care theory, economy-of-effort theory,* and *expendability theory.*

The *strength theory* focuses on the generally greater strength of males and their superior capacity to mobilize their strength in quick bursts of energy (because of greater aerobic work capacity). Certainly, males may generally best perform activities that require lifting heavy

TABLE 1 Worldwide Patterns in the Division of Labor by Gender

Type of Activity	Males Almost Always	Males Usually	Either Gender or Both	Females Usually	Females Almost Always
Primary subsistence activities	Hunt and trap animals, large and small	Fish Herd large animals Collect wild honey Clear land and prepare soil for planting	Collect shellfish Care for small animals Plant crops Tend crops Harvest crops Milk animals	Gather wild plants	
Secondary subsistence and household activities		Butcher animals	Preserve meat and fish	Care for children Cook Prepare vegetable foods, drinks, and dairy products Launder Fetch water Collect fuel	Care for infants
Other	Lumber Mine and quarry Make boats, musical instruments, and bone, horn, and shell objects Engage in combat	Build houses Make nets and rope Exercise political leadership	Prepare skins Make leather products, baskets, mats, clothing, and pottery	Spin yarn	

Source: Mostly adapted from Murdock and Provost 1973, 203–25. The information on political leadership and warfare comes from Whyte 1978a, 217. The information on child care comes from Weisner and Gallimore 1977, 169–80.

Hmong women carry large loads of firewood to market.

objects (hunting large animals, butchering, clearing land, or working with stone, metal, or lumber), throwing weapons, and running with great speed (as in hunting). And none of the activities females usually perform, with the possible exception of collecting firewood, seem to require the same degree of physical strength or quick bursts of energy. But the strength theory is not completely convincing, if only because it cannot readily explain all the observed patterns. For example, it is not clear that the male activities of trapping small animals, collecting wild honey, or making musical instruments require much physical strength. Moreover, as we will see shortly, women do hunt in some societies, suggesting that differences in strength cannot play a very important role.

The *compatibility-with-child-care theory* emphasizes that women's tasks need to be compatible with child care. Although males can take care of infants, most traditional societies rely on breast-feeding of infants, which men cannot do. (In most societies, women breast-feed their children for 2 years on the average.) Women's tasks may be those that do not take them far from home for long periods, that do not place children in potential danger if they are taken along, and that can be stopped and resumed if an infant needs care.[10]

The compatibility theory may explain why *no* activities other than infant care are listed in the right-hand column of Table 1. That is, it may be that there are practically no universal or near-universal women-only activities because until recently most women have had to devote much of their time to nursing and caring for infants, as well as caring for other children. This theory may also explain why men usually perform tasks such as hunting, trapping, fishing, collecting honey, lumbering, and mining. Those tasks are dangerous for infants to be around, and in any case, would be difficult to coordinate with infant care.[11]

Finally, the compatibility theory may also explain why men seem to take over certain crafts in societies with full-time specialization. Although the distinction is not shown in Table 1, crafts such as making baskets, mats, and pottery are women's activities in noncommercial societies but tend to be men's activities in societies with full-time craft specialists.[12] Similarly, weaving tends to be a female activity unless it is produced for trade.[13] Full-time specialization and production for trade may increase incompatibility with child care. Cooking is a good example in our own society. Many women are excellent cooks and traditionally did most of the cooking at home, but chefs and bakers tend to be men. Women might be more likely to work as chefs if they could leave their babies and young children in safe places to be cared for by other people or if the hours chefs and bakers work were not so long.

But the compatibility theory does not explain why men usually prepare soil for planting, make objects out of wood, or work bone, horn, and shell. All of those tasks could probably be stopped to tend to a child, and none of them is any more dangerous to children nearby than is cooking. Why, then, do males tend to do them? The *economy-of-effort theory* may help explain patterns that cannot readily be explained by the strength and compatibility theories. For example, it may be advantageous for men to make wooden musical instruments because men generally lumber.[14] Lumbering may give men more knowledge about the physical properties of various woods and make it more likely that they know how to work with different woods. The economy-of-effort interpretation also suggests that it would be advantageous for one gender to perform tasks that are physically located near each other. If women have to be near home to take care of nursing and young children, it would be economical for them to perform other chores in or near the home.

In many farming societies, women can do some agriculture and take care of their young children at the same time, as this mother in Zambia demonstrates.

Expendability theory suggests that men, rather than women, will tend to do the dangerous work in a society because the loss of men is less disadvantageous reproductively than the loss of women. If some men lose their lives in hunting, deep-water fishing, mining, quarrying, lumbering, and the like, reproduction need not suffer as long as most fertile women have sexual access to men—for example, if the society permits two or more women to be married to the same man.[15] If something is dangerous, why would anybody, male or female, be willing to do it? Perhaps only when society glorifies those roles and endows them with high prestige and other rewards.

Although the various theories, singly or in combination, seem to explain much of the division of labor by gender, there are some unresolved problems. Critics of the strength theory have pointed out that women in some societies do engage in very heavy labor.[16] If women in some societies can develop the strength to do such work, perhaps strength is more a function of training than traditionally has been believed.

The compatibility theory also has some problems. It suggests that labor is divided to conform to the requirements of child care. But sometimes it seems the other way around. For example, women who spend a good deal of time in agricultural work outside the home often ask others to watch and feed their infants while they are unavailable to nurse.[17] Consider, too, the mountain areas of Nepal, where agricultural work is incompatible with child care; heavy loads must be carried up and down steep slopes, fields are far apart, and labor takes up most of the day. Yet women do this work anyway and leave their infants with others for long stretches of time.[18]

Furthermore, in some societies, women hunt—one of the activities most incompatible with child care and generally not done by women. Many Agta women of the Philippines regularly hunt wild pig and deer; women alone or in groups kill almost 30 percent of the large game.[19] Women take nursing babies on hunting trips, and the women who hunt do not have lower reproductive rates than the women who choose not to hunt. Agta women may find it possible to hunt because the hunting grounds are only about a half hour from camp, the dogs that accompany the women assist in the hunting and protect the women and babies, and the women generally hunt in groups, so others can help carry babies as well as carcasses. Hunting by women is also fairly common among the Aka, forest foragers in the Central African Republic. Aka women participate in and sometimes lead in organizing cooperative net-hunting, in which an area is circled and animals are flushed out and caught in nets. Women spend approximately 18 percent of their time net-hunting, which is more than men do.[20] In the Canadian subarctic, teams of Chipewyan women would hunt small animals such as muskrats or rabbits, and would commonly join their husbands to hunt large animals such as moose. Women did not participate in long-distance hunts,[21] which also suggests that compatibility with child care was a consideration.

As the cases just described suggest, we need to know a lot more about labor requirements. More precisely, we need to know exactly how much strength is required in particular tasks, how dangerous those tasks are, and whether a person could stop working at a task to care for a child. So far, we have mostly guesses. When there is more systematically collected evidence on aspects of particular tasks, we will be in a better position to evaluate the various theories. In any case, none of the available theories implies that the worldwide patterns of division of labor shown in Table 1 will persist. As we know from our own and other industrial societies, a strict gender division of labor begins to disappear when machines replace human strength, when women have fewer children, and when women can assign child care to others.

Relative Contributions to Work

In the United States, there is a tendency to equate "work" with a job earning income. Until relatively recently, being a "homemaker" was not counted as an occupation. Anthropologists also tended to ignore household work; indeed, most of the research on division of labor by gender focuses on **primary subsistence activities**—gathering, hunting, fishing, herding, and farming—and relatively less attention is paid to gender contributions to **secondary subsistence activities**, those that involve the processing and preparation of food for eating or storing.

Overall Work

If we count all the kinds of economic activities shown in Table 1, women typically work more total hours per day than men in intensive agricultural and horticultural societies.[22] We do not know if this is a truly cross-cultural universal. However, we do know that, in many societies where women earn wages, they are still responsible for the bulk of the household work as well as the child care at home.

Subsistence Work

If we focus on contribution to primary subsistence activities, which are generally located further from the home, female and male contributions are more variable cross-culturally. Estimates of time actually working are not generally available, so most comparisons estimate how much each gender contributes to the diet in terms of caloric intake from primary subsistence activities.

In some societies, women have traditionally contributed more to the economy than men by any measure. For example, among the Tchambuli of New Guinea in the 1930s, the women did all the fishing—going out early in the morning by canoe to their fish traps and returning when the sun was hot. Some of the catch was traded for sago (a starch) and sugarcane, and it was the women who went on the long canoe trips to do the trading.[23]

In contrast, men did almost all of the primary subsistence work among the Toda of India. As they were described early in the 20th century, they depended for subsistence almost entirely on the dairy products of their water buffalo, either by using the products directly or by selling them for grain. Women were not allowed to have anything to do with dairy work; only men tended the buffalo and prepared the dairy products. Women's work was largely household work. Women prepared the purchased grain for cooking, cleaned house, and decorated clothing.[24]

A survey of a wide variety of societies has revealed that both women and men contribute a good deal to primary food-getting activities, but men usually contribute more in most societies.[25] Because women are almost always occupied with infant and child care responsibilities, it is not surprising that men usually do most of the primary subsistence work, which generally has to be done away from the home.

Some of the variation is explained by the type of food-getting activities in the society. In societies that depend on hunting, fishing, and herding for most of their calories—generally male activities—men usually contribute more than women.[26] For example, among the Inuit who traditionally depended mostly on hunting and fishing, as well as among the Toda who depended mostly on herding, men did most of the primary subsistence work. In societies that depend on gathering, primarily women's work, women tend to do most of the food-getting.[27] The San are an example. But the predominant type of food-getting is not always predictive. For example, among the Tchambuli who depended mostly on fishing, women did most of the work. Most societies depend upon some form of food production, rather than foraging. With the exception of clearing land, preparing the soil, and herding large animals, which are usually men's tasks, men, women, or both do the work of planting, crop tending (weeding, irrigating), and harvesting (see Table 1). So we need some explanation of why women do most of the farming work in some societies but men do it in others. Different patterns predominate in different areas of the world. In Africa, south of the Sahara, women generally do most of the farming. In much of Asia and Europe and the areas around the Mediterranean, men do more.[28]

The type of agriculture may help explain some of the variation. Many have pointed out that men's contribution to primary subsistence tends to be much higher than women's in intensive agricultural societies, particularly with plow agriculture. In contrast, women's contribution is relatively high compared with men's and sometimes higher in horticultural societies. According to Ester Boserup, when population increases and there is pressure to make more intensive use of the land, cultivators begin to use the plow and irrigation, and males start to do more.[29] But it is not clear why.

Why should women not contribute a lot to farming just because plows are used? In trying to answer this question, most researchers shift to considering how much time males and females spend in various farming tasks, rather than estimating the total caloric contribution of females versus males. The reason for this shift is that gender contribution to farming varies substantially over the various phases of the production sequence, as well as from one crop to another. Thus, the total amount of time females versus males work at farming tasks is easier to estimate than how much each gender contributes to the diet in terms of calories. How would caloric contribution be judged, for example, if men do the clearing and plowing, women do the planting and weeding, and both do the harvesting?

Perhaps plow agriculture increases male contribution to subsistence because plowing takes longer and minimizes weeding time. Cross-culturally, men usually clear land. It has been estimated that, in one district in Nigeria, 100 days of work are required to clear one acre of virgin land for plowing by tractor; only 20 days are required to prepare the land for shifting cultivation.

Grinding corn is very time-consuming hard work. A woman in the highlands of Guatemala is grinding corn for tortillas.

Weeding is a task that probably can be combined with child care, and perhaps women may have mostly performed it previously for that reason.[30] But the fact that men do the plowing, which may take a lot of time, does not explain why women do relatively fewer farming tasks, including weeding, in societies that have the plow.[31]

Another explanation is that household chores increase substantially with intensive agriculture and limit the time women can spend in the fields. Intensive agriculturalists rely heavily on grain crops (such as corn, wheat, and oats) that are usually dried before storing. To make these dried foods edible, they either have to be cooked in water for a long time or they have to be processed first to make cooking faster. Cooking usually requires collecting water and firewood, neither usually close by, and both tasks are usually done by women. In addition, there is more cleaning of pots and utensils. Soaking, grinding, or pounding can reduce cooking time for hard grains, but the process that speeds up cooking the most—grinding—is itself very time-consuming unless done by machine.[32] Finally, household work may increase substantially with intensive agriculture because women in such societies have *more* children than women in horticultural societies.[33] If household work increases in these ways, it is easy to understand why women cannot contribute more time than men, or as much time as men, to intensive agriculture. But women's contribution, although less than men's, is nonetheless substantial; they seem to work outside the home 4½ hours a day, 7 days a week, on the average.[34]

We still have not explained why women contribute so much to horticulture in the first place. They may not have as much household work as intensive agricultural women, but neither do the men. Why, then, don't men do relatively more in horticulture also? Men in horticultural societies are often drawn away from cultivation into other types of activities. One of the most common is warfare, in which all able-bodied men are expected to participate. There is evidence that, if males are engaged in warfare when primary subsistence work has to be done, the women must do that subsistence work.[35] Men may also be withdrawn from primary subsistence work if they have to work in distant towns and cities for wages or if they periodically go on long-distance trading trips.[36]

When women contribute a lot to primary food-getting activities, we might expect effects on their childrearing. Several cross-cultural studies suggest that this expectation is correct. In societies with a high female contribution to primary subsistence (in terms of contributing calories), infants are fed solid foods earlier (so that other people besides mothers can feed them) than in societies with a low female contribution.[37] Girls are likely to be trained to be industrious (probably to help their mothers), and girl babies are more valued.[38]

Political Leadership and Warfare

In almost every known society, men rather than women are generally the leaders in the political arena. One cross-cultural survey found that, in about 88 percent of the surveyed societies, only men were leaders. In 10 percent of societies in which some women occupied leadership positions, the women were either outnumbered by or less powerful than the male leaders.[39] In the remaining 2 percent, leadership was fairly evenly distributed between men and women. If we look at countries, not cultures, women on the average make up only around 16 percent of the representatives in national parliaments or legislative bodies.[40] Whether or not we consider warfare to be part of the political sphere of life, we find an almost universal dominance of males in that arena. In 87 percent of the world's societies, women never participate actively in war.[41]

Even in *matrilineal* societies, which seem to be oriented around women, men usually occupy formal political positions. Among the Iroquois of what is now New York State, women had control over resources, but men, not women, held political office. The highest political body among the League of the Iroquois, which comprised five societies, was a council of 50 male chiefs. Nonetheless, women could nominate, elect, and impeach their male representatives. Women also could decide between life and death for prisoners of war, forbid the men of their households to go to war, and intervene to bring about peace.[42]

Women in some societies engage in combat, as this Israeli helicopter gunner does.

Why have men (at least so far) almost always dominated the political sphere of life? Some scholars have suggested that men's role in warfare gives them the edge in all kinds of political leadership, particularly because they control weapons, an important resource.[43] But evidence suggests that force is rarely used to obtain leadership positions;[44] superior strength is not the deciding factor. Still, warfare may be related to political leadership for another reason. Warfare clearly affects survival, and it occurs regularly in most societies. Therefore, decision making about war may be among the most important kinds of politics in most societies. If so, then the people who know the most about warfare should be making the decisions about it.

To explain why males and not females usually engage in fighting, let us refer to three of the possible explanations of the worldwide patterns in the gender division of labor. Warfare, like hunting, probably requires strength (for throwing weapons) and quick bursts of energy (for running). And certainly combat is one of the most dangerous and uninterruptible activities imaginable, hardly compatible with child care. Also, even if they do not at the time have children, women may generally be kept out of combat because their potential fertility is more important to a population's reproduction and survival than their potential usefulness as warriors.[45] So the strength theory, the compatibility theory, and the expendability theory might all explain the predominance of men in warfare.

Two other factors may be involved in male predominance in politics. One is the generally greater height of men. Why height should be a factor in leadership is unclear, but studies suggest that taller people are more likely to be leaders.[46] Finally, there is the possibility that men dominate politics because they get around more in the outside world than do women. Men's activities typically take them farther from home; women tend to work more around the home. If societies choose leaders at least in part because of what they know about the larger world, then men will generally have some advantage. In support of this reasoning, Patricia Draper found that, in settled San groups, women no longer engaged in long-distance gathering, and they seemed to have lost much of their former influence in decision making.[47] Involvement in child care may also detract from influence in decision making. In a study of village leadership among the Kayapo of Brazil, Dennis Werner found that women with heavy child care burdens were less influential than women not as involved in child care; he suggests that they had fewer friends and missed many details of what was going on in the village.[48]

These various explanations suggest why men generally dominate politics, but we still need to explain why women participate in politics more in some societies than in others. Marc Ross investigated this question in a cross-cultural survey of 90 societies.[49] In that sample, the degree of female participation in politics varied considerably. For example, among the Mende of Sierra Leone, women regularly held high office, but among the Azande of Zaire, women took no part in public life. One factor that predicts the exclusion of women from politics is the organization of communities around male kin. When they marry, women usually have to leave their communities and move to their husband's place. If women are "strangers" in a community with many related males, then the males will have political advantages because of their knowledge of community members and past events.

The Relative Status of Women

There are probably as many definitions of status as there are researchers interested in the topic. To some, the relative status of the sexes means how much importance society confers on females versus males. To others, it means how much power and authority men and women have relative to each other. And to still others, it means what kinds of rights women and men possess to do what they want to do. In any case, many social scientists ask why the status of women appears to vary from one society to another. Why do women have few rights and little influence in some societies and more of each in other societies? In other words, why is there variation in degree of **gender stratification**?

In the small Iraqi town of Daghara, women and men live very separate lives.[50] In many respects, women appear to have very little status. Like women in some other parts of the Islamic world, women in Daghara live their lives mostly in seclusion, staying in their houses and interior courtyards. If women must go out, which they can do only with male approval, they must shroud their faces and bodies in long black cloaks. These cloaks must be worn in mixed company, even at home. Women are essentially excluded from political activities. Legally, they are considered to be under the authority of their fathers and husbands. Even the sexuality of women is controlled. There is strict emphasis on virginity before marriage. Because women are not permitted even casual conversations with strange men, the possibilities for extramarital or even premarital relationships are very slight. In contrast, hardly any sexual restrictions are imposed on men.

But some societies such as the Mbuti seem to approach equal status for males and females. Like most food collectors, the Mbuti have no formal political organization to make decisions or to settle disputes. Public disputes occur, and both women and men take part in the uproar that is part of such disputes. Not only do women make their positions known, but their opinions are often heeded. Even in domestic quarrels involving physical violence between husband and wife, others usually intervene to stop them, regardless of who hit whom first.[51] Women control the use of dwellings; they usually have equal say over the disposal of resources they or the men collect, over the upbringing of their children, and about whom their children should marry. One of the few signs of inequality is that women are somewhat more restricted than men with respect to extramarital sex.[52]

There are many theories about why women have relatively high or low status. One of the most common is that women's status will be high when they contribute substantially to primary subsistence activities. This theory would predict that women should have very little status when food-getting depends largely on hunting, herding, or intensive agriculture. A second theory suggests that men will be more valued and esteemed than women where warfare is particularly important. A third theory suggests that men will have higher status where there are centralized political hierarchies. The reasoning in this theory is essentially the same as the reasoning in the warfare theory: Men usually play the dominant role in political behavior, so men's status should be higher wherever political behavior is more important or frequent. Finally, there is the theory that women will have higher status where kin groups and couples' places of residence after marriage are organized around women.

One of the problems in evaluating these theories is that decisions have to be made about the meaning of *status*. Does it mean value? Rights? Influence? And do all these aspects of status vary together? Cross-cultural research by Martin Whyte suggests that they do not. For each sample society in his study, Whyte rated 52 items that might be used to define the relative status of the sexes. These items included such things as which sex can inherit property, who has final authority over disciplining unmarried children, and whether the gods in the society are male, female, or both. The results of the study indicate that very few of these items are related. Therefore, Whyte concluded, we cannot talk about status as a single concept. Rather, it seems more appropriate to talk about the relative status of women in different spheres of life.[53]

Women as well as men serve on political councils in many Coast Salish communities. Here, we see a swearing-in ceremony for the Special Chiefs' Council in Sardis, British Columbia.

Even though Whyte found no necessary connection between one aspect of status and another, he decided to ask whether some of the theories correctly predict why some societies have many, as opposed to few, areas in which the status of women is high. Let us turn first to the ideas *not* supported by the available cross-cultural evidence. The idea that generally high status stems from a greater caloric contribution to primary subsistence activities is not supported.[54] For example, women seem to have higher status the more a society depends on hunting, but women do little of the primary subsistence work in hunting societies. And it is commonly thought that warfare should bolster male status, but there is no consistent evidence that a high frequency of warfare generally lowers women's status in different spheres of life.[55]

What does predict higher status for women in many areas of life? Although the results are not strong, there is some support in Whyte's study for the theory that women have somewhat higher status where kin groups and marital residence are organized around women. The Iroquois are a good example. Even though Iroquois women could not hold formal political office, they had considerable authority within and beyond the household. Related women lived together in longhouses with husbands who belonged to other kin groups. In the longhouse, the women's authority was clear, and they could ask objectionable men to leave. The women controlled the allocation of the food they produced. Allocation could influence the timing of war parties because men could not undertake a raid without provisions. Women were involved in the selection of religious leaders, half of whom were women. Even in politics, although women could not speak or serve on the council, they largely controlled the selection of councilmen and could institute impeachment proceedings against those to whom they objected.[56]

In preindustrial societies, women have generally lower status in societies with more political hierarchy.[57] Lower status for women is also associated with other indicators of cultural complexity—social stratification, plow and irrigation agriculture, large settlements, private property, and craft specialization. Only one type of influence for women increases with cultural complexity: informal influence. However, informal influence may simply reflect a lack of *real* influence.[58] Why cultural complexity in preindustrial societies is associated with women having less authority in the home, less control over property, and more restricted sexual lives is not yet understood. However, the relationship between cultural complexity and gender equality appears to be reversed in industrial and postindustrial societies. Judging by a comparative study of gender attitudes in 61 countries, it seems that countries relying on agriculture such as Nigeria and Peru have the least favorable attitudes toward gender equality, industrial societies such as Russia and Taiwan have moderately favorable attitudes, and postindustrial societies such as Sweden and the United States have the most favorable attitudes toward gender equality.[59]

Western colonialism appears to have been generally detrimental to women's status. Although the relative status of men and women may not have been equal before the Europeans arrived, colonial influences seem generally to have undermined the position of women. There are plenty of examples of Europeans restructuring landownership around men and teaching men modern farming techniques, even in places where women were usually the farmers. In addition, men more often than women could earn cash through wage labor or through sales of goods (such as furs) to Europeans.[60] We are beginning to understand some of the conditions that may enhance or decrease certain aspects of women's status. If we can understand which of these conditions are most important, society may be able to reduce gender inequality if it wants to.[61]

ANTHROPOLOGY ● ● ● ● ● ● ●

Economic Development and Women's Status

Based on the writings of Ester Boserup and subsequent scholarship on women in development, the prevailing opinion was that development usually made things worse for women. Development agents commonly targeted men for learning new technology and how to produce crops for sale. Today, women in developing countries are still largely left out and women still face difficulties, but recent research has documented how women often find creative solutions to participating in commercial enterprises. In many cases, involvement in commercial activity leads to improvement in women's lives, at least as judged from material and status benefits they receive. Producing for a market might range in scale from raising a few extra pigs for sale in southwestern China, to more complex involvement such as contract farming for crop exports in Kenya, or market trading in Ghana.

Some of the creative strategies women use in Kenya to get around their structural disadvantages include buying or renting land with their proceeds, "pooling" small pieces of land to meet minimum requirements for commercial growers, joining women's rotating credit associations, and looking to the private sector for training and materials for contract agriculture.

Almost everywhere, women in developing countries use money from their commercial enterprise to purchase things for their households. At first the money might go to food purchases, household goods, and education for their children. If their incomes or savings grow, women may pay for large appliances, furniture, and farm machinery and vehicles. Women, in contrast to men, tend to plow all their earnings into household expenditures.

Most of these recent studies suggest that bringing money into the household generally translates into lasting changes, including increased educational opportunities, greater say in household decisions, and higher social status in the community.

Some opportunities for women open up when men move into other domains. For example, among the Asante of Ghana, many men moved out of market trading to take advantage of more lucrative cocoa production. Women had long been traders along with men, but with the departure of men, women took over many of men's former market niches and began to engage in longer-distance trade. And, in Kenya, male migration has increased the number of women who manage the farm and head households.

The places we have discussed so far are largely agricultural. Women's work is primarily in or near the household. Commercial involvement gets women more into the public sector. But what about industrial societies, where only a small proportion of people engage in farming? According to a survey of 61 countries, gender equality is more favored in industrializing countries than in agricultural societies. With industrialization, infant and child mortality decline, lessening the pressure on women to reproduce. Perhaps this frees them to pursue education and work outside the home. Postindustrial countries, with even lower fertility rates, are even more accepting of gender equality. As women learn more and get out in the world more, gender inequality appears to decline.

Sources: Bossen 2000; G. Clark 2000; Doyle 2005; Spring 2000a; 2000b; 2000c.

Personality Differences

Much of the research on gender differences in personality has taken place in the United States and other Western countries where psychology is a major field of study. Although such studies are informative, they do not tell us whether the observed differences hold true in cultures very different from our own. Fortunately, we now have systematic observational studies for various non-Western societies. These studies recorded the minute details of behavior of substantial numbers of males and females. Any conclusions about female–male differences in aggressiveness, for example, are based on actual counts of the number of times a particular individual tried to hurt or injure another person during a given amount of observation time. Almost all of these differences are subtle and a matter of degree, not a matter of a behavior being present or absent in females or males.

Which differences in personality are suggested by these systematic studies? Most of them have observed children in different cultural settings. The most consistent difference is in the area of aggression; boys try to hurt others more frequently than girls do. In an extensive comparative study of children's behavior, the Six Cultures project, this difference showed up as early as 3–6 years of age.[62] In the Six Cultures project, six different research teams observed children's behavior in Kenya (among the Gusii), Mexico, India, the Philippines, Okinawa, and the United States. A more recent cross-cultural comparison of four other cultures (the Logoli of Kenya, Nepal, Belize, and American Samoa) supports the sex difference in aggression.[63] Studies in the United States are consistent with the cross-cultural findings: In a large number of observation and experimental studies, boys exhibited more aggression than girls.[64]

Other female–male differences have turned up with considerable consistency, but we have to be cautious in accepting them, either because they have not been documented as well or because there are more exceptions. There seems to be a tendency for girls to exhibit more responsible behavior, including nurturance (trying to help others). Girls seem more likely to conform to adult wishes and commands. Boys try more often to exert dominance over others to get their own way. In play, boys and girls show a preference for their own gender. Boys seem to play in large groups, girls in small ones. And boys seem to maintain more distance between each other than girls do.[65]

If we assume that these differences are consistent across cultures, how can we explain them? Many writers and researchers believe that because certain female–male differences are so consistent, they are probably rooted in the biological differences between the two sexes. Aggression is one of the traits talked about most often in this connection, particularly because this male–female difference appears so early in life.[66] But an alternative argument is that societies bring up boys and girls differently because they almost universally require adult males and females to perform different types of roles. If most societies expect adult males to be warriors or to be prepared to be warriors, shouldn't we expect most societies to encourage or idealize aggression in males? And if females are almost always the caretakers of infants, shouldn't we also expect societies generally to encourage nurturant behaviors in females?

Researchers tend to adopt either the biological or the socialization view, but it is possible that both kinds of causes are important in the development of gender differences. For example, parents might turn a slight genetic difference into a large gender difference by maximizing that difference in the way they socialize boys versus girls.

It is difficult for researchers to distinguish the influence of genes and other biological conditions from the influence of socialization. We have research indicating that parents treat boy and girl infants differently as early as birth.[67] In spite of the fact that objective observers can see no major "personality" differences between girl and boy infants, parents often claim to.[68] But parents may unconsciously want to see differences and may therefore produce them in socialization. So even early differences could be learned rather than genetic. Remember, too, that researchers cannot do experiments with people; for example, parents' behavior cannot be manipulated to find out what would happen if boys and girls were treated in exactly the same ways.

However, there is considerable experimental research on aggression in nonhuman animals. These experiments suggest that the hormone androgen is partly responsible for higher levels of aggression. For example, in some experiments, females injected with androgen at about the time the sexual organs develop (before or shortly after birth) behave more aggressively when they are older than do females without the hormone. These results may or may not apply to humans, of course, but some researchers have investigated human females who were "androgenized" in the womb because of drugs given to their mothers to prevent miscarriage. By and large, the results of these studies are similar to the experimental studies—androgenized human females show similar patterns of higher aggression.[69] Some scholars take these results to indicate that biological differences between males and females are responsible for the male–female difference in aggression;[70] others suggest that even these results are not conclusive because females who get more androgen show generally disturbed metabolic systems, and general metabolic disturbance may itself increase aggressiveness. Furthermore, androgen-injected females may look more like males because they develop male-like genitals; therefore, they may be treated like males.[71]

Is there any evidence that socialization differences may account for differences in aggression? Although a cross-cultural survey of ethnographers' reports on 101 societies does show that more societies encourage aggression in boys than in girls, most societies show no difference in aggression training.[72] The few societies that do show differences in aggression training can hardly account for the widespread sex differences in actual aggressiveness. But the survey does not necessarily mean that there are no consistent differences in aggression training for boys and girls. All it shows is that there are no *obvious* differences. For all we know, the learning of aggression and other "masculine" traits by boys could be produced by subtle types of socialization.

One possible type of subtle socialization that could create gender differences in behavior is the chores children are assigned. It is possible that little boys and girls learn to behave differently because their parents ask them to do different kinds of work. Beatrice and John Whiting reported from the Six Cultures project that, in societies where children were asked to do a great deal of work, they generally showed more responsible and nurturant behavior. Because girls are almost always asked to do more work than boys, they may be more responsible and nurturant for this reason alone.[73] If this reasoning is correct, we should find that, if boys are asked to do girls' work, they will learn to behave more like girls.

A study of Luo children in Kenya by Carol Ember supports this view.[74] Girls were usually asked to babysit, cook, clean house, and fetch water and firewood. Boys were usually asked to do very little because boys' traditional work was herding cattle, and most families in the community studied had few cattle. But for some reason, more boys than girls had been born, and many mothers without girls at home asked their sons to do girls' chores. Systematic behavior observations showed that much of the behavior of the boys who did girls' work was intermediary between the behavior of other boys and the behavior of girls. The boys who did girls' work were more like girls in that they were less aggressive, less domineering, and more responsible than other boys, even when they weren't working. So it is possible that task assignment has an important influence on how boys and girls learn to behave. These and other subtle forms of socialization need to be investigated more thoroughly.

Misconceptions about Differences in Behavior

Before we leave the subject of behavior differences, we should note some widespread beliefs about them that research does not support. Some of these mistaken beliefs are that girls are more dependent than boys, that girls are more sociable, and that girls are more passive. The results obtained by the Six Cultures project cast doubt on all these notions.[75] First, if we think of dependency as seeking help and emotional support from others, girls are generally no more likely to behave this way than boys. To be sure, the results do indicate that boys and girls have somewhat

Cross-culturally, girls more often play in small, intimate groups, boys in larger groups.

different styles of dependency. Girls more often seek help and contact; boys more often seek attention and approval. As for sociability, which means seeking and offering friendship, the Six Cultures results showed no reliable differences between the sexes. Of course, boys and girls may be sociable in different ways because boys generally play in larger groups than girls. As for the supposed passivity of girls, the evidence is also not particularly convincing. Girls in the Six Cultures project did not consistently withdraw from aggressive attacks or comply with unreasonable demands. The only thing that emerged as a female–male difference was that older girls were less likely than boys to respond to aggression with aggression. But this finding may not reflect passivity as much as the fact that girls are less aggressive than boys, which we already knew.

So some of our common ideas about female–male differences are unfounded. Others, such as those dealing with aggression and responsibility, cannot be readily dismissed and should be investigated further.

As we noted, an observed difference in aggression does not mean that males are aggressive and females are not. Perhaps because males are generally more aggressive, aggression in females has been studied less often. For that reason, Victoria Burbank focused on female aggression in an Australian aborigine community she calls Mangrove. During the 18 months that she was there, Burbank observed some act of aggression almost every other day. Consistent with the cross-cultural evidence, men initiated aggression more often than women, but women were initiators about 43 percent of the time. The women of Mangrove engaged in almost all the same kinds of aggression as men did, including fighting, except that it tended not to be as lethal as male violence. Men most often used lethal weapons; when women fought with weapons, they mostly used sticks, not spears, guns, or knives. Burbank points out that, in contrast to Western cultures, female aggression is not viewed as unnatural or deviant but rather as a natural expression of anger.[76]

Sexuality

In view of the way the human species reproduces, it is not surprising that sexuality is part of our nature. But no society we know of leaves sexuality to nature; all have at least some rules governing "proper" conduct. There is much variation from one society to another in the degree of sexual activity permitted or encouraged before marriage, outside marriage, and even within marriage. And societies vary markedly in their tolerance of nonheterosexual sexuality.

Cultural Regulations of Sexuality: Permissiveness versus Restrictiveness

All societies seek to regulate sexual activity to some degree, and there is a lot of variation cross-culturally. Some societies allow premarital sex; others forbid it. The same is true for extramarital sex. In addition, a society's degree of restrictiveness is not always consistent throughout the life span or for all aspects of sex. For example, a number of societies ease sexual restrictions somewhat for adolescents, and many become more restrictive for adults.[77] Then, too, societies change over time. The United States has traditionally been restrictive, but until recently—before the emergence of the AIDS epidemic—more permissive attitudes were gaining acceptance.

Premarital Sex The degree to which sex before marriage is approved or disapproved of varies greatly from society to society. The Trobriand Islanders, for example, approved of and encouraged premarital sex, seeing it as an important preparation for later marriage roles. Both girls and boys were given complete instruction in all forms of sexual expression at the onset of puberty and were allowed plenty of opportunity for intimacy. Some societies not only allow premarital sex on a casual basis but specifically encourage trial marriages between adolescents. Among the Ila-speaking peoples of central Africa, at harvest time, girls were given houses of their own where they could play at being wife with the boys of their choice.[78]

On the other hand, premarital sex was discouraged in many societies. For example, among the Tepoztlan Indians of Mexico, a girl's life became "crabbed, cribbed, confined" from the time of her first menstruation. She was not to speak to or encourage boys in the least way. To do so would be to court disgrace, to show herself to be crazy. The responsibility of guarding the chastity and reputation of one or more daughters of marriageable age was often a burden for the mother. One mother said she wished her 15-year-old daughter would marry soon because it was inconvenient to "spy" on her all the time.[79] In many Muslim societies, a girl's premarital chastity was tested after her marriage. After the wedding night, blood-stained sheets were displayed as proof of the bride's virginity.

Cultures do not remain the same; attitudes and practices can change markedly over time, as in the United States. In the past, sex was generally delayed until after marriage; in the 1990s, most Americans accepted or approved of premarital sex.[80]

Sex in Marriage In most societies, some form of face-to-face sexual intercourse or coitus is the usual pattern, most preferring the woman on her back and the man on top. Couples in most cultures prefer privacy. This is easier in societies with single-family dwellings or separate rooms, but privacy is difficult to attain in the house in societies with unpartitioned dwellings and multiple families living there. For example, the Siriono of Bolivia had as many as 50 hammocks 10 feet apart in their houses. Not surprisingly, couples in such societies prefer to have sex outdoors in a secluded location.[81]

Night is often preferred for sex, but some cultures specifically opted for day. For example, the Chenchu of India believed that a child conceived at night might be born blind. In some societies, couples engage in sex quickly with little or no foreplay; in others, foreplay may take hours.[82] Attitudes toward marital sex and the frequency of it vary widely from culture to culture. In one cross-cultural survey, frequent marital sex is generally viewed as a good thing, but frequent sex is viewed as undesirable, causing weakness, illness, and sometimes death in 9 percent of the societies.[83] People in most societies abstain from intercourse during menstruation, during at least part of pregnancy, and for a period after childbirth. Some societies prohibit sexual relations before various activities, such as hunting, fighting, planting, brewing, and iron smelting. Our own society is among the most lenient regarding restrictions on intercourse within marriage, imposing only rather loose restraints during mourning, menstruation, and pregnancy.[84]

Extramarital Sex Extramarital sex is not uncommon in many societies. In about 69 percent of the world's societies, men have extramarital sex more than occasionally, and in about 57 percent of the societies women do so. The frequency of such sexual activity is higher than we might expect, given that only a slight majority of societies say they allow extramarital sex for men, and only a small number (11 percent) say they allow it for women.[85]

In quite a few societies, then, there is quite a difference between the restrictive code and actual practice. The Navajo of the 1940s were said to forbid adultery, but young married men under the age of 30 had about a quarter of their heterosexual contacts with women other than their wives.[86] And although people in the United States in the 1970s almost overwhelmingly rejected extramarital sex, 41 percent of married men and about 18 percent of married women had had extramarital sex. In the 1990s, proportionately more men and women reported that they had been faithful to their spouses.[87] Cross-culturally, most societies have a double standard with regard to men and women, with restrictions considerably greater for women.[88] A substantial number of societies openly accept extramarital relationships. The Chukchee of Siberia, who often traveled long distances, allowed a married man to engage in sex with his host's wife, with the understanding that he would offer the same hospitality when the host visited him.[89]

Although a society may allow extramarital sex, a recent cross-cultural study of individual reactions to extramarital sex finds that men and women try a variety of strategies to curtail such sex. Men are much more likely than women to resort to physical violence against their wives; women are more likely to distance themselves from their husbands. Gossip may be employed to shame the relationship and a higher authority may be asked to intervene in more complex societies. The researchers conclude that married women and men universally consider extramarital sex inappropriate, even in societies that permit it sometimes.[90]

Some cultures are more relaxed about sexuality than others. Does public sculpture reflect that? A park in Oslo, Norway, is dedicated to sculptures by Gustav Vigeland.

Sex and Gender

Homosexuality When most anthropologists discuss homosexuality, they usually refer to sex between males or sex between females. But although the biological male–female dichotomy corresponds to the gender male–female dichotomy in the West, other societies do not have the same gender concepts, so that the meaning of homosexuality may be different in different societies. For example, the Navajo of the American Southwest traditionally recognized four genders. Only relationships between people of the same gender would be considered homosexual, and they considered such relationships inappropriate.[91] Biologically speaking, some of the cross-gender relationships would be considered homosexual in the Western view. Most of the research to date has adopted the biological view that homosexuality is between people of the same biological sex.

The range in permissiveness or restrictiveness toward homosexual relations is as great as that for any other kind of sexual activity. Among the Lepcha of the Himalayas, a man was believed to become homosexual if he ate the flesh of an uncastrated pig. But the Lepcha said that homosexual behavior was practically unheard of, and they viewed it with disgust.[92] Perhaps because many societies deny that homosexuality exists, little is known about homosexual practices in the restrictive societies. Among the permissive ones, there is variation in the type and pervasiveness of homosexuality. In some societies, homosexuality is accepted but limited to certain times and certain individuals. For example, among the Papago of the southwestern United States, there were "nights of saturnalia" in which homosexual tendencies could be expressed. The Papago also had many male transvestites who wore women's clothing, did women's chores, and, if not married, could be visited by men.[93] A woman did not have the same freedom of expression. She could participate in the saturnalia feasts but only with her husband's permission, and female transvestites were nonexistent.

Homosexuality occurs even more widely in other societies. The Berber-speaking Siwans of North Africa expected all males to engage in homosexual relations. In fact, fathers made arrangements for their unmarried sons to be given to an older man in a homosexual arrangement. Siwan custom limited a man to one boy. Fear of the Egyptian government made this a secret matter, but before 1909, such arrangements were made openly. Almost all men were reported to have engaged in a homosexual relationship as boys; later, when they were between 16 and 20, they married girls.[94] Such prescribed homosexual relationships between people of different ages are a common form of homosexuality.[95] Among the most extremely pro-homosexual societies, the Etoro of New Guinea preferred homosexuality to heterosexuality. Heterosexuality was prohibited as many as 260 days a year and was forbidden in or near the house and gardens. Male homosexuality, on the other hand, was not prohibited at any time and was believed to make crops flourish and boys become strong.[96] Even among the Etoro, however, men were expected to marry women after a certain age.[97]

Only recently have researchers paid much attention to erotic relationships between females. Although early studies found relatively few societies with female–female sexual relationships, Evelyn Blackwood located reports of 95 societies with such practices, suggesting that it is more common than previously thought.[98] As with male homosexuality, some societies institutionalize same-sex sexual relationships—the Kaguru of Tanzania have female homosexual relationships between older and younger women as part of their initiation ceremonies, reminiscent of the male–male "mentor" relationships in ancient Greece.

Cross-culturally, it is extremely unusual to find "gays" or exclusive male or female homosexuals. In most societies, males and females are expected to marry, and homosexuality, if tolerated or approved, either occurs as a phase in one's life or occurs along with heterosexuality.[99]

Reasons for Restrictiveness

The research to date suggests that societies that are restrictive with regard to one aspect of heterosexual sex tend to be restrictive with regard to other aspects. Thus, societies that frown on sexual expression by young children also punish premarital and extramarital sex.[100] Furthermore, such societies tend to insist on modesty in clothing and are constrained in their talk about sex.[101] But societies that are generally restrictive about heterosexuality are not necessarily restrictive about homosexuality. Societies restrictive about premarital sex are neither more nor less likely to restrict homosexuality. In the case of extramarital sex, the situation is somewhat different. Societies that have a considerable amount of male homosexuality tend to disapprove of males having extramarital heterosexual relationships.[102] If we are going to explain restrictiveness, then, it appears we have to consider heterosexual and homosexual restrictiveness separately.

Let us consider homosexual restrictiveness first. Research so far has not yielded any clear-cut predictions, although several cross-cultural predictors about male homosexuality are intriguing. One such finding is that societies that forbid abortion and infanticide for married women (most societies permit these practices for illegitimate births) are likely to be intolerant of male homosexuality.[103] This and other findings are consistent with the point of view that homosexuality is less tolerated in societies that would like to increase population. Such societies may be intolerant of all kinds of behaviors that minimize population growth. Homosexuality would have this effect, if we assume that a higher frequency of homosexual relations is associated with a lower frequency of heterosexual relations. The less frequently heterosexual relations occur, the lower the number of conceptions there might be. Another indication that intolerance may be related to a desire for population growth is that societies with famines and severe food shortages are more likely to allow homosexuality. Famines and food shortages suggest population pressure on resources; under these conditions, homosexuality and other practices that minimize population growth may be tolerated or even encouraged.[104] Population pressure may also explain why our own society has become somewhat more tolerant of homosexuality recently. Of course, population pressure does not explain why certain individuals become homosexual or why most individuals in some societies engage in such behavior, but it might explain why some societies view such behavior more or less permissively.

Let us now turn to heterosexual behavior. Greater restrictiveness toward premarital sex tends to occur in more complex societies—societies that have hierarchies of political officials, part-time or full-time craft specialists, cities and towns, and class stratification.[105] It may be that, as social inequality increases and various groups come to have differential wealth, parents become more concerned with preventing their children from marrying "beneath them." Permissiveness toward premarital sexual relationships might lead a person to become attached to someone not considered a desirable marriage partner. Even worse, from the family's point of view, such "unsuitable" sexual liaisons might result in a pregnancy that could make it impossible for a girl to marry "well." Controlling mating, then, may be a way of trying to control property. Consistent with this view is the finding that virginity is emphasized in rank and stratified societies, in which families are likely to exchange goods and money in the course of arranging marriages.[106]

The biological fact that humans depend on sexual reproduction does not by itself help explain why females and males differ in so many ways across cultures, or why societies vary in the way they handle male and female roles. We are only beginning to investigate these questions. When we eventually understand more about how and why females and males are different or the same in roles, personality, and sexuality, we may be better able to decide how much we want the biology of sex to shape our lives.

Sex and Gender

Summary

1. That humans reproduce sexually does not explain why males and females tend to differ in appearance and behavior, and to be treated differently, in all societies.

2. All or nearly all societies assign certain activities to females and other activities to males. These worldwide gender patterns of division of labor may be explained by male–female differences in strength, by differences in compatibility of tasks with child care, or by economy-of-effort considerations and/or the expendability of men.

3. Perhaps because women almost always have infant and child care responsibilities, men in most societies contribute more to primary subsistence activities, in terms of calories. When primary and secondary subsistence work is counted, women typically work more hours than men. In most societies, men are the leaders in the political arena, and warfare is almost exclusively a male activity.

4. The relative status of women compared with that of men seems to vary from one area of life to another. Whether women have relatively high status in one area does not necessarily indicate that they will have high status in another. Less complex societies, however, seem to approach more equal status for males and females in a variety of areas of life.

5. Field studies have suggested some consistent female–male differences in personality: Boys tend to be more aggressive than girls, and girls seem to be more responsible and helpful than boys.

6. Societies that are restrictive toward one aspect of heterosexual sex tend to be restrictive with regard to other aspects. And more complex societies tend to be more restrictive toward premarital heterosexual sex than less complex societies.

7. Societal attitudes toward homosexuality are not completely consistent with attitudes toward sexual relationships between the sexes. Societal tolerance of homosexuality is associated with tolerance of abortion and infanticide and with famines and food shortages.

Glossary Terms

gender differences
gender roles
gender stratification
primary subsistence
  activities

secondary subsistence
  activities
sex differences

Critical Questions

1. Would you expect female–male differences in personality to disappear in a society with complete gender equality in the workplace?
2. Under what circumstances would you expect male–female differences in athletic performance to disappear?
3. What conditions may make the election of a female head of state most likely?

Read the Original Source on myanthrolab.com

Read "Andean Mestizos: Growing Up Female and Male" by Lauris McKee in MyAnthroLibrary and answer the following questions.

1. Which of the Andean Mestizos' ideas about conception, pregnancy, and birth are different from those of your own culture? (Identify your own culture in your answer.)
2. According to McKee, what do the Mestizos say is the reason for the shorter breast-feeding of girls?
3. What are the consequences of the gender difference in breast-feeding? Are the parents aware of these consequences?

Photo Credits

Glossary

Gender differences Differences between females and males that reflect cultural expectations and experiences.

Gender roles Roles that are culturally assigned to genders.

Gender stratification The degree of unequal access by the different genders to prestige, authority, power, rights, and economic resources.

Primary subsistence activities The food-getting activities: gathering, hunting, fishing, herding, and agriculture.

Secondary subsistence activities Activities that involve the preparation and processing of food either to make it edible or to store it.

Sex differences The typical differences between females and males that are most likely due to biological differences.

Notes

1. Leibowitz 1978, 43–44.
2. Chafetz 1990, 28; Epstein 1988, 5–6; Schlegel 1989, 266.
3. Jacobs and Roberts 1989.
4. Segal 2004; Segal also cites the work of W. Williams 1992.
5. Blackwood 1984b; Lang 1999, 93–94.
6. Wikan 1982, 168–86.
7. Stini 1971.
8. Frayer and Wolpoff 1985, 431–32.
9. For reviews of theories and research on sexual dimorphism and possible genetic and cultural determinants of variation in degree of dimorphism over time and place, see Frayer and Wolpoff 1985 and Gray 1985, 201–09, 217–25.
10. J. K. Brown 1970b, 1074.
11. Among the Aché hunter-gatherers of Paraguay, women collect the type of honey produced by stingless bees (men collect other honey); this division of labor is consistent with the compatibility theory. See Hurtado et al. 1985, 23.
12. Byrne 1994; Murdock and Provost 1973, 213.
13. R. O'Brian 1999.
14. D. R. White, Burton, and Brudner 1977, 1–24.
15. Mukhopadhyay and Higgins 1988, 473.
16. J. K. Brown 1970b, 1073–78; D. R. White et al. 1977.
17. Nerlove 1974.
18. N. E. Levine 1988.
19. M. J. Goodman et al. 1985.
20. Noss and Hewlett 2001.
21. Brumbach and Jarvenpa 2006; Jarvenpa and Brumbach 2006.
22. C. R. Ember 1983, 288–89.
23. Mead 1950 [originally published 1935], 180–84.
24. Rivers 1967 [originally published 1906], 567.
25. M. Ember and Ember 1971, 573, Table 1.
26. Schlegel and Barry 1986.
27. Wood and Eagly 2002, 706, drawing on data from H. Kaplan et al. 2000.
28. Boserup 1970, 22–25; see also Schlegel and Barry 1986, 144–45.
29. Boserup 1970, 22–25.
30. Bossen 2000, 31–34.
31. C. R. Ember 1983, 286–87; data from Murdock and Provost 1973, 212; Bradley 1995.
32. C. R. Ember 1983.
33. Ibid.
34. Ibid., 287–93.
35. M. Ember and Ember 1971, 579–80.
36. Ibid., 581; see also Sanday 1973, 1684.
37. Nerlove 1974.
38. Schlegel and Barry 1986.
39. Whyte 1978a, 217.
40. *Human Development Report 2010.*
41. D. B. Adams 1983; Whyte 1978a.
42. J. K. Brown 1970a.
43. Divale and Harris 1976; Sanday 1974.
44. Quinn 1977, 189–90.

45. Graham 1979.
46. D. Werner 1982; Stogdill 1974, cited in Ibid.; see also Handwerker and Crosbie 1982.
47. Draper 1975, 103.
48. D. Werner 1984.
49. M. H. Ross 1986.
50. This description is based on the fieldwork of Elizabeth and Robert Fearnea (1956–1958), as reported in M. K. Martin and Voorhies 1975, 304–31.
51. Begler 1978.
52. Ibid. See also Whyte 1978a, 229–32.
53. Whyte 1978b, 95–120; see also Quinn 1977.
54. Whyte 1978b, 124–29, 145; see also Sanday 1973.
55. Whyte 1978b, 129–30.
56. J. K. Brown 1970a.
57. Whyte 1978b, 135–36.
58. Ibid., 135.
59. Doyle 2005.
60. Quinn 1977, 85; see also Etienne and Leacock 1980, 19–20.
61. Chafetz 1990, 11–19.
62. B. B. Whiting and Edwards 1973.
63. R. L. Munroe et al. 2000, 8–9.
64. Maccoby and Jacklin 1974.
65. For a more extensive discussion of behavior differences and possible explanations of them, see C. R. Ember 1981.
66. B. B. Whiting and Edwards 1973.
67. For references to this research, see C. R. Ember 1981, 559.
68. Rubin, Provenzano, and Haskett 1974.
69. For a discussion of this evidence, see Ellis 1986, 525–27; C. R. Ember 1981.
70. For example, Ellis (1986) considers the evidence for the biological view of aggression "beyond reasonable dispute."
71. For a discussion of other possibilities, see C. R. Ember 1981.
72. Rohner 1976.
73. B. B. Whiting and Whiting 1975; see also B. B. Whiting and Edwards 1988, 273.
74. C. R. Ember 1973, 424–39.
75. B. B. Whiting and Edwards 1973, 175–79; see also Maccoby and Jacklin 1974.
76. Burbank 1994.
77. Heise 1967.
78. C. S. Ford and Beach 1951, 191.
79. O. Lewis 1951, 397.
80. Farley 1996, 60.
81. C. S. Ford and Beach 1951, 23–25, 68–71.
82. Ibid., 40–41, 73.
83. Broude 2009.
84. C. S. Ford and Beach 1951, 82–83.
85. Broude and Greene 1976.
86. Kluckhohn 1948, 101.
87. M. Hunt 1974, 254–57; Lewin 1994.
88. Broude 1980, 184.
89. C. S. Ford and Beach 1951, 114.
90. Jankowiak, Nell, and Buckmaster 2002.
91. Lang 1999, 97, citing Thomas 1993.
92. J. Morris 1938, 191.
93. Underhill 1938, 117, 186.
94. 'Abd Allah 1917, 7, 20.
95. Cardoso and Werner 2004.
96. R. C. Kelly 1974.
97. Cardoso and Werner 2004.
98. Blackwood 1984a; Blackwood and Wieringa 1999, 49.
99. Cardoso and Werner 2004, 207.
100. Data from Textor 1967.
101. W. N. Stephens 1972, 1–28.
102. Broude 1976, 243.
103. D. Werner 1975; 1979.
104. D. Werner 1979, 345–62; see also D. Werner 1975, 36.
105. Data from Textor 1967.
106. Schlegel 1991.

Bibliography

'Abd Allah, Mahmud M. 1917. Siwan customs. *Harvard African Studies* 1:1–28.

Adams, David B. 1983. Why there are so few women warriors. *Behavior Science Research* 18:196–212.

Begler, Elsie B. 1978. Sex, status, and authority in egalitarian society. *American Anthropologist* 80:571–88.

Blackwood, Evelyn. 1984a. *Cross-cultural dimensions of lesbian relations.* Master's thesis, San Francisco State University.

Blackwood, Evelyn. 1984b. Sexuality and gender in certain Native American tribes: The case of cross-gender females. *Signs* 10:27–42.

Blackwood, Evelyn, and Saskia E. Wieringa. 1999. Sapphic shadows: Challenging the silence in the study of sexuality. In *Female desires: Same-sex relations and transgender practices across cultures,* eds. Evelyn Blackwood and Saskia E. Weiringa, 39–63. New York: Columbia University Press.

Boserup, Ester. 1970. *Woman's role in economic development.* New York: St. Martin's Press.

Bossen, Laurel. 2000. Women farmers, small plots, and changing markets in China. In *Women farmers and commercial ventures: Increasing food security in developing countries,* ed. Anita Spring, 171–89. Boulder, CO: Lynne Rienner Press.

Bradley, Candice. 1995. Keeping the soil in good heart: Weeding, women and ecofeminism. In *Ecofeminism,* ed. K. Warren. Bloomington: Indiana University Press.

Broude, Gwen J. 1976. Cross-cultural patterning of some sexual attitudes and practices. *Behavior Science Research* 11:227–62.

Broude, Gwen J. 1980. Extramarital sex norms in cross-cultural perspective. *Behavior Science Research* 15:181–218.

Broude, Gwen J. 2009. Variations in sexual attitudes, norms, and practices. In MyAnthroLibrary, eds. C. R. Ember, M. Ember, and P. N. Peregrine. MyAnthroLibrary.com. Pearson.

Broude, Gwen J., and Sarah J. Greene. 1976. Cross-cultural codes on twenty sexual attitudes and practices. *Ethnology* 15:409–29.

Brown, Judith K. 1970a. Economic organization and the position of women among the Iroquois. *Ethnohistory* 17:151–67.

Brown, Judith K. 1970b. A note on the division of labor by sex. *American Anthropologist* 72:1073–78.

Brumbach, Hetty Jo, and Robert Jarvenpa. 2006. Chipewyan society and gender relations. In *Circumpolar lives and livelihood: A comparative ethnoarchaeology of gender and subsistence,* eds. R. Jarvenpa and H. J. Brumbach, 24–53. Lincoln: University of Nebraska Press.

Byrne, Bryan. 1994. Access to subsistence resources and the sexual division of labor among potters. *Cross-Cultural Research* 28:225–50.

Cardoso, Fernando Luis and Dennis Werner. 2004. Homosexuality. In *Encyclopedia of sex and gender: Men and women in the world's cultures,* vol 1., eds. C. Ember and M. Ember, 204–15. New York: Kluwer Academic/Plenum Press.

Chafetz, Janet Saltzman. 1990. *Gender equity: An integrated theory of stability and change.* Sage Library of Social Research No. 176. Newbury Park, CA: Sage.

Divale, William T., and Marvin Harris. 1976. Population, warfare, and the male supremacist complex. *American Anthropologist* 78:521–38.

Doyle, Rodger. 2005. Leveling the playing field: Economic development helps women pull even with men. *Scientific American* (June):32.

Draper, Patricia. 1975. !Kung women: Contrasts in sexual egalitarianism in foraging and sedentary contexts. In *Toward an anthropology of women,* ed. R. R. Reiter. New York: Monthly Review Press.

Ellis, Lee. 1986. Evidence of neuroandrogenic etiology of sex roles from a combined analysis of human, nonhuman primate and nonprimate mammalian studies. *Personality and Individual Differences* 7:519–52.

Ember, Carol R. 1973. Feminine task assignment and the social behavior of boys. *Ethos* 1:424–39.

Ember, Carol R. 1981. A cross-cultural perspective on sex differences. In *Handbook of cross-cultural human development,* eds. R. H. Munroe, R. L. Munroe, and B. B. Whiting. New York: Garland.

Ember, Carol R. 1983. The relative decline in women's contribution to agriculture with intensification. *American Anthropologist* 85:285–304.

Ember, Melvin, and Carol R. Ember. 1971. The conditions favoring matrilocal versus patrilocal residence. *American Anthropologist* 73:571–94.

Ember, Melvin, and Carol R. Ember. 1979. Male-Female bonding: A cross-species study of mammals and birds. *Behavior Science Research* 14:37–56.

Epstein, Cynthia Fuchs. 1988. *Deceptive distinctions: Sex, gender, and the social order.* New York: Russell Sage Foundation.

Etienne, Mona, and Eleanor Leacock, eds. 1980. *Women and colonization: Anthropological perspectives.* New York: Praeger.

Farley, Reynolds. 1996. *The new American reality: Who we are, how we got here, where we are going.* New York: Russell Sage Foundation.

Ford, Clellan S., and Frank A. Beach. 1951. *Patterns of sexual behavior.* New York: Harper.

Frayer, David W., and Milford H. Wolpoff. 1985. Sexual dimorphism. *Annual Review of Anthropology* 14:429–73.

Goodman, Madeleine J., P. Bion Griffin, Agnes A. Estioko-Griffin, and John S. Grove. 1985. The compatibility of hunting and mothering among the Agta hunter-gatherers of the Philippines. *Sex Roles* 12:1199–209.

Graham, Susan Brandt. 1979. Biology and human social behavior: A response to van den Berghe and Barash. *American Anthropologist* 81:357–60.

Gray, J. Patrick. 1985. *Primate sociobiology.* New Haven, CT: HRAF Press.

Handwerker, W. Penn, and Paul V. Crosbie. 1982. Sex and dominance. *American Anthropologist* 84:97–104.

Heise, David R. 1967. Cultural patterning of sexual socialization. *American Sociological Review* 32:726–39.

Human Development Report 2010. Statistical Tables. http://hdr.undp.org/en/statistics/gii/ (accessed March 12, 2011).

Hunt, Morton. 1974. *Sexual behavior in the 1970s.* Chicago: Playboy Press.

Hurtado, Ana M., Kristen Hawkes, Kim Hill, and Hillard Kaplan. 1985. Female subsistence strategies among the Aché hunter-gatherers of eastern Paraguay. *Human Ecology* 13:1–28.

Jacobs, Sue-Ellen, and Christine Roberts. 1989. Sex, sexuality, gender and gender variance. In *Gender and anthropology,* ed. S. Morgen. Washington, DC: American Anthropological Association.

Jankowiak, William, M. Diane Nell, and Ann Buckmaster. 2002. Managing infidelity: A cross-cultural perspective. *Ethnology* 41:85–101.

Jarvenpa, Robert, and Hetty Jo Brumbach. 2006. Chipewyan hunters: A task differentiation analysis. In *Circumpolar lives and livelihood: A comparative ethnoarchaeology of gender and subsistence,* eds. Robert Jarvenpa and Hetty Jo Brumbach, 54–78. Lincoln: University of Nebraska Press.

Kaplan, Hillard, Kim Hill, Jane Lancaster, and A. Magdalena Hurtado. 2000. A theory of human life history evolution, diet, intelligence, and longevity. *Evolutionary Anthropology* 9:156–84.

Sex and Gender

Kelly, Raymond C. 1974. Witchcraft and sexual relations: An exploration in the social and semantic implications of the structure of belief. Paper presented at the annual meeting of the American Anthropological Association, Mexico City (November).

Kluckhohn, Clyde. 1948. As an anthropologist views it. In *Sex habits of American men*, ed. A. Deutsch. Upper Saddle River, NJ: Prentice Hall.

Lang, Sabine. 1999. Lesbians, men-women and two-spirits: Homosexuality and gender in Native American cultures. In *Female desires: Same-sex relations and transgender practices across cultures*, eds. Evelyn Blackwood and Saskia E. Weiringa, 91–116. New York: Columbia University Press.

Leibowitz, Lila. 1978. *Females, males, families: A biosocial approach*. North Scituate, MA: Duxbury.

Levine, Nancy E. 1988. Women's work and infant feeding: A case from rural Nepal. *Ethnology* 27:231–51.

Lewin, Tamar. 1994. Sex in America: Faithfulness in marriage is overwhelming. *New York Times*, National, October 7, pp. A1, A18.

Lewis, Oscar. 1951. *Life in a Mexican village: Tepoztlan revisited*. Urbana: University of Illinois Press.

Maccoby, Eleanor E., and Carol N. Jacklin. 1974. *The psychology of sex differences*. Stanford, CA: Stanford University Press.

Martin, M. Kay, and Barbara Voorhies. 1975. *Female of the species*. New York: Columbia University Press.

Mead, Margaret. 1950/1935. *Sex and temperament in three primitive societies*. New York: Mentor.

Morris, John. 1938. *Living with Lepchas: A book about the Sikkim Himalayas*. London: Heinemann.

Mukhopadhyay, Carol C., and Patricia J. Higgins. 1988. Anthropological studies of women's status revisited: 1977–1987. *Annual Review of Anthropology* 17:461–95.

Munroe, Robert L., Robert Hulefeld, James M. Rodgers, Damon L. Tomeo, and Steven K. Yamazaki. 2000. Aggression among children in four cultures. *Cross-Cultural Research* 34:3–25.

Murdock, George P., and Caterina Provost. 1973. Factors in the division of labor by sex: A cross-cultural analysis. *Ethnology* 12:203–25.

Nerlove, Sara B. 1974. Women's workload and infant feeding practices: A relationship with demographic implications. *Ethnology* 13:207–14.

Noss, Andrew J., and Barry S. Hewlett. 2001. The contexts of female hunting in central Africa. *American Anthropologist* 103:1024–40.

O'Brian, Robin. 1999. Who weaves and why? Weaving, loom complexity, and trade. *Cross-Cultural Research* 33:30–42.

Quinn, Naomi. 1977. Anthropological studies on women's status. *Annual Review of Anthropology* 6:181–225.

Rivers, William H. R. 1967/1906. *The Todas*. Oosterhout, N.B., The Netherlands: Anthropological Publications.

Roberts, Derek F. 1953. Body weight, race, and climate. *American Journal of Physical Anthropology*, 533–58.

Rohner, Ronald P. 1976. Sex differences in aggression: Phylogenetic and enculturation perspectives. *Ethos* 4:57–72.

Ross, Marc Howard. 1986. Female political participation: A cross-cultural explanation. *American Anthropologist* 88:843–58.

Rubin, Jeffrey Z., F. J. Provenzano, and R. F. Haskett. 1974. The eye of the beholder: Parents' views on the sex of newborns. *American Journal of Orthopsychiatry* 44:512–19.

Sanday, Peggy R. 1973. Toward a theory of the status of women. *American Anthropologist* 75:1682–700.

Sanday, Peggy R. 1974. Female status in the public domain. In *Woman, culture, and society*, eds. M. Z. Rosaldo and L. Lamphere. Stanford, CA: Stanford University Press.

Schlegel, Alice. 1989. Gender issues and cross-cultural research. *Behavior Science Research* 23:265–80.

Schlegel, Alice. 1991. Status, property, and the value on virginity. *American Ethnologist* 18:719–34.

Schlegel, Alice, and Herbert Barry III. 1986. The cultural consequences of female contribution to subsistence. *American Anthropologist* 88:142–50.

Segal, Edwin S. 2004. Cultural constructions of gender. In *Encyclopedia of sex and gender: Men and women in the world's cultures*, vol. 1, eds. C. Ember and M. Ember, 3–10. New York: Kluwer Academic/Plenum Press.

Stephens, William N. 1972. A cross-cultural study of modesty. *Behavior Science Research* 7:1–28.

Stini, William A. 1971. Evolutionary implications of changing nutritional patterns in human populations. *American Anthropologist* 73:1019–30.

Stogdill, Ralph M. 1974. *Handbook of leadership: A survey of theory and research*. New York: Macmillan.

Textor, Robert B., comp. 1967. *A cross-cultural summary*. New Haven, CT: HRAF Press.

Thomas, Wesley. 1993. *A traditional Navajo's perspectives on the cultural construction of gender in the Navajo world*. Paper presented at the University of Frankfurt, Germany. As referred to in Lang 1999.

Underhill, Ruth M. 1938. *Social organization of the Papago Indians*. New York: Columbia University Press.

Werner, Dennis. 1975. *On the societal acceptance or rejection of male homosexuality*. Master's thesis, Hunter College of the City University of New York.

Werner, Dennis. 1979. A cross-cultural perspective on theory and research on male homosexuality. *Journal of Homosexuality* 4:345–62.

Werner, Dennis. 1982. Chiefs and presidents: A comparison of leadership traits in the United States and among the Mekranoti-Kayapo of central Brazil. *Ethos* 10:136–48.

Werner, Dennis. 1984. Child care and influence among the Mekranoti of central Brazil. *Sex Roles* 10:395–404.

White, Douglas R., Michael L. Burton, and Lilyan A. Brudner. 1977. Entailment theory and method: A cross-cultural analysis of the sexual division of labor. *Behavior Science Research* 12:1–24.

Whiting, Beatrice B., and Carolyn Pope Edwards. 1973. A cross-cultural analysis of sex differences in the behavior of children aged three through eleven. *Journal of Social Psychology* 91:171–88.

Whiting, Beatrice B., and Carolyn Pope Edwards (in collaboration with Carol R. Ember, Gerald M. Erchak, Sara Harkness, Robert L. Munroe, Ruth H. Munroe, Sara B. Nerlove, Susan Seymour, Charles M. Super, Thomas S. Weisner, and Martha Wenger). 1988. *Children of different worlds: The formation of social behavior*. Cambridge, MA: Harvard University Press.

Whiting, Beatrice B., and John W. M. Whiting (in collaboration with Richard Longabaugh). 1975. *Children of six cultures: A psycho-cultural analysis*. Cambridge, MA: Harvard University Press.

Whyte, Martin K. 1978a. Cross-cultural codes dealing with the relative status of women. *Ethnology* 17:211–37.

Whyte, Martin K. 1978b. *The status of women in preindustrial societies*. Princeton, NJ: Princeton University Press.

Wikan, Unni. 1982. *Beyond the veil in Arabia*. Baltimore: Johns Hopkins University Press.

Williams, Walter L. 1992. *The spirit and the flesh*. Boston: Beacon Press.

Wood, Wendy, and Alice H. Eagly. 2002. A cross-cultural analysis of the behavior of women and men: Implications for the origins of sex differences. *Psychological Bulletin* 128:699–727.

Social Stratification:
Class, Ethnicity,
and Racism

From Chapter 6 of *Human Culture*, Second Edition. Carol R. Ember, Melvin Ember. Copyright © 2012 by Pearson Education, Inc. All rights reserved.

Social Stratification: Class, Ethnicity, and Racism

A long-enduring value in the United States is the belief that "all men are created equal." These famous words from the American Declaration of Independence do not mean that all people are equal in wealth or status but rather that all (including women nowadays) are supposed to be equal before the law. Equality before the law is the ideal. But the ideal is not always the actuality. Some people have advantages in legal treatment, and they generally also tend to have advantages of other kinds, including economic advantages. Without exception, recent and modern industrial and postindustrial societies such as our own are *socially stratified*—that is, they contain social groups such as families, classes, or ethnic groups that have unequal access to important advantages such as economic resources, power, and prestige.

Hasn't such inequality always existed? Anthropologists, based on firsthand observations of recent societies, would say not. To be sure, even the simplest societies (in the technological sense) have some differences in advantages based on age, ability, or gender—adults have higher status than children, the skilled more than the unskilled, men more than women. But anthropologists would argue that *egalitarian* societies exist where *social groups* (e.g., families) have more or less the same access to rights or advantages. The economic systems of many food collectors and horticulturalists promote equal access to economic resources for all families in the community. Moreover, such societies also tend to emphasize the sharing of food and other goods, which tends to equalize any small inequalities in resources between families. Until about 10,000 years ago, all human societies depended on food they hunted, gathered, and/or fished. And so we might expect that egalitarianism characterized most of human history. That is indeed what archaeologists suggest. Substantial inequality generally appears only with permanent communities, centralized political systems, and intensive agriculture, which are cultural features that began to appear in the world only in the last 10,000 years. Before that time, then, most societies were probably egalitarian. In the world today, egalitarian societies have all but disappeared because of two processes: the global spread of commercial or market exchange and the voluntary or involuntary incorporation of many diverse people into large, centralized political systems. In modern societies, some groups have more advantages than others. These groups may include *ethnic* groups. That is, ethnic diversity is almost always associated with differential access to advantages. When ethnic diversity is also associated with differences in physical features such as skin color, the social stratification may involve *racism,* the belief that some "racial" groups are inferior.

Systems of social stratification are strongly linked to the customary ways in which economic resources are allocated, distributed, and converted through labor into goods and services. So we would not expect much inequality if all people had relatively equal access to economic resources. But stratification cannot be understood solely in terms of economic resources; there are other benefits such as prestige and power that may be unequally distributed. We first examine how societies vary in their systems of stratification. Then we turn to possible explanations of why they vary.

Variation in Degree of Social Inequality

Societies vary in the extent to which social groups, as well as individuals, have unequal access to advantages. Here, we are concerned with differential or unequal access to three types of advantages: (1) wealth or economic resources, (2) power, and (3) prestige. **Economic resources** are things that have value in a culture; they include land, tools and other technology, goods, and money. **Power**, a second and usually related advantage, is the ability to make others do what they do not want to do; power is influence based on the threat of force. When groups in a society have rules or customs that give them unequal access to wealth or resources, they generally also have unequal access to power. So, for example, when we speak of a "company town" in the United States, we are referring to the fact that the company that employs most of the residents of the town usually has considerable control over them. Finally, there is the advantage of **prestige**. When we speak of prestige, we mean that someone or some group is accorded particular respect or honor. Even if it is true that there is always unequal access by individuals to prestige (because of differences in age, gender, or ability), some societies in the ethnographic record have no social groups with unequal access to prestige.

Thus, anthropologists conventionally distinguish three types of society in terms of the degree to which different social groups have unequal access to advantages: *egalitarian, rank,* and *class societies* (see Table 1). Some societies in the ethnographic record do not fit easily into any of these three types; as with any classification scheme, some cases seem to straddle the line between types.[1] **Egalitarian societies** contain no social groups with greater or lesser access to economic resources, power, or prestige. **Rank societies** do not have very unequal access to economic resources or to power, but they do contain social groups with unequal access to prestige. Rank societies, then, are partly stratified. **Class societies** have unequal access to all three advantages—economic resources, power, and prestige.

Egalitarian Societies

Egalitarian societies can be found not only among foragers such as the San, Mbuti, Australian aborigines, Inuit, and Aché, but also among horticulturalists such as the Yanomamö and pastoralists such as the Saami. An important point to keep in mind is that egalitarian does not mean that all people within such societies are the same. There will always be differences among individuals in age and gender and in such abilities or traits as hunting skill, perception, health, creativity, physical prowess, attractiveness, and intelligence. According to Morton Fried, egalitarian means that, within a given society, "there are as many positions of prestige in any given age/sex grade as there are persons capable of filling them."[2] For instance, if a person can achieve high status by fashioning fine spears, and if many people in the society fashion such spears, then many acquire high status as spear makers. If high status is also acquired by carving bones into artifacts, and if only three people are considered expert carvers of bones, then only those three achieve high status as carvers. But the next generation might produce eight spear makers and 20 carvers. In an egalitarian society, the number of prestigious positions is adjusted to fit the number of qualified candidates. We would say, therefore, that such a society is not socially stratified.

TABLE 1 Stratification in Three Types of Societies

| Type of Society | Some Social Groups Have Greater Access To: | | | |
	Economic Resources	Power	Prestige	Examples
Egalitarian	No	No	No	San, Mbuti, Australian aborigines, Inuit, Aché, Yanomamö
Rank	No	No	Yes	Samoans, Tahiti, Trobriand Islanders, Ifaluk
Class/caste	Yes	Yes	Yes	United States, Canada, Greece, India, Inca

Social Stratification: Class, Ethnicity, and Racism

There are, of course, differences in position and prestige arising out of differences in ability. Even in an egalitarian society, differential prestige exists. But, although some people may be better hunters or more skilled artists than others, there is still *equal access* to status positions for people of the same ability. Any prestige gained by achieving high status as a great hunter, for instance, is neither transferable nor inheritable. Because a man is a great hunter, it is not assumed that his sons are also great hunters. There also may be individuals with more influence, but it cannot be inherited, and there are no groups with appreciably more influence over time. An egalitarian society keeps inequality at a minimal level.

Any differences in prestige that do exist are not related to economic differences. Egalitarian groups depend heavily on *sharing*, which ensures equal access to economic resources despite differences in acquired prestige. For instance, in some egalitarian communities, some members achieve higher status through hunting. But even before the hunt begins, how the animal will be divided and distributed among the members of the band has already been decided according to custom. The culture works to separate the status that members achieve—recognition as great hunters—from actual possession of the wealth, which in this case would be the slain animal.

Just as egalitarian societies do not have social groups with unequal access to economic resources, they also do not have social groups with unequal access to power. Unequal access to power by social groups seems to occur only in state societies, which have full-time political officials and marked differences in wealth. Egalitarian societies use a number of customs to keep leaders from dominating others. Criticism and ridicule can be very effective. The Mbuti of central Africa shout down an overassertive leader. When a Hadza man (in Tanzania) tried to get people to work for him, other Hadza made fun of him. Disobedience is another strategy. If a leader tries to command, people just ignore the command. In extreme cases, a particularly domineering leader may be killed by community agreement; this behavior was reported among the San and the Hadza. Finally, particularly among more nomadic groups, people may just move away from a leader they don't like. The active attempts to put down upstarts in many egalitarian societies prompts Christopher Boehm to suggest that dominance comes naturally to humans. Egalitarian societies work hard to reverse that tendency.[3] The Mbuti provide an example of a society almost totally equal: "Neither in ritual, hunting, kinship nor band relations do they exhibit any discernible inequalities of rank or advantage."[4] Their hunting bands have no

In egalitarian societies, such as among the Mbuti hunter-gatherers, houses tend to look the same.

leaders, and recognition of the achievement of one person is not accompanied by privilege of any sort. Economic resources such as food are communally shared, and even tools and weapons are frequently passed from person to person. Only within the family are rights and privileges differentiated.

Rank Societies

Most societies with social *ranking* practice agriculture or herding, but not all agricultural or pastoral societies are ranked. Ranking is characterized by social groups with unequal access to prestige or status but *not* significantly unequal access to economic resources or power. Unequal access to prestige is often reflected in the position of chief, a rank that only some members of a specified group in the society can achieve.

Unusual among rank societies were the 19th-century Native Americans who lived along the northwestern coast of the United States and the southwestern coast of Canada. An example were the Nimpkish, a Kwakiutl group.[5] These societies were unusual because their economy was based on food-collecting. But huge catches of salmon—which were preserved for year-round consumption—enabled them to support fairly large and permanent villages. These societies were similar to food-producing societies in many ways, not just in their development of social ranking. Still, the principal means of proving one's high status was to give away wealth. The tribal chiefs celebrated solemn rites by grand feasts called **potlatches,** at which they gave gifts to every guest.[6]

In rank societies, the position of chief is at least partly hereditary. The criterion of superior rank in some Polynesian societies, for example, was genealogical. Usually the eldest son succeeded to the position of chief, and different kinship groups were differentially ranked according to their genealogical distance from the chiefly line. In rank societies, chiefs are often treated with deference by people of lower rank. For example, among the Trobriand Islanders of Melanesia, people of lower rank must keep their heads lower than a person of higher rank. So, when a chief is standing, commoners must bend low. When commoners have to walk past a chief who happens to be sitting, he may rise and they will bend. If the chief chooses to remain seated, they must crawl.[7]

Although there is no question that chiefs in a rank society enjoy special prestige, there is some controversy over whether they really do not also have material advantages. Chiefs may sometimes look as if they are substantially richer than commoners, for they may receive many gifts and have larger storehouses. In some instances, the chief may even be called the "owner" of the land. However, Marshall Sahlins maintains that the chief's storehouses only house temporary accumulations for feasts or other redistributions. And although the chief may be designated the "owner" of the land, others have the right to use the land. Furthermore, Sahlins suggests that the chief in a rank society lacks power because he usually cannot make people give him gifts or force them to work on communal projects. Often the chief can encourage production only by working furiously on his own cultivation.[8]

This picture of economic equality in rank societies is beginning to be questioned. Laura Betzig studied patterns of food-sharing and labor on Ifaluk, a small atoll in the Western Carolines.[9] Chiefly status is inherited geneaologically in the female line, although most chiefs are male. As in other chiefly societies, Ifaluk chiefs are accorded deference. For example, during collective meals prepared by all the island women, chiefs were served first and were bowed to. The Ifaluk chiefs are said to control the fishing areas. Were the catches equitably distributed? Betzig measured the amount of fish each household got. All the commoners received an equal share, but the chiefs got extra fish; their households got twice as much per person as other households. Did the chiefs give away more later?

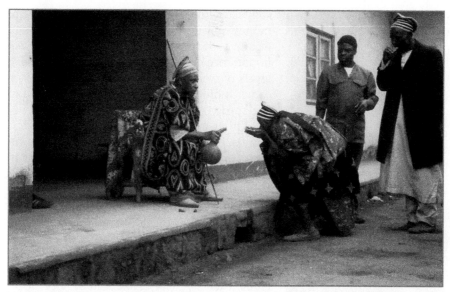

In societies with rank and class, deference is usually shown to political leaders. Among the Nso of northwestern Cameroon, people bow to the Fon or cheif of a village, shown here in his courtyard.

Theoretically, generosity is supposed to even things out, but Betzig found that the gifts from chiefs to other households did not equal the amount the chiefs received from others. Furthermore, although everyone gave to the chiefs, the chiefs gave mostly to their close relatives. On Ifaluk, the chiefs did not work harder than others; in fact, they worked less. Is this true in other societies conventionally considered to be rank societies? We do not know. However, we need to keep in mind that the chiefs in Ifaluk were not noticeably better off either. If they lived in palaces with servants, had elaborate meals, or were dressed in fine clothes and jewelry, we would not need measures of food received or a special study to see if the chiefs had greater access to economic resources because their wealth would be obvious. But rank societies may not have had as much economic equality as we used to think.

Class Societies

In class societies, as in rank societies, there is unequal access to prestige. But, unlike rank societies, class societies are characterized by groups of people that have substantially greater or lesser access to economic resources and power. That is, not every social group has the same opportunity to obtain land, animals, money, or other economic benefits or the same opportunity to exercise power that other groups have. Fully stratified or class societies range from somewhat open to virtually closed class, or *caste*, systems.

Open Class Systems

A **class** is a category of people who all have about the same opportunity to obtain economic resources, power, and prestige. Different classes have differing opportunities. We call class systems *open* if there is some possibility of moving from one class to another. Although class status is not fully determined at birth in open class societies, there is a high probability that most people will stay close to the class into which they were born and will marry within that class. Classes tend to perpetuate themselves through the inheritance of wealth. John Brittain

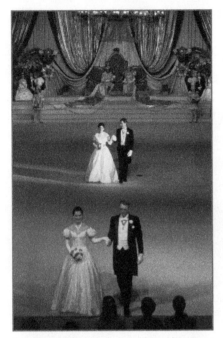

People of the same social class tend to socialize together, where they live, where they vacation, or through shared activities. Debutantes and their escorts are presented at the Krewe of Rex ball during Mardi Gras in New Orleans.

suggested that, in the United States, the transfer of money through bequests accounts for much of the wealth of the next generation. As we might expect, the importance of inheritance seems to increase at higher levels of wealth. That is, the wealth of richer people comes more from inheritance than does the wealth of not-so-rich people.[10]

Other mechanisms of class perpetuation may be more subtle, but they are still powerful. In the United States, many institutions make it possible for an upper-class person to have little contact with other classes. Private day and boarding schools put upper-class children in close contact mostly with others of their class. Attending these schools makes it more likely they will get into universities with higher prestige. Debutante balls and exclusive private parties ensure that young people meet the "right people." Country clubs, exclusive city clubs, and service in particular charities continue the process of limited association. People of the same class also tend to live in the same neighborhoods. Before 1948, explicit restrictions kept certain groups out of particular neighborhoods, but after the U.S. Supreme Court ruled such discrimination unconstitutional, more subtle methods were developed. For instance, zoning restrictions may prohibit multiple-family dwellings in a town or neighborhood and lots below a certain acreage.[11]

Identification with a social class begins early in life. In addition to differences in occupation, wealth, and prestige, social classes vary in many other ways, including religious affiliation, closeness to kin, ideas about childrearing, job satisfaction, leisure-time activities, style of clothes and furniture, and even in styles of speech.[12] People from each class tend to be more comfortable with those from the same class; they talk similarly and are more likely to have similar interests and tastes.

Degree of Openness Some class systems are more open than others; that is, it is easier in some societies to move from one class position to another. Social scientists typically compare the class of people with the class of their parent or parents to measure the degree of mobility. Although most people aspire to move up, mobility also includes moving down. Obtaining more education, particularly a university education, is one of the most effective ways to move upward in contemporary societies. For example, in the United States, individuals with a college bachelor's degree average 75 percent more income than those with only a high school diploma. And individuals with professional degrees earn on average 119 percent more than those with a bachelor's degree.[13] In many countries, educational attainment predicts one's social class better than parents' occupation does.[14]

How do the United States and Canada compare with other countries in degree of class mobility? Canada, Finland, and Sweden have more mobility than the United States and Britain. Mexico and Peru have less mobility than the United States and Brazil, and Colombia considerably less.[15]

Class openness also varies over time. In Paradise, Ontario, Barrett found that the rigid stratification system of the 1950s opened up considerably as new people moved into the community. No one disputed who belonged to the elite in the past. They were of British background, lived in the largest houses, had new cars, and vacationed in Florida. Moreover, they controlled all the leadership positions in the town. By the 1980s, though, the leaders came mostly from the middle and working classes.[16]

Degree of Inequality Degree of class mobility, however, is not the same as degree of economic inequality. For example, Japan, Italy, and Germany have less mobility than the United States, but less inequality. Degree of inequality can vary considerably over time. In the United States, inequality has fluctuated considerably from the 1900s to the present. The greatest inequality was just before the 1929 stock market crash, when the top 1 percent had 42.6 percent of all the wealth. The least inequality was in the mid-1970s, after the stock market declined by 42 percent. Then the top 1 percent controlled 17.6 percent of the wealth.

Change over time in the degree of inequality sometimes appears to have economic causes; for example, the 1929 crash made the wealthy less wealthy. But some of the change over time is due to shifts in public policy. During the New Deal of the 1930s, tax changes and work programs shifted more income to ordinary people; in the 1980s, tax cuts for the wealthy helped the rich get richer. In the 1990s, the rich continued to get richer and the poor got poorer.[17] By 2006, inequality was more concentrated at the top than since the 1929 crash. Only since the severe recession between 2007 and 2009 have the rich gotten somewhat less rich.[18] One way of calculating the disparity between rich and poor is to use the ratio of income held by the top fifth of the households divided by the income held by the bottom fifth. Comparatively speaking, the United States has more inequality than any of the countries in western Europe, with a ratio of 8.5 to 1 (see Figure 1). That is, the top 20 percent of U.S. households controls 8.5 times the wealth controlled by the bottom 20 percent. Norway, on the other hand, has a ratio of about 4 to 1. And Germany has a ratio of about 4.3 to 1. The degree of inequality in the United States exceeds that of India, with a ratio of about 4.7 to 1. Brazil is one of the most unequal countries, with ratios of 32 to 1.

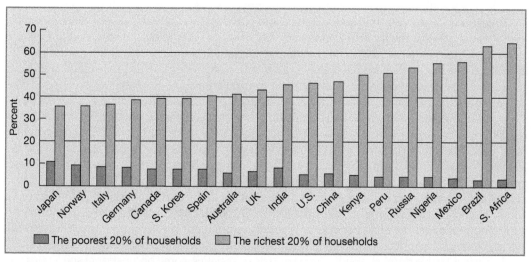

Figure 1 **Proportion of National Income Earned by the Richest 20 Percent of Households Compared with the Poorest 20 Percent: Selected Country Comparisons**

Source: These data are abstracted from World Bank 2004, 60–62.

Recognition of Class

Societies that have open class systems vary in the degree to which members of the society recognize that there are classes, albeit somewhat open classes. The United States is unusual in that, despite objective evidence of multiple social classes, many people deny their existence. The ideology that hard work and strong character can transform anyone into a success appears to be so powerful that it masks the realities of social inequality.[19] When we were growing up, we were told that "Anyone can be President of the United States." As "proof," people pointed to a few individuals who rose from humble beginnings. But consider the odds. How many presidents have come from poor families? How many were not European in background? How many were not Protestant? How many were not male? So far, almost all of the presidents of the United States have been mainly European in ancestry, all but one have been Protestant, and all have been male. And only a handful came from humble beginnings. The paradox of an open class system is that, to move up in the social ladder, people seem to have to believe that it is possible to do so. However, it is one thing to believe in mobility; it is another thing to deny the existence of classes. Why might people need to deny that classes exist?

Caste Systems

Some societies have classes (called castes) that are virtually closed. A **caste** is a ranked group in which membership is determined at birth, and marriage is restricted to members of one's own caste. The only way you can belong is by being born into the group; and because you cannot marry outside the group, your children cannot acquire another caste status either. In India, for example, there are several thousand hereditary castes. Although the precise ranking of these thousands of groups is not clear, there appear to be four main levels of hierarchy. The castes in India are often thought to be associated with different occupations, but that is not quite true. Most Indians live in rural areas and have agricultural occupations, but their castes vary widely.[20]

Castes may exist in conjunction with a more open class system. Indeed, in India today, members of a low caste who can get wage-paying jobs, chiefly those in urban areas, may improve their social standing in the same ways available to people in other class societies. In general, however, they still cannot marry someone in a higher caste, so the caste system is perpetuated.

Questions basic to all stratified societies, and particularly to a caste society, were posed by John Ruskin, a 19th-century British essayist: "Which of us . . . is to do the hard and dirty work for the rest—and for what pay? Who is to do the pleasant and clean work, and for what pay?"[21] In India, those questions have been answered by the caste system, which mainly dictates how goods and services are exchanged, particularly in rural areas.[22]

Japan also had a caste group within a class society. Now called *burakumin* (instead of the pejorative *eta*), this group traditionally had occupations that were considered unclean.[23] Comparable to India's Untouchables, they were a hereditary, endogamous (in-marrying) group. Their occupations were traditionally those of farm laborer, leatherworker, and basket weaver; their standard of living was very low. The burakumin are physically indistinguishable from other Japanese.[24] The Japanese government officially abolished discrimination against the burakumin ih 1871, but the burakumin did not begin organizing to bring about change until the 20th century. As of 1995, 73 percent of burakumin marriages were with non-burakumin. In public opinion polls, two-thirds of burakumin now said that they had not encountered discrimination. However, most burakumin still live in segregated neighborhoods where unemployment, crime, and alcoholism rates are high.[25]

In a considerable number of sub-Saharan African societies, some occupational specialties are only performed by certain castes. The specialties usually involve metalworking, pottery, woodworking, leatherworking, playing musical instruments, and praise-singing. In some cases, the caste consists of people who traditionally hunted and gathered. These castes usually constituted only a small minority of the society's population and were not the lowest ranking groups in society. Only slaves had a lower rank. The caste vocational distinctions have weakened in recent times as people have become more educated.[26]

In Rwanda, long before the ethnic division arose between the Hutu and Tutsi (see discussion later in the ethnicity section), the Twa, who comprised less than 1 percent of the population, were subject to serious discrimination. Their bodies were viewed as dangerous and polluting and they were avoided whenever possible. For example, if a Twa were present while others were

Caste is somewhat less important in India, but has not disappeared. In Mumbai, the washers of the Dhobi caste process laundry.

eating or drinking, separate utensils were reserved only for Twa. The Twa traditional occupations were foraging, making pottery, entertaining, and serving as torturers or executioners for the Rwandan king. Mutton was considered a Twa food and other Rwandans would not eat mutton.[27]

In the United States, African Americans used to have more of a castelike status determined partly by the inherited characteristic of skin color. Until recently, some states had laws prohibiting an African American from marrying a European American. When interethnic marriage did occur, children of the union were often regarded as having lower status than European American children, even though they may have had blond hair and light skin. In the South, where treatment of African Americans as a caste was most apparent, European Americans refused to eat with African Americans or sit next to them at lunch counters, on buses, and in schools. Separate drinking fountains and toilets reinforced the idea of ritual uncleanness. The economic advantages and gains in prestige that European Americans enjoyed are well documented.[28] In the following sections on slavery, racism, and inequality, we discuss the social status of African Americans in more detail.

Slavery

Slavery has existed in some form in almost every part of the world at one time or another, in simpler as well as in more complex societies. Slaves are often obtained from other cultures directly: kidnapped, captured in war, or given as tribute. Or they may be obtained indirectly as payment in barter or trade. Slaves sometimes come from the same culture; one became a slave as payment of a debt, as a punishment for a crime, or even as a chosen alternative to poverty. Slave societies vary in the degree to which it is possible to become freed from slavery.[29] Sometimes the slavery system has been a closed class, or caste, system, sometimes a relatively open class system. In different slave-owning societies, slaves have had different, but always some, legal rights.[30] Because of the variability of slavery systems, the meaning of a slave is hard to define, but a common definition is that **slaves** are people who do not own their own labor, and as such they represent a class.

In the United States, slavery originated as a means of obtaining cheap labor, but the slaves soon came to be regarded as deserving of their low status because of their alleged inherent inferiority. Because the slaves were from Africa and were dark-skinned, some European Americans justified slavery and the belief in "black" people's inferiority by quoting scripture out of context ("They shall be hewers of wood and drawers of water"). Slaves could not marry or make any other contracts, nor could they own property. In addition, their children were also slaves, and the master had sexual rights over the female slaves. Because the status of slavery was determined by birth in the United

States, slaves constituted a caste. During the days of slavery, therefore, the United States had both a caste and a class system. It is widely assumed that slavery occurred only in the southern United States, but although not on as large a scale, slavery existed in the northern states as well. New Jersey was the last northern state to legally give up slavery around the time of the U.S. Civil War.[31]

Among the Nupe, a society in central Nigeria, slavery was of quite another type.[32] The methods of obtaining slaves—as part of the booty of warfare and, later, by purchase—were similar to those of Europeans, but the position of the slaves was very different. Mistreatment was rare. Male slaves were given the same opportunities to earn money as other dependent males in the household—younger brothers, sons, or other relatives. A slave might be given a garden plot of his own to cultivate, or he might be given a commission if his master was a craftsman or a tradesman. Slaves could acquire property, wealth, and even slaves of their own. But all of a slave's belongings went to the master at the slave's death.

Manumission—the granting of freedom to slaves—was built into the Nupe system. If a male slave could afford the marriage payment for a free woman, the children of the resulting marriage were free; the man himself, however, remained a slave. Marriage and concubinage were the easiest ways out of bondage for a slave woman. Once she had produced a child by her master, both she and the child had free status. The woman, however, was only figuratively free; if a concubine, she had to remain in that role. As might be expected, the family trees of the nobility and the wealthy were liberally grafted with branches descended from slave concubines.

The most fortunate slaves among the Nupe were the house slaves. They could rise to positions of power in the household as overseers and bailiffs, charged with law enforcement and judicial duties. (Recall the Old Testament story of Joseph, who was sold into slavery by his brothers. Joseph became a household slave of the pharaoh and rose to the position of second in the kingdom because he devised an ingenious system of taxation.) There was even a titled group of Nupe slaves, the Order of Court Slaves, who were trusted officers of the king and members of an elite. Slave status in general, though, placed one at the bottom of the social ladder. In the Nupe system, few slaves, mainly princes from their own societies, ever achieved membership in the titled group. Nupe slavery was abolished at the beginning of the 20th century.

As for why slavery may have developed in the first place, cross-cultural research is as yet inconclusive. We do know, however, that slavery is not an inevitable stage in economic development, contrary to what some have assumed. In other words, slavery is not found mainly in certain economies, such as those dependent on intensive agriculture. Unlike the United States until the Civil War, many societies with intensive agriculture did not develop any variety of slavery. Also, the theory that slavery develops where available resources are plentiful but labor is scarce is not supported by the cross-cultural evidence. All we can say definitely is that slavery does not occur in developed or industrial economies; either it disappears or it was never present in them.[33]

Racism and Inequality

Racism is the belief that some "races" are inferior to others. In a society composed of people with noticeably different physical features, such as differences in skin color, racism is almost invariably associated with social stratification. Those "races" considered inferior make up a larger proportion of the lower social classes or castes. Even in more open class systems, where individuals from all backgrounds can achieve higher status positions, individuals from groups deemed inferior may be subject to discrimination in housing or may be more likely to be searched or stopped by the police.

In some societies, such as the United States, the idea that humans are divided into "races" is taken so much for granted that people are asked for their "race" on the census. Most Americans probably assume that the classification of people into categories such as "white" or "black" reflects important biological categories. We put "race" in quotes to reflect the fact that most anthropologists are now persuaded that the biological concept of "race" is not scientifically useful when applied to humans.

Racial classification is problematic because there is sometimes more physical, physiological, and genetic diversity *within* a single geographic group that might be called a "race" (e.g., Africans) than there is *between* supposed "racial" groups. Africans vary more among themselves than they do in comparison with people elsewhere.[34] Analyses of all human populations have demonstrated that between 93 and 95 percent of genetic variation is due to individual differences within populations, whereas only 3–5 percent of genetic variation is due to differences between major human population groups.[35] "Race," when applied to humans, is a social category, not a scientific one.

Race as a Social Category

Racial classifications are social categories to which individuals are assigned, by themselves and others, to separate "our" group from others. We have seen that people tend to be *ethnocentric,* to view their culture as better than other cultures. Racial classifications may reflect the same tendency to divide "us" from "them," except that the divisions are supposedly based on biological differences.[36] The "them" are almost always viewed as inferior to "us."

We know that racial classifications have often been, and still are, used by certain groups to justify discrimination, exploitation, or genocide. The "Aryan race" was supposed to be the group

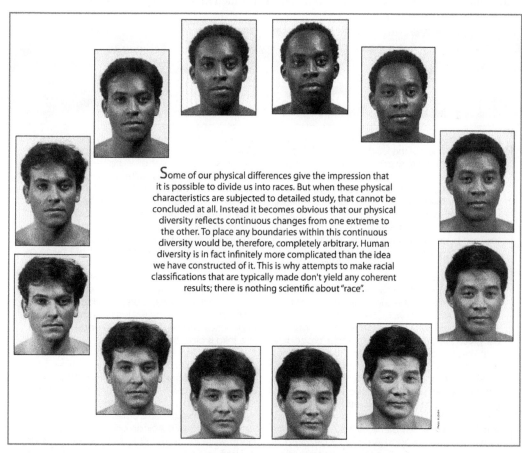

Some of our physical differences give the impression that it is possible to divide us into races. But when these physical characteristics are subjected to detailed study, that cannot be concluded at all. Instead it becomes obvious that our physical diversity reflects continuous changes from one extreme to the other. To place any boundaries within this continuous diversity would be, therefore, completely arbitrary. Human diversity is in fact infinitely more complicated than the idea we have constructed of it. This is why attempts to make racial classifications that are typically made don't yield any coherent results; there is nothing scientific about "race".

It is an illusion that there are races. The diversity of human beings is so great and so complicated that it is impossible to classify 5.8 billion individuals into discrete "races."

of blond-haired, blue-eyed, white-skinned people whom Adolf Hitler wanted to dominate the world, to which end he and others attempted to destroy as many members of the Jewish "race" as they could. (An estimated 6 million Jews and others were murdered in what is now called the Holocaust.[37]) But who were the Aryans? Technically, Aryans are any people, including the German-speaking Jews in Hitler's Germany, who speak one of the Indo-European languages. The Indo-European languages include such disparate modern tongues as Greek, Spanish, Hindi, Polish, French, Icelandic, German, Gaelic, and English. And many Aryans speaking these languages have neither blond hair nor blue eyes. Similarly, all kinds of people may be Jews, whether or not they descend from the ancient Near Eastern population that spoke the Hebrew language. There are light-skinned Danish Jews and darker Jewish Arabs. One of the most orthodox Jewish groups in the United States is based in New York City and is composed entirely of African Americans.

The arbitrary and social basis of most racial classifications becomes apparent when you compare how they differ from one place to another. Consider, for example, what used to be thought about the "races" in South Africa. Under apartheid, which was a system of racial segregation and discrimination, someone with mixed "white" and "black" ancestry was considered "colored." However, when important people of African ancestry (from other countries) would visit South Africa, they were often considered "white." Chinese were considered "Asian"; but the Japanese, who were important economically to South Africa, were considered "white."[38] In some parts of the United States, laws against interracial marriage continued in force through the 1960s. You would

APPLIED ANTHROPOLOGY

Unequal in Death: African Americans Compared with European Americans

Everyone dies of something. Yet, if you consider cardiovascular disease, the leading cause of death in the United States, it turns out that after controlling for the effects of age and gender, African Americans die more often from that disease than European Americans. The same kind of disparity occurs also with almost every other major cause of death—cancer, cirrhosis of the liver, kidney disease, diabetes, injuries, infant mortality, and homicide. Medical anthropologists and health policy researchers want to know why. Without such understanding, it is hard to know how to reduce the disparity.

One reason may be subtle discrimination by the medical profession itself. For example, a European American with chest pain in the United States is more likely than an African American to be given an angiogram, a medical procedure that injects radioactive dye into the heart to look for deficits in blood flow through the coronary arteries that supply blood to the heart. And even if coronary heart disease is detected by an angiogram, an African American is less likely to receive bypass surgery. Thus, the death rate from cardiovascular disease may be higher for African Americans than for European Americans because of unequal medical care. Seeing a patient physically

appears to make a difference. When heart specialists reviewed cases to make decisions about subsequent treatment after catheterization, recommendations did not differ by "race" when the doctors did not know the "race" of the patient.

Yet, although some difference in mortality may be due to disparity in medical treatment, this could only be part of the picture. African Americans may be more prone to cardiovascular disease because they are about twice as likely as European Americans to have high rates of hypertension (high blood pressure). But why the disparity in hypertension? Three possible explanations, not mutually exclusive, are discussed in the research literature. The first is a possible difference in genetics. The second is a difference in lifestyle. The third is class difference.

Most of the Africans that came to the Americas were forcibly taken as slaves between the 16th and 19th centuries, largely from West Africa. In one comparative study of hypertension, African Americans had much higher blood pressure than Africans in Nigeria and Cameroon, even in urban areas. People with African ancestry in the Caribbean were in the middle of the range. Lifestyle differences were also vast—the West Africans had be considered a "negro" if you had an eighth or more "negro" ancestry (if one or more of your eight grandparents were "negro").[39] In some states, an even smaller proportion made you "negro." Some refer to this concept as the "one-drop" rule—just a tiny bit of "negro" (now called "black") ancestry was sufficient to determine your "racial" classification.[40] So only a small amount of "negro" ancestry made a person "negro." But a small amount of "white" ancestry did not make a person "white." Biologically speaking, this makes no sense, but socially it was another story.[41]

In much of Latin America and the Caribbean, the reverse rule is the case. A small amount of European blood can make you "white." When people from Dominica, Haiti, or Cuba come to the United States, they often find that their "race" has changed. They might have been considered "white" at home, but they are considered "black" in the United States. In contrast to the United States, with a two-part division of "white" and "black," concepts of race in Latin America are on more of a continuum from light to dark, with important middle positions (such as "mestizo"). Wealth makes a difference too—if you are dark-skinned but wealthy, you will tend to be considered "whiter."[42]

If people of different "races" are viewed as inferior, they are more likely going to end up on the lower rungs of the social ladder in a socially stratified society. Discrimination will keep them out of the better-paying or higher-status jobs and in neighborhoods that are poorer. As the box "Unequal in Death" shows, people of different "races" also suffer from differential access to health care and have more health problems.

plenty of exercise, were lean, and ate low-fat and low-salt diets. Any possible difference in genes would seem to be insignificant. Jared Diamond has suggested that individuals who could retain salt would have been most likely to survive the terrible conditions of the sailing ships that brought slaves to the New World. Many died from diarrhea and dehydration (salt-depleting conditions) on those voyages. Retention of salt would have been a genetic advantage then, but disadvantageous in places such as the United States with high-salt, high-fat diets. Critics of this theory suggest that salt-depleting diseases were not the leading causes of death in the slave voyages; tuberculosis and violence were more frequent causes of death. Furthermore, critics say that the slave ship theory would predict little genetic diversity in African American populations with respect to hypertension, but in fact there is great diversity.

Hypertension could be related also to differences in lifestyle and wealth. As we noted in the section on racism and inequality, African Americans in the United States are disproportionately poorer. Study after study has noted that healthier lifestyle habits are generally correlated with higher positions on the socioeconomic ladder. Moreover,

individuals from higher social positions are more likely to have health insurance and access to care in superior hospitals. But even after correcting for factors such as obesity, physical activity, and social class, the health differential persists— African Americans still have a much higher incidence of hypertension than European Americans.

William Dressler suggests that stress is another possible cause of higher rates of hypertension. Despite increased economic mobility in recent years, African Americans are still subject to prejudice and may consequently have more stress even if they have higher income. Stress is related to higher blood pressure. In a color-conscious society, a very dark-skinned individual walking in a wealthy neighborhood at night may be thought not to live there and may be stopped by the police. If Dressler is correct, darker-skinned African Americans who have objective indicators of higher status should have much higher blood pressure than would be expected from their relative education, age, body mass, or social class alone. And that seems to be true. Racism may affect health.

Sources: Cooper, Rotimi, and Ward 1999, 56–63; Diamond 1991; Dressler 1993; Geiger 2003; Smedley, Stith, and Nelson 2003, 3.

Ethnicity and Inequality

If "race" is not a scientifically useful category because people cannot be clearly divided into different "racial" categories based on sets of physical traits, then racial classifications such as "black" and "white" in the United States might better be described as *ethnic* classifications. How else can we account for the following facts? Groups that are thought of as "white" now in the United States were earlier thought of as belonging to inferior "races." For example, in the latter half of the 19th century, newspapers would often talk about the new immigrants from Ireland as belonging to the Irish "race." Similarly, before World War II, Jews were thought of as a separate "racial" group, and only became "white" afterward.[43] It is hard to escape the idea that changes in "racial" classification occurred as the Irish, Jews, and other immigrant groups became more accepted by the majority in the United States.[44]

It is apparent that *ethnic groups* and *ethnic identities* emerge as part of a social and political process. The process of defining **ethnicity** usually involves a group of people emphasizing common origins and language, shared history, and selected cultural differences such as a difference in religion. Those doing the defining can be outside or inside the ethnic group. Outsiders and insiders often perceive ethnic groups differently. In a country with one large core majority group, often the majority group doesn't think of itself as an ethnic group. Rather, they consider only the minority groups to have ethnic identities. For example, in the United States, it is not common for the majority to call themselves European Americans, but other groups may be called African Americans, Asian Americans, or Native Americans. The minority groups, on the other hand, may also have different named identities.[45] Asian Americans may identify themselves more specifically as Japanese Americans, Korean Americans, Chinese Americans, or Hmong. The majority population often uses derogatory names to identify people who are different. The majority may also tend to lump people of diverse ethnicities together. Naming a group establishes a boundary between it and other ethnic groups.[46]

Ethnic identity may be manipulated, by insiders and by outsiders, in different situations. A particularly repressive regime that emphasizes nationalism and loyalty to the state may not only suppress the assertiveness of ethnic claims; it may also act to minimize communication among people who might otherwise embrace the same ethnic identity.[47] More democratic regimes may allow more expression of difference and celebrate ethnic difference. However, manipulation of ethnicity does not come just from the top. It may be to the advantage of minority groups to lobby for more equal treatment as a larger entity, such as Asian American, rather than as Japanese, Chinese, Hmong, Filipino, or Korean American. Similarly, even though there are hundreds of Native American groups, originally speaking different languages, there may be political advantages for all if they are treated as Native Americans.

In many multiethnic societies, ethnicity and diversity are things to be proud of and celebrated. Shared ethnic identity often makes people feel comfortable with similar people and gives them a strong sense of belonging. Still, ethnic differences in multiethnic societies are usually associated with inequities in wealth, power, and prestige. In other words, ethnicity is part of the system of *stratification*.

Although some people believe that inequities are deserved, the origins of ethnic stereotypes, prejudice, and discrimination usually follow from historical and political events that give some groups dominance over others. For example, even though there were many early stories of help given by native peoples to the English settlers in the 17th century in the land now known as North America, the English were the invaders, and negative stereotypes about native peoples developed to justify taking their land and their lives. Referring to the negative stereotypes of

Social Stratification: Class, Ethnicity, and Racism

Members of minority ethnic groups are more often at the bottom of the socioeconomic "ladder," but not always, as these pictures from the United States illustrate.

Native Americans that developed, J. Milton Yinger said, "One would almost think that it had been the Indian who had invaded Europe, driven back the inhabitants, cut their population to one-third of its original size, unilaterally changed treaties, and brought the dubious glories of firewater and firearms."[48]

Similarly, as we noted in the section on slavery, African slaves were initially acquired as cheap labor, but inhumane treatment of slaves was justified by beliefs about their inferiority. Unfortunately, stereotypes can become self-fulfilling prophesies, especially if those discriminated against come to believe the stereotypes. It is easy to see how this can happen. If there is a widespread belief that a group is inferior, and that group is given inferior schools and little chance for improvement or little chance for a good job, the members of that group may acquire few skills and not try hard. The result is often a vicious cycle.[49]

And yet, the picture is not all bleak. Change has occurred. The ethnic identity a minority group forges can help promote political activism, such as the nonviolent civil rights movement in the United States in the 1960s. That activism, helped by some people in the more advantaged groups, helped break down many of the legal barriers and segregationist practices that reinforced inequality.

The traditional barriers in the United States have mostly been lifted in recent years, but the "color line" has not disappeared. African Americans are found in all social classes, but they remain underrepresented in the wealthiest group and overrepresented at the bottom. Discrimination may be lessened, but it is still not gone. In research done with matched pairs of "whites" and "blacks" applying for jobs or for housing, discrimination is still evident.[50] Thus, African Americans may have to be better than others to get promoted, or it may be assumed that they got ahead just because they were African American and were hired because of affirmative action programs. European Americans often expect African Americans to be "ambassadors," to be called on mainly for knowledge about how to handle situations involving other African Americans. African Americans may work with others, but they usually go home to African American neighborhoods. Or they may live in mixed neighborhoods and experience considerable isolation. Few African Americans can completely avoid the anguish of racism.[51]

The Emergence of Stratification

Anthropologists are not certain why social stratification developed. Nevertheless, they are reasonably sure that higher levels of stratification emerged relatively recently in human history. Archaeological sites dating before about 8,000 years ago do not show extensive evidence of inequality. Houses do not appear to vary much in size or content, and different communities of the same culture are similar in size and otherwise. Signs of inequality appear first in the Near East, about 2,000 years after agriculture emerged in that region. Inequality in burial suggests inequality in life. Particularly telling are unequal child burials. It is unlikely that children could achieve high status by their own achievements. So, when archaeologists find statues and ornaments only in some children's tombs, as at the 7,500-year-old site of Tell es-Sawwan in Iraq,[52] the grave goods suggest that those children belonged to a higher-ranking family or a higher class.

Another indication that stratification is a relatively recent development in human history is the fact that certain cultural features associated with stratification also developed relatively recently. For example, most societies that depend primarily on agriculture or herding have social classes.[53] Agriculture and herding developed within the past 10,000 years, so we may assume that most food collectors in the distant past lacked social classes. Other recently developed cultural features associated with class stratification include fixed settlements, political integration beyond the community level, the use of money as a medium of exchange, and the presence of at least some full-time specialization.[54]

In 1966, comparative sociologist Gerhard Lenski suggested that the trend toward increasing inequality since 8,000 years ago was reversing. He argued that inequalities of power and privilege in industrial societies—measured in terms of the concentration of political power and the distribution of income—are less pronounced than inequalities in complex preindustrial societies. Technology in industrialized societies is so complex, he suggested, that those in power are compelled to delegate some authority to subordinates if the system is to work. In addition, a decline in the birth rate in industrialized societies, coupled with the need for skilled labor, has pushed the average wage of workers far above the subsistence level, resulting in greater equality in the distribution of income. Finally, Lenski also suggested that the spread of the democratic ideology, and particularly its acceptance by elites, has significantly broadened the political power of the lower classes.[55] A few studies have tested and supported Lenski's hypothesis that inequality has decreased with industrialization. In general, nations that are highly industrialized exhibit a lower level of inequality than nations that are only somewhat industrialized.[56] But, as we have seen, even the most industrialized societies may still have an enormous degree of inequality.

Why did social stratification develop in the first place? On the basis of his study of Polynesian societies, Marshall Sahlins suggested that an increase in agricultural productivity results in social stratification.[57] According to Sahlins, the degree of stratification is directly related to the production of a surplus, which is made possible by greater technological efficiency. The higher the level of productivity and the larger the agricultural surplus, the greater the scope and complexity of the distribution system. The status of the chief, who serves as redistributing agent, is enhanced. Sahlins argued that the differentiation between distributor and producer inevitably gives rise to differentiation in other aspects of life:

First, there would be a tendency for the regulator of distribution to exert some authority over production itself—especially over productive activities which necessitate subsidization, such as communal labor or specialist labor. A degree of control of production implies a degree of control over the utilization of resources, or, in other words, some preeminent property rights. In turn, regulation of these economic processes necessitates the exercise of authority in interpersonal affairs; differences in social power emerge.[58]

Sahlins later rejected the idea that a surplus leads to chiefships, postulating instead that the relationship may be the other way around—that is, leaders encourage the development of a surplus so as to enhance their prestige through feasts, potlatches, and other redistributive events.[59] Of course, both trajectories are possible—surpluses may generate stratification, and stratification may generate surpluses; they are not mutually exclusive.

Lenski's theory of the causes of stratification is similar to Sahlins's original idea. Lenski, too, argued that production of a surplus is the stimulus in the development of stratification, but he focused primarily on the conflict that arises over control of that surplus. Lenski concluded that the distribution of the surplus will be determined on the basis of power. Thus, inequalities in power promote unequal access to economic resources and simultaneously give rise to inequalities in privilege and prestige.[60]

The "surplus" theories of Sahlins and Lenski do not really address the question of why the redistributors or leaders will want, or be able, to acquire greater control over resources. After all, the redistributors or leaders in many rank societies do not have greater wealth than others, and custom seems to keep things that way. One suggestion is that, as long as followers have mobility, they can vote with their feet by moving away from leaders they do not like. But when people start to make more permanent "investments" in land or technology (e.g., irrigation systems or weirs for fishing), they are more likely to put up with a leader's aggrandizement in exchange for protection.[61] Another suggestion is that access to economic resources becomes unequal only when there is population pressure on resources in rank or chiefdom societies.[62] Such pressure may be what induces redistributors to try to keep more land and other resources for themselves and their families.

C. K. Meek offered an example of how population pressure in northern Nigeria may have led to economic stratification. At one time, a tribal member could obtain the right to use land by asking permission of the chief and presenting him with a token gift in recognition of his higher status. But, by 1921, the reduction in the amount of available land had led to a system under which applicants offered the chief large payments for scarce land. As a result of these payments, farms came to be regarded as private property, and differential access to such property became institutionalized.[63]

Future research by archaeologists, sociologists, historians, and anthropologists should provide more understanding of the emergence of social stratification in human societies and how and why it may vary in degree.

✓●┤Study and Review on **myanthrolab.com**

Summary

1. Without exception, recent and modern industrial and postindustrial societies such as our own are socially stratified—that is, they contain social groups such as families, classes, or ethnic groups that have unequal access to important advantages, such as economic resources, power, and prestige. Anthropologists, based on firsthand observations, would

say that such inequality has not always existed among the societies they have studied. Although even the simplest societies (in the technological sense) have some differences in advantages based on age, ability, or gender—adults have higher status than children, the skilled more than the unskilled, men more than women—anthropologists would argue that egalitarian societies exist where social groups (e.g., families) have more or less the same access to rights or advantages.

2. The presence or absence of customs or rules that give certain groups unequal access to economic resources, power, and prestige can be used to distinguish three types of societies. In egalitarian societies, social groups do not have unequal access to economic resources, power, or prestige; they are unstratified. In rank societies, social groups do not have very unequal access to economic resources or power, but they do have unequal access to prestige. Rank societies, then, are partially stratified. In class societies, social groups have unequal access to economic resources, power, and prestige. They are more completely stratified than are rank societies.

3. Stratified societies range from somewhat open class systems to caste systems, which are extremely rigid because caste membership is fixed permanently at birth.

4. Slaves are people who do not own their own labor; as such, they represent a class and sometimes even a caste. Slavery has existed in various forms in many times and places, regardless of "race" and culture. Sometimes slavery is a rigid and closed, or caste, system; sometimes it is a relatively open class system.

5. Within a society composed of people from widely divergent backgrounds and different physical features, such as skin color, racism is almost invariably associated with social stratification. Those "races" considered inferior make up a larger proportion of the lower social classes or castes. In the opinion of many biological anthropologists, "race" is not a scientifically useful device for classifying humans. "Racial" classifications should be recognized for what they mostly are—social categories to which individuals are assigned, by themselves and others, on the basis of supposedly shared biological traits.

6. In multiethnic societies, ethnic differences are usually associated with inequities in wealth, power, and prestige. In other words, ethnicity is part of the system of stratification.

7. Social stratification appears to have emerged relatively recently in human history, about 8,000 years ago. This conclusion is based on archaeological evidence and on the fact that certain cultural features associated with stratification developed relatively recently.

8. One theory suggests that social stratification developed as productivity increased and surpluses were produced. Another suggestion is that stratification can develop only when people have "investments" in land or technology and therefore cannot move away from leaders they do not like. A third theory suggests that stratification emerges only when there is population pressure on resources in rank societies.

Glossary Terms

caste	egalitarian societies	power
class	ethnicity	prestige
class societies	manumission	rank societies
economic resources	potlatch	slaves

Critical Questions

1. What might be some of the social consequences of large differences in wealth? Explain your reasoning.

2. Is an industrial or a developed economy incompatible with a more egalitarian distribution of resources? Why or why not?

3. In a multiethnic society, does ethnic identity help or hinder social equality? Explain your answer.

4. Why do you suppose the degree of inequality has decreased in some countries in recent years?

Read the Original Source on myanthrolab.com

Read "Haitians: From Political Repression to Chaos" by Robert Lawless on MyAnthroLab. Answer the questions below.

1. In what ways does Lawless suggest that the elite in Haiti maintain their power?
2. Why does Lawless say that "Voodoo" is an egalitarian religion?
3. Explain what role slavery played in Haitian history.

Photo Credits

Credits are listed in order of appearance.

Catherine Karnow/Corbis; Wendy Stone/Corbis; Aidan Gullickson; Philip Gould/Corbis; sinopictures/Photolibrary/Peter Arnold, Inc./ Getty Images; Syracuse Univeristy; (left): Kevin Fleming/Corbis; (right): Ghislain & Marie David de Lossy/The Image Bank/Getty Images. From Sahlins, Marshall D. 1958. Social stratification in Polynesia. Seattle: University of Washington Press.

Glossary

Caste A ranked group, often associated with a certain occupation, in which membership is determined at birth and marriage is restricted to members of one's own caste.

Class A category of people who have about the same opportunity to obtain economic resources, power, and prestige.

Class societies Societies containing social groups that have unequal access to economic resources, power, and prestige.

Economic resources Things that have value in a culture, including land, tools and other technology, goods, and money.

Egalitarian societies Societies in which all people of a given age-sex category have equal access to economic resources, power, and prestige.

Ethnicity The process of defining ethnicity usually involves a group of people emphasizing common origins and language, shared history, and selected aspects of cultural difference such as a difference in religion. Because different groups are doing the perceiving, ethnic identities often vary with whether one is inside or outside the group.

Manumission The granting of freedom to a slave.

Potlatch A feast among Pacific Northwest Native Americans at which great quantities of food and goods are given to the guests in order to gain prestige for the host(s).

Power The ability to make others do what they do not want to do or influence based on the threat of force.

Prestige Being accorded particular respect or honor.

Rank societies Societies that do not have any unequal access to economic resources or power, but with social groups that have unequal access to status positions and prestige.

Slaves A class of people who do not own their own labor or the products thereof.

Notes

1. In an analysis of many native societies in the New World, Gary Feinman and Jill Neitzel argue that egalitarian and rank societies ("tribes" and "chiefdoms," respectively) are not systematically distinguishable. See Feinman and Neitzel (1984, 57).
2. Fried 1967, 33.
3. Boehm 1993, 230–31; 1999.
4. M. G. Smith 1966, 152.
5. D. Mitchell 2009.
6. Drucker 1965, 56–64.
7. Service 1978, 249.
8. Sahlins 1958, 80–81.
9. Betzig 1988.
10. Brittain 1978.
11. Higley 1995, 1–47.
12. Argyle 1994.
13. U.S. Census Bureau 2002.
14. Featherman and Hauser 1978, 4, 481; Treiman and Ganzeboom 1990, 117.
15. Behrman, Gaviria, and Székely, 2001; Solon 2002.
16. S. R. Barrett 1994, 17, 41.
17. Johnston 1999, 16; *New York Times International*, Tuesday, September 30, 1997, p. A26; K. Phillips 1990; U.S. Census Bureau 1993.
18. Leonhardt and Fabrikant 2009.
19. Durrenberger 2001b, who refers to Goldschmidt 1999 and Newman 1988; 1993.
20. Klass 2009.
21. Ruskin 1963, 296–314.
22. O. Lewis 1958.
23. Kristof 1995, A18.
24. For more information about caste in Japan, see Berreman 1972, 403–14; 1973.
25. Kristof 1995; 1997.
26. Tamari 1991; 2005.
27. Taylor 2005.
28. Berreman 1960, 120–27.
29. O. Patterson 1982, vii–xiii, 105.
30. Pryor 1977, 219.
31. Harper 2003.
32. Nadel 1942.

33. Pryor 1977, 217–47.
34. Marks 1994; Shanklin 1993, 15–17.
35. Molnar 1998, 19.
36. M. D. Williams 2009.
37. S. S. Friedman 1980, 206.
38. M. H. Ross 2009a.
39. Marks 1994, 32.
40. Fluehr-Lobban 2006, 12.
41. Marks 1994, 32.
42. Fluehr-Lobban 2006, 12.
43. Armelagos and Goodman 1998, 365.
44. O. Patterson 2000.
45. M. Nash 1989, 2.
46. Ibid., 10.
47. Barth 1994, 27.
48. Yinger 1994, 169.
49. Ibid., 169–71.
50. Ibid., 216–17.
51. Benjamin 1991; see also M. D. Williams 2004.
52. Flannery 1972.
53. Data from Textor 1967.
54. Ibid.
55. Lenski 1984/1966, 308–18.
56. Cutright 1967, 564; Treiman and Ganzeboom 1990, 117.
57. Sahlins 1958.
58. Ibid., 4.
59. Sahlins 1972.
60. Lenski 1984/1966.
61. Gilman 1990.
62. Fried 1967, 201ff; Harner 1975.
63. Meek 1940, 149–50.

Bibliography

Argyle, Michael. 1994. *The psychology of social class.* New York: Routledge.
Armelagos, George J., and Alan H. Goodman. 1998. Race, racism, and anthropology. In *Building a new biocultural synthesis: Political-economic perspectives on human biology,* eds. A. H. Goodman and T. L. Leatherman. Ann Arbor: University of Michigan Press.
Barrett, Stanley R. 1994. *Paradise: Class, commuters, and ethnicity in rural Ontario.* Toronto: University of Toronto Press.
Barth, Fredrik. 1994. Enduring and emerging issues in the analysis of ethnicity. In *The anthropology of ethnicity,* eds. H. Vermeulen and C. Govers. Amsterdam: Het Spinhuis.
Behrman, Jere R., Alejandro Gaviria, and Miguel Székely. 2001. Intergenerational mobility in Latin America. Inter-American Development Bank, Working Paper #45. http://www.iadb.org/res/publications/pubfiles/pubWP-452.pdf (accessed June 2009).
Benjamin, Lois. 1991. *The black elite: Facing the color line in the twilight of the twentieth century.* Chicago: Nelson-Hall.
Berreman, Gerald D. 1960. Caste in India and the United States. *American Journal of Sociology* 66:120–27.
Berreman, Gerald D. 1972. Race, caste and other invidious distinctions in social stratification. *Race* 13:403–14.
Berreman, Gerald D. 1973. *Caste in the modern world.* Morristown, NJ: General Learning Press.
Betzig, Laura. 1988. Redistribution: Equity or exploitation? In *Human reproductive behavior,* eds. L. Betzig, M. B. Mulder, and P. Turke, 49–63. Cambridge, UK: Cambridge University Press.
Boehm, Christopher. 1993. Egalitarian behavior and reverse dominance hierarchy. *Current Anthropology* 34:230–31.
Brittain, John A. 1978. *Inheritance and the inequality of material wealth.* Washington, DC: Brookings Institution.
Cutright, Phillips. 1967. Inequality: A cross-national analysis. *American Sociological Review* 32:562–78.
Drucker, Philip. 1965. *Cultures of the north Pacific coast.* San Francisco: Chandler.
Durrenberger, E. Paul. 2001b. Explorations of class and consciousness in the U.S. *Journal of Anthropological Research* 57:41–60.
Featherman, David L., and Robert M. Hauser. 1978. *Opportunity and change.* New York: Academic Press.
Feinman, Gary, and Jill Neitzel. 1984. Too many types: An overview of sedentary prestate societies in the Americas. In *Advances in archaeological methods and theory,* vol. 7, ed. M. B. Schiffer. Orlando, FL: Academic Press.
Flannery, Kent V. 1972. The cultural evolution of civilizations. *Annual Review of Ecology and Systematics* 3:399–426.
Fluehr-Lobban, Carolyn. 2006. *Race and racism: An introduction.* Lanham: AltaMira Press.
Fried, Morton H. 1967. *The evolution of political society: An essay in political anthropology.* New York: Random House.

Social Stratification: Class, Ethnicity, and Racism

Friedman, Saul S. 1980. Holocaust. In *Academic American Encyclopedia*, vol. 10. Princeton, NJ: Areté.

Gilman, Antonio. 1990. The development of social stratification in Bronze Age Europe. *Current Anthropology* 22:1–23.

Goldschmidt, Walter. 1999. Dynamics and status in America. *Anthropology Newsletter* 40(5):62, 64.

Harner, Michael J. 1975. Scarcity, the factors of production, and social evolution. In *Population, ecology, and social evolution*, ed. S. Polgar. The Hague: Mouton.

Harper, Douglas. 2003. Slavery in the North. http://www.slavenorth.com (accessed June, 2009).

Higley, Stephen Richard. 1995. *Privilege, power, and place: The geography of the American upper class.* Lanham, MD: Rowman & Littlefield.

Johnston, David Cay. 1999. Gap between rich and poor found substantially wider. *New York Times,* National, September 5, p. 16.

Klass, Morton. 2009. Is there "caste" outside of India? In MyAnthroLibrary, eds. C. R. Ember, M. Ember, and P. N. Peregrine. MyAnthroLibrary.com. Pearson.

Kristof, Nicholas D. 1995. Japan's invisible minority: Better off than in past, but still outcasts. *New York Times,* International, November 30, p. A18.

Kristof, Nicholas D. 1997. Japan's invisible minority: Burakumin. *Britannica Online,* December.

Lenski, Gerhard. 1984/1966. *Power and privilege: A theory of social stratification.* Chapel Hill: University of North Carolina Press.

Leonhardt, David, and Geraldine Fabrikant. 2009. Rise of the super-rich hits a sobering wall. *New York Times,* New York Edition, August 20, p. A1.

Lewis, Oscar (with the assistance of Victor Barnouw). 1958. *Village life in northern India.* Urbana: University of Illinois Press.

Marks, Jonathan. 1994. Black, white, other: Racial categories are cultural constructs masquerading as biology. *Natural History* (December):32–35.

Meek, Charles K. 1940. *Land law and custom in the colonies.* London: Oxford University Press.

Mitchell, Donald. 2009. Nimpkish: Complex foragers on the northwest coast of North America. In MyAnthroLibrary, eds. C. R. Ember, M. Ember, and P. N. Peregrine. MyAnthroLibrary.com. Pearson.

Nadel, Siegfried F. 1942. *A black Byzantium: The kingdom of Nupe in Nigeria.* London: Oxford University Press.

Nash, Manning. 1989. *The cauldron of ethnicity in the modern world.* Chicago: University of Chicago Press.

Newman, Katherine S. 1988. *Falling from grace: The experience of downward mobility in the American middle class.* New York: Free Press.

Newman, Katherine S. 1993. *Declining fortunes: The withering of the American dream.* New York: Basic Books.

Patterson, Orlando. 1982. *Slavery and social death: A comparative study.* Cambridge, MA: Harvard University Press.

Patterson, Orlando. 2000. Review of *One drop of blood: The American misadventure of race,* by Scott L. Malcomson. *New York Times Book Review,* October 22, pp. 15–16.

Phillips, Kevin. 1990. *The politics of rich and poor: Wealth and the American electorate in the Reagan aftermath.* New York: Random House.

Pryor, Frederic L. 1977. *The origins of the economy: A comparative study of distribution in primitive and peasant economies.* New York: Academic Press.

Ross, Marc Howard. 2009a. Ethnocentrism and ethnic conflict. In MyAnthroLibrary, eds. C. R. Ember, M. Ember, and P. N. Peregrine. MyAnthroLibrary.com. Pearson.

Ruskin, John. 1963. Of king's treasures. In *The genius of John Ruskin,* ed. J. D. Rosenberg. New York: Braziller.

Sahlins, Marshall D. 1958. *Social stratification in Polynesia.* Seattle: University of Washington Press.

Sahlins, Marshall D. 1972. *Stone Age economics.* Chicago: Aldine.

Service, Elman R. 1978. *Profiles in ethnology.* 3rd ed. New York: Harper & Row.

Smith, Michael G. 1966. Preindustrial stratification systems. In *Social structure and mobility in economic development,* eds. N. J. Smelser and S. M. Lipset. Chicago: Aldine.

Solon, Gary. 2002. Cross-country differences in intergenerational earnings mobility. *Journal of Economic Perspectives* 16:59–66.

Tamari, Tal. 1991. The development of caste systems in West Africa. *Journal of African History* 32:221–50.

Tamari, Tal. 2005. Kingship and caste in Africa: History, diffusion and evolution. In *The character of kingship,* ed. Declan Quigley, 141–70. Oxford, UK: Berg.

Taylor, Christopher C. 2005. Mutton, mud, and runny noses: A hierarchy of distaste in early Rwanda. *Social Analysis* 49:213–30.

Treiman, Donald J., and Harry B. G. Ganzeboom. 1990. Cross-national comparative status-attainment research. *Research in Social Stratification and Mobility* 9:117.

U.S. Census Bureau. 1993. *Statistical abstract of the United States: 1993,* 113th ed. Washington, DC: U.S. Government Printing Office.

U.S. Census Bureau. 2002. The big payoff: Educational entertainment and synthetic estimates of work-life earnings. *Statistical abstract of the United States: 1993,* 113th ed. Washington, DC: U.S. Government Printing Office. http://www.census.gov/prod/2002pubs/p23-210.pdf.

Williams, Melvin D. 2009. Racism: The production, reproduction, and obsolescence of social inferiority. In MyAnthroLibrary, eds. C. R. Ember, M. Ember, and P. N. Peregrine. MyAnthroLibrary.com. Pearson.

Yinger, J. Milton. 1994. *Ethnicity: Source of strength? Source of conflict?* Albany: State University Press.

Economics

CHAPTER OUTLINE

Getting Food

The Origin, Spread, and Intensification of Food Production

The Allocation of Resources

The Conversion of Resources

The Distribution of Goods and Services

The Worldwide Trend Toward Commercialization

From Chapter 5 of *Human Culture*, Second Edition. Carol R. Ember, Melvin Ember. Copyright © 2012 by Pearson Education, Inc. All rights reserved.

((•—[Listen to the **Chapter Audio** on **myanthrolab.com**   [▣]—[Read on **myanthrolab.com**

When we think of economics, we think of things and activities involving money. We think of the costs of goods and services, such as food, rent, haircuts, and movie tickets. We may also think of factories, farms, and other enterprises that produce the goods and services we need, or think we need. In industrial societies, workers may stand before a moving belt for 8 hours, tightening identical bolts that glide by. For this task, they are given bits of paper that may be exchanged for food, shelter, and other goods or services. But many societies—indeed, most that are known to anthropology—did not have money or the equivalent of the factory worker until relatively recently. Still, all societies have economic systems, whether or not they involve money. All societies have customary ways of getting food. They also have customs specifying how people gain access to natural resources; customary ways of transforming or converting those resources, through labor, into necessities and other desired goods and services. Finally, all societies have customs for distributing and perhaps exchanging goods and services.

As we shall see, a great deal of the cross-cultural variation in economic systems is related to how a society primarily gets its food. However, other aspects of the culture also affect the economies. These other influences include the presence or absence of social (class and gender) inequality, family and kinship groups, and the political system.

Getting Food

For most people in our society, getting food consists of a trip to the supermarket. Within an hour, we can gather enough food from the shelves to last us a week. Seasons don't daunt us. Week after week, we know food will be there. But we do not think of what would happen if the food were not delivered to the supermarket. We wouldn't be able to eat, and without eating for a while, we would die. Despite the old adage "Man [or woman] does not live by bread alone," we could not live at all without bread or the equivalent. Food-getting activities, then, take precedence over other activities important to survival. Reproduction, social control (the maintenance of peace and order within a group), defense against external threat, and the transmission of knowledge and skills to future generations—none could take place without energy derived from food. But it is not merely energy that is required for survival and long-term reproduction. Food-getting strategies need to provide the appropriate combination of nutrients throughout varying seasons and changing environmental conditions.

In this text, we look at the ways different societies get food and discuss some of the features associated with the different patterns.

Foraging

Foraging or *food collection* may be generally defined as a food-getting strategy that obtains wild plant and animal resources through gathering, hunting, scavenging, or fishing. Although this was the way humans got their food for most of human history, foragers in the world today, also commonly referred to as **hunter-gatherers,** are not very numerous, and most of them live in what have been called the *marginal areas* of the earth—deserts, the Arctic, and dense tropical forests—habitats that do not allow easy exploitation by modern agricultural technologies. In the last few hundred years, only about 5 million people are or were foragers.[1]

Anthropologists are interested in studying the relatively few foraging societies still available for observation because these groups may help us understand some aspects of human life in the past, when all people were foragers. But we must be cautious in drawing inferences about the past from our observations of recent and contemporary foragers, for three reasons. First, early foragers lived in almost all types of environments, including some very bountiful ones. Therefore, what we observe among recent and contemporary foragers—who generally live in deserts, the Arctic, and tropical forests—may not be comparable to what would have been observable in more favorable environments in the past.[2] Second, contemporary foragers are not relics of the past. Like all contemporary societies, they have evolved and are still evolving. Indeed, recent research reveals considerable variation in economic behavior as well as in social structure in foraging groups that share common ancestry; this implies that recent foragers have responded to differences in local environmental conditions.[3] Third, recent and contemporary foragers have been interacting with kinds of societies that did not exist until after 10,000 years ago—agriculturalists, pastoralists, and intrusive, powerful state societies.[4] For example, evidence from South Asia and Southeast Asia suggests that trade with agriculturalists was probably an important component of foragers' economic strategies for millennia.[5] And, in the recent past, foraging people have increasingly depended on agriculture and commercial activities as well as trade, so what we see recently may be very different from the distant past when foraging was the only means of subsistence. Let us examine one area of the world where recent foragers were the only inhabitants until about 200 years ago.

Australian Aborigines Before Europeans came to the Australian continent, all the aboriginal people who lived there depended on foraging. Although the way of life of Australian aborigines is now considerably altered, we consider the life of the Ngatatjara as described by Richard Gould in the 1960s, when they still lived by gathering wild plants and hunting wild animals in the Gibson Desert of western Australia.[6]

The desert environment of the Ngatatjara averages less than 8 inches of rain per year, and the temperature in summer may rise to 118°F. The few permanent water holes are separated by hundreds of square miles of sand, scrub, and rock. Even before Europeans arrived in Australia, the area was sparsely populated—fewer than one person per 35–40 square miles. Now there are even fewer people because the aboriginal population was decimated by introduced diseases and mistreatment after the Europeans arrived.

On a typical day, the camp begins to stir just before sunrise, while it is still dark. Children are sent to fetch water, and the people breakfast on water and food left over from the night before. In the cool of the early morning, the adults talk and make plans for the day. The talking goes on for a while. Where should they go for food—to places they have been to recently or to new places? Sometimes there are other considerations. For example, one woman may want to search for plants whose bark she needs to make new sandals. When the women decide which plants they want to gather and where they think those plants are most likely to be found, they take up their digging sticks and set out with large wooden bowls of drinking water on their heads. Their children ride on their hips or walk alongside. Meanwhile, the men may have decided to hunt emus, 6-foot-tall ostrichlike birds that do not fly. The men go to a creek bed where they will wait to ambush any game that may come along. They lie patiently behind a screen of brush they have set up, hoping for a chance to throw a spear at an emu or even a kangaroo. They can throw only once because the game will run away if they miss.

By noon, the men and women are usually back at camp, the women with their wooden bowls each filled with up to 15 pounds of fruit or other plant foods, the men more often than not with only some small game, such as lizards and rabbits. The men's food-getting is less certain of success than the women's, so most of the Ngatatjara aborigines' diet is plant food. The daily cooked meal is eaten toward evening, after an afternoon spent resting, gossiping, and making or repairing tools.

The aborigines traditionally were nomadic, moving their campsites fairly frequently. The campsites were isolated and inhabited by only a small number of people, or they were clusters of groups including as many as 80 people. The aborigines never established a campsite right next to a place with water. If they were too close, their presence would frighten away game and might cause tension with neighboring bands, who would also wait for game to come to the scarce watering spots.

Today, many aborigines live in small settled villages. For example, in the 1980s, Victoria Burbank worked in a village she calls "Mangrove" in the Northern Territory of Australia. The once-nomadic aborigines now live in a village of about 600, which was founded in the 1950s around a Protestant mission. Their houses have stoves, refrigerators, toilets, washing machines, and even television sets. Their children attend school full time, and there is a health clinic for their medical needs. They still do some foraging, but most of their food comes from the store. Some earn wages, but many subsist on government welfare checks.[7]

General Features of Foragers Despite the differences in terrain and climate under which they live and the different food-collecting technologies they use, Australian aborigines and most other recent foragers have certain characteristic cultural patterns (see Table 1). Most live in small communities in sparsely populated territories and follow a nomadic lifestyle, forming no permanent settlements. As a rule, they do not recognize individuals' land rights. Their communities generally do not have different classes of people and tend to have no specialized or

TABLE 1 Variation in Food-Getting and Associated Features

	Food Collectors	Food Producers		
	Foragers	Horticulturalists	Pastoralists	Intensive Agriculturalists
Population density	Lowest	Low to moderate	Low	Highest
Maximum community size	Small	Small to moderate	Small	Large (towns and cities)
Nomadism/ permanence of settlements	Generally nomadic or seminomadic	More sedentary: communities may move after several years	Generally nomadic or seminomadic	Permanent communities
Food shortages	Infrequent	Infrequent	Frequent	Frequent
Trade	Minimal	Minimal	Very important	Very important
Full-time craft specialists	None	None or few	Some	Many (high degree of craft specialization)
Individual differences in wealth	Generally none	Generally minimal	Moderate	Considerable
Political leadership	Informal	Some part-time political officials	Part- and full-time political officials	Many full-time political officials

full-time political officials.[8] Division of labor in foraging societies is based largely on age and gender: Men exclusively hunt large marine and land animals and usually do most of the fishing, and women usually gather wild plant foods.[9]

Is there a typical pattern of food-getting among foragers? Many anthropologists have assumed that foragers typically get their food more from gathering than from hunting, and that women contribute more than men to subsistence, because women generally do the gathering.[10] Although gathering is the most important food-getting activity for some foragers (e.g., the Ngatatjara aborigines and the San of southern Africa), this is not true for most food-collecting societies known to us. A survey of 180 such societies indicates that there is a lot of variation with regard to which food-getting activity is most important to the society. Gathering is the most important activity for 30 percent of the surveyed societies, hunting for 25 percent, and fishing for 38 percent. (That is why we prefer the term *foragers* rather than the often-used *hunter-gatherers;* the term "foragers" allows us to recognize the importance of fishing.) In any case, because men generally do the fishing as well as the hunting, the men usually contribute more to food-getting than do the women among recent foragers.[11]

Because foragers move their camps often and walk great distances, it may seem that the food-collecting way of life is difficult. Although we do not have enough quantitative studies to tell us what is typical of most foragers, studies of two Australian aborigine groups[12] and of one San group[13] indicate that those foragers do not spend many hours getting food. For example, San adults spend an average of about 17 hours per week collecting food. Even when you add the time spent making tools (about 6 hours a week) and doing housework (about 19 hours a week), the San seem to have more leisure time than many agriculturalists, as we discuss later.

When we say that foragers tend to have certain traits, this does not mean that all of them have those traits. There is considerable variability among societies that depend on foraging. Foraging societies that depend heavily on fishing (such as on the Pacific Coast of the northwestern United States and Canada or on the south coast of New Guinea) are more likely to have bigger and more permanent communities and more social inequality than foraging societies elsewhere who mostly depend on game and plants.[14] The Pacific Coast and New Guinea coastal people also tend to have higher population densities, food storage,[15] occupational specialization, resource ownership, slavery, and competitiveness.[16] Two foraging groups that depended heavily on annual salmon runs were the Tlingit of southeastern Alaska and the Nimpkish of British Columbia. Both groups had a three-tiered class system with a high class, commoners, and slaves. The high-status individuals were obliged to stage competitive elaborate feasts and distributions of valuables.[17] This type of inequality and competitiveness was very different from what we find in typical foragers, who generally show little social differentiation. In New Guinea, Paul Roscoe has found that the amount of dependence upon fishing is strongly associated with density of population and settlement size. For example, societies with more than 75 percent dependence upon fishing have average community sizes of about 350 people, as compared with community size of about 50 for those with less than 25 percent dependence upon fishing. Some villages were much larger. One Asmat village had over 1,400 people and a Waropen village over 1,700.[18]

Food Production

Beginning about 10,000 years ago, certain peoples in widely separated geographic locations made the revolutionary changeover to **food production.** That is, they began to cultivate and then domesticate plants and animals. (Domesticated plants and animals are different from the ancestral wild forms.) With domestication of these food sources, people acquired control over certain natural processes, such as animal breeding and plant seeding. Today, most peoples in the world depend for their food on some combination of domesticated plants and animals.

Anthropologists generally distinguish three major types of food production systems: *horticulture, intensive agriculture,* and *pastoralism.*

Horticulture The word **horticulture** may conjure up visions of people with "green thumbs" growing orchids and other flowers in greenhouses. But to anthropologists, the word means the growing of crops of all kinds with relatively simple tools and methods, in the absence of permanently cultivated fields. The tools are usually hand tools, such as the digging stick or hoe, not plows or other equipment pulled by animals or tractors. And the methods used do not include fertilization, irrigation, or other ways to restore soil fertility after a growing season.

There are two kinds of horticulture. The more common one involves a dependence on **extensive (shifting) cultivation.** The land is worked for short periods and then left idle for some years. During the years when the land is not cultivated, wild plants and brush grow; when the fields are later cleared by *slash-and-burn techniques,* nutrients are returned to the soil. The other kind of horticulture involves a dependence on long-growing tree crops. The two kinds of horticulture may be practiced in the same society, but in neither case is there permanent cultivation of field crops.

Most horticultural societies do not rely on crops alone for food. Many also hunt or fish; a few are nomadic for part of the year. For example, the Kayapo of the Brazilian Amazon leave their villages for as long as 3 months at a time to trek through the forest in search of game. The entire village participates in a trek, carrying large quantities of garden produce and moving their camp every day.[19] Other horticulturalists raise domestic animals, but these are usually not large animals, such as cattle and camels.[20] More often than not, horticulturalists raise smaller animals, such as pigs, chickens, goats, and sheep.

Let us look now at a horticultural society, the Yanomamö of the Brazilian–Venezuelan Amazon.

A Yanomamö boy peels cassava.

The Yanomamö Dense tropical forest covers most of Yanomamö territory. From the air, the typical village is located in a forest clearing and looks like a single, large, circular lean-to with its inner side open to the central plaza. Each individual family has its own portion of the lean-to under a common roof and each has a back wall (part of the closed back wall around the circular village structure), but the portions are open on the sides to each other as well as onto the central plaza of the village. The Yanomamö get most of their calories from garden produce, but according to Raymond Hames, the Yanomamö actually spend most of their time foraging.[21]

Before the people can plant, the forest must be cleared of trees and brush. Like most shifting cultivators, the Yanomamö use a combination of techniques: slashing the undergrowth, felling trees, and using controlled burning to clear a garden spot—in other words, **slash-and-burn** horticulture. Before the

1950s, the Yanomamö had only stone axes, so felling trees was quite difficult. Now they have steel machetes and axes given or traded to them by missionaries.

Because of the work involved in clearing a garden, the Yanomamö prefer to make use of forest patches that have little thorny brush and not too many large trees.[22] After the ground is cleared, the Yanomamö plant plantains, manioc, sweet potatoes, taro, and a variety of plants for medicine, condiments, and craft materials. Men do the heavy clearing work to prepare a garden, and they as well as women plant the crops. Women usually go to the gardens daily to weed and harvest. After two or three years, the yields diminish and the forest starts growing back, making continued cultivation less desirable and more difficult, so they abandon the garden and clear a new one. If they can, they clear adjacent forest, but if gardens are far from the village, they will move the village to a new location. Villages are moved about every 5 years because of gardening needs and warfare. There is a great deal of intervillage raiding, so villages are often forced to flee to another location.

Extensive cultivation requires a lot of territory because new gardens are not cleared until the forest grows back. What is often misunderstood is why it is so important to shift gardens. Not only is a burned field easier to plant, but the organic matter that is burned provides necessary nutrients for a good yield. If horticulturalists come back too quickly to a spot with little plant cover, a garden made there will not produce a satisfactory yield.

The Yanomamö crops do not provide much protein, so hunting and fishing are important to their diet. Men hunt birds, peccaries, monkeys, and tapir with bows and arrows. Women, men, and children enjoy fishing. They catch fish by hand, with small bows and arrows, and by stream poisoning. Everybody gathers honey, hearts of palm, Brazil nuts, and cashews, although the men usually climb trees to shake down the nuts. Much of the foraging is done from the village base, but the Yanomamö, like the Kayapo, may go on treks to forage from time to time.

General Features of Horticulturalists In most horticultural societies, simple farming techniques have tended to yield more food from a given area than is generally available to foragers. Consequently, horticulture is able to support larger, more densely populated communities. The way of life of horticulturalists is more sedentary than that of foragers, although communities may move after some years to farm a new series of plots. (Some horticulturalists have permanent villages because they depend mostly on food from trees that keep producing for a long time.) In contrast with most recent food-collecting groups, horticultural societies exhibit the beginnings of social differentiation. For example, some individuals may be part-time craftworkers or part-time political officials, and certain members of a kin group may have more status than other individuals in the society.

Intensive Agriculture People engaged in **intensive agriculture** use techniques that enable them to cultivate fields permanently. Essential nutrients may be put back in the soil through the use of fertilizers, which may be organic material (most commonly dung from humans or other animals) or inorganic (chemical) fertilizers. But there are other ways to restore nutrients. The Luo of western Kenya plant beans around corn plants. Bacteria growing around the roots of the bean plant replace lost nitrogen, and the corn plant conveniently provides a pole for the bean plant to wind around as it grows. Some intensive agriculturalists use irrigation from streams and rivers to ensure an adequate supply of waterborne nutrients. Crop rotation and plant stubble that has been plowed under also restore nutrients to the soil.

In general, the technology of intensive agriculturalists is more complex than that of horticulturalists. Plows rather than digging sticks are generally employed. But there is enormous variation in the degree to which intensive agriculturalists rely on mechanization rather than hand labor. In some societies, the most complex machine is an animal-drawn plow; in the corn and wheat belts of the United States, huge tractors till, seed, and fertilize 12 rows at a time.[23]

Let's look at one group of intensive agriculturalists, those of the Mekong Delta in Vietnam.

Rural Vietnam: The Mekong Delta The village of Khanh Hau, situated along the flat Mekong Delta, comprised about 600 families when Gerald Hickey described it in the late 1950s, before the Vietnam War.[24] The delta area has a tropical climate, with a rainy season that lasts from May to November. As a whole, the area has been made habitable only through extensive drainage.

Wet rice cultivation is the principal agricultural activity of Khanh Hau. It is part of a complex, specialized arrangement that involves three interacting components: (1) a complex system of irrigation and water control; (2) a variety of specialized equipment, including plows, waterwheels, threshing sledges, and winnowing machines; and (3) a clearly defined set of socioeconomic roles—from those of landlord, tenant, and laborer to those of rice miller and rice merchant.

In the dry season, the farmer decides what sort of rice crop to plant, whether of long (120 days) or short (90 days) maturation. The choice depends on the capital at his disposal, the current cost of fertilizer, and the anticipated demand for rice. The seedbeds are prepared as soon as the rains have softened the ground in May. The soil is turned over (plowed) and broken up (harrowed) as many as six separate times, with two-day intervals for "airing" between operations. During this time, the rice seeds are soaked in water for at least 2 days to stimulate sprouting. Before the seedlings are planted, the paddy is plowed once more and harrowed twice in two directions at right angles.

Planting is a delicate, specialized operation that must be done quickly and is performed most often by hired male laborers. But efficient planting is not enough to guarantee a good crop. Proper fertilization and irrigation are equally important. In the irrigating, steps must be taken to ensure that the water level remains at exactly the proper depth over the entire paddy. Water is distributed by means of scoops, wheels, and mechanical pumps. Successive crops of rice ripen

Vietnamese farmers in the Mekong Delta working in a flooded rice paddy. Much of the delta was originally tropical forest.

from late September to May; all members of the family may be called upon to help with the harvest. After each crop is harvested, it is threshed, winnowed, and dried. Normally, the rice is sorted into three portions: one is set aside for use by the household in the following year; one is for payment of hired labor and other services (such as loans from agricultural banks); and one is for cash sale on the market. Aside from the harvesting, women do little work in the fields, spending most of their time on household chores. In families with little land, however, young daughters help in the fields and older daughters may hire themselves out to other farmers.

The villagers also cultivate vegetables; raise pigs, chickens, and other animals; and frequently engage in fishing. The village economy usually supports three or four implement makers and a much larger number of carpenters.

General Features of Intensive Agricultural Societies Societies with intensive agriculture are more likely than horticulturalists to have towns and cities, a high degree of craft specialization, complex political organization, and large differences in wealth and power. Studies suggest that intensive agriculturalists work longer hours than horticulturalists.[25] For example, men engaged in intensive agriculture average 9 hours of work a day, 7 days a week; women average almost 11 hours of work per day. Most of the work for women in intensive agricultural societies involves food processing and work in and around the home, but they also spend a lot of time working in the fields.

Intensive agricultural societies are more likely than horticultural societies to face famines and food shortages, even though intensive agriculture is generally more productive than horticulture.[26] Why, if more food can be produced per acre, is there more risk of shortage among intensive agriculturalists? Intensive agriculturalists may be more likely to face food shortages because they are often producing crops for a market. Producing for a market pushes farmers to cultivate plants that give them the highest yield rather than cultivating plants that are drought-resistant or that require fewer nutrients. Farmers producing for a market also tend to concentrate on one crop. Crop diversity is often a protection against total crop failure because fluctuations in weather, plant diseases, or insect pests are not likely to affect all the crops. There are also fluctuations in market demand. If the market demand drops and the price falls for a particular crop, farmers may not have enough cash to buy the other food they need.

The Commercialization and Mechanization of Agriculture Some intensive agriculturalists produce very little for sale; most of what they produce is for their own use. But there is a worldwide trend for intensive agriculturalists to produce more and more for a market. This trend is called **commercialization,** which may occur in any area of life and which involves increasing dependence on buying and selling, usually with money as the medium of exchange. Some of the push toward commercialization comes from external pressures, from governments that impose taxes that must be paid by money. But some of the shift occurs when subsistence farmers choose to plant a cash crop to earn money for various reasons. For example, the Malaiyali farmers of India grow a cash crop, tapioca (cassava), as a way of responding to unpredictable rainfall. Tapioca is fairly drought-tolerant, grows in poor soils, and can be planted later in the year when the rainfall has become more predictable.[27]

The increasing commercialization of agriculture is associated with several other trends. One is that farm work is becoming more mechanized as hand labor becomes scarce, because of migration to industrial and service jobs in towns and cities, or because hired hand labor has become too expensive. A second trend is the emergence and spread of *agribusiness,* large corporation-owned farms that may be operated by multinational companies and worked entirely by hired, as opposed to family, labor. For example, consider how cotton farming has changed in the southeastern United States. In the 1930s, tractors replaced mules and horses used in plowing. This change allowed some landowners to evict their sharecroppers and expand their holdings. After World War II, mechanical cotton pickers replaced most of the harvest laborers. But a farmer had to have a good deal of money to acquire those machines, each of which cost many tens of thousands of dollars.[28] So the mechanization of cotton farming sent many rural farm laborers off to the cities of the North in search of employment, and the agricultural sector increasingly became big business. A third trend associated with the commercialization of agriculture, including animal raising, is a reduction in the proportion of the population engaged in food production. In the United States today, for example, less than 1 percent of the total population work on farms.[29] A fourth trend is that much of what people produce for sale nowadays is shipped to or received from markets in other countries. For example, in the summer months, fruits and vegetables are often shipped to markets where consumers have little local fresh produce.

Pastoralism Most agriculturalists keep and breed some animals (practice animal husbandry), but a small number of societies depend mostly for their living on domesticated herds of animals that feed on natural pasture.[30] We call such a system **pastoralism.** We might assume that pastoralists breed animals to eat their meat, but most do not. Pastoralists more often get their animal protein from live animals in the form of milk, and some pastoralists regularly take blood, which is rich in protein, from their animals to mix with other foods. The herds often indirectly provide food because many pastoralists trade animal products for plant foods and other necessities. In fact, a large proportion of their food may actually come from trade with agricultural groups.[31] For example, some pastoral groups in the Middle East derive much of their livelihood from the sale of what we call oriental rugs, which are made from the wool of their sheep on hand looms. One pastoral society we examine are the Saami or Lapps of Scandinavia.

The Saami The Saami practice reindeer herding in northwestern Scandinavia where Finland, Sweden, and Norway share common frontiers. It is a typical Arctic habitat: cold, windswept, with long, dark days for half the year. Considerable change has occurred recently, so we first discuss the food-getting strategy in the 1950s, as described by Ian Whitaker and T. I. Itkonen.[32]

A Saami reindeer herder feeds two of her animals in the snow.

The Saami herd their reindeer either intensively or, more often, extensively. In the *intensive system,* the herd is constantly under observation within a fenced area for the whole year. Intensively herded reindeer and other animals are accustomed to human contact. Hence, the summer corralling of the females for milking and the breaking-in of the oxen for use as work animals are not difficult tasks. The *extensive system* involves allowing the animals to migrate over a large area. It requires little surveillance and encompasses large herds. Under this system, the reindeer are allowed to move through their seasonal feeding cycles watched by only one or two scouts. The other Saami stay with the herd only when it has settled in its summer or winter habitat. But milking, breaking-in, and corralling are harder in the extensive than in the intensive system because the animals are less accustomed to humans.

Even under the extensive system, which theoretically permits Saami to engage in subsidiary economic activities such as hunting and fishing, the reindeer herd is the essential, if not the only, source of income. A family might possess as many as 1,000 reindeer, but usually the figure is half that number. Studies show 200 to be the minimum number of reindeer needed to provide for a family of four or five adults. Women may have shared the herding chores in the past under the intensive system, but now, under the extensive system, men do the herding. Women still do the milking. The Saami eat the meat of the bull reindeer; the female reindeer are kept for breeding purposes. Bulls are slaughtered in the fall, after the mating season. Meat and hides are frequently sold or bartered for other food and necessities.

Reindeer are still herded nowadays, but snowmobiles, all-terrain vehicles, and even helicopters have replaced sleds for herding. Ferries move reindeer to and from different pastures, and the herders communicate by field telephones. With faster transportation, many Saami now live in permanent homes and can still get to their herds in hours. Saami children spend much of their time in school and, consequently, do not learn much of the herding ways. The Norwegian government now regulates pastoralism, licensing pastoralists and trying to limit the number of reindeer they can herd.[33] And many Saami no longer have reindeer.

General Features of Pastoralism In recent times, pastoralism has been practiced mainly in grassland and other semiarid habitats that are not especially suitable for cultivation without some significant technological input such as irrigation. Most pastoralists are nomadic, moving camp fairly frequently to find water and new pasture for their herds. But other pastoralists have somewhat more sedentary lives. They may move from one settlement to another in different seasons, or they may send some people out to travel with the herds in different seasons. Pastoral communities are usually small, consisting of a group of related families.[34] Individuals or families may own their own animals, but the community makes decisions about when and where to move the herds. There is a great deal of interdependence between pastoral and agricultural groups. That is, trade is usually necessary for pastoral groups to survive. Like agriculturalists, pastoralists are more vulnerable than foragers and horticulturalists to famine and food shortages. Pastoralists usually inhabit drought-prone regions, but recent pastoralists have had their access to grazing lands reduced, and political pressures have pushed them to decrease their movement over large areas. Mobility kept the risk of overgrazing to a minimum, but overgrazing in small territories has increased the risk of desertification.[35]

The Origin, Spread, and Intensification of Food Production

We see the first evidence of a changeover to food production—the cultivation and domestication of plants and animals—in the Near East about 8000 B.C. This shift occurred, probably independently, in other areas as well. There is evidence of cultivation some time around 6000 B.C. in China, Southeast Asia (what is now Malaysia, Thailand, Cambodia, and Vietnam), and Africa. In the New World, there appear to have been several places of original cultivation and domestication. The highlands of Mexico (about 7000 B.C.) and the central Andes around Peru (by about 6000 B.C.) were probably the most important in terms of food plants used today.

There are many theories of why food production developed; most have tried to explain the origin of domestication in the Near East. The possible reasons include the following:

1. Population growth in regions of bountiful wild resources pushed people to move to marginal areas, where they tried to reproduce their former abundance.

2. Global population growth filled up most of the world's habitable regions and forced people to utilize a broader spectrum of wild resources and to domesticate plants and animals.

3. Climatic change—hotter, drier summers and colder winters—favored settling near seasonal stands of wild grain; population growth in such areas would force people to plant crops and raise animals.

Whatever the reasons for the switch to food production, we still need to explain why food production has supplanted foraging as the primary mode of subsistence. We cannot assume that collectors would automatically adopt production as a superior way of life once they understood the process of domestication. After all, as we have noted, domestication may entail more work and provide less security than the food-collecting way of life.

The spread of agriculture may be linked to the need for territorial expansion. As a sedentary, food-producing population grew, it may have been forced to expand into new territory. Some of this territory may have been vacant, but foragers probably already occupied much of it. Although food production is not necessarily easier than collection, it is generally more productive per unit of land. Greater productivity enables more people to be supported in a given territory. In the competition for land between the faster-expanding food producers and the foragers, the food producers may have had a significant advantage: They had more people in a given area. Thus, the foraging groups may have been more likely to lose out in the competition for land. Some groups may have adopted cultivation, abandoning the foraging way of life to survive. Other groups, continuing as foragers, may have been forced to retreat into areas not desired by the cultivators. Today, as we have seen, the small number of remaining foragers inhabit areas not particularly suitable for cultivation—dry lands, dense tropical forests, and polar regions.

Just as prior population growth might account for the origins of domestication, further population growth and ensuing pressure on resources at later periods might also at least partly explain the transformation of horticultural systems into intensive agricultural systems. Ester Boserup suggested that intensification of agriculture, with a consequent increase in yield per acre, is not likely to develop naturally out of horticulture because intensification requires much more work.[36] She argued that people will be willing to intensify their labor only if they have to. Where emigration is not feasible, the prime mover behind intensification may be prior population growth. The need to pay taxes or tribute to a political authority may also stimulate intensification.

This area of Montana is cultivated now. In the past, only foraging was practiced.

The Effect of Food-Getting on the Environment

Many people are now aware of industrial pollution—the dumping of industrial wastes in the ground or into rivers, the spewing of chemicals into the air through smokestacks—but we don't often realize how much humans have altered the environment by the ways they collect and produce food. Consider irrigation. Irrigation has made agriculture productive in arid or unpredictable rainfall environments. There are various ways to capture water for irrigation. Water can be channeled from rivers; rainwater can be caught in terraces carved out of hillsides; ancient water can be pumped up from vast underground reservoirs called aquifers. But much of the water use is wasteful, seeping into the channels or evaporating into the air before reaching the plants. Plants absorb water and leave behind the salts. But the extensive evaporation of water during irrigation mostly leads to higher concentration of minerals and salts. If drainage is poor and if the water table rises, the salt concentrations are not washed away. Often, the more a piece of land has been irrigated, the saltier the ground becomes. Eventually, the soil becomes too salty to grow crops effectively and crops have to be grown elsewhere.

Some archaeologists have suggested that the accumulation of toxic salts in the soil at least partly explains the doom or decline of various groups in the past. For example, salinization probably contributed to the decline of Sumer, an early empire in Mesopotamia, and other early states in what is now southern Iraq and southwestern Iran. Over time, the concentration of people shifted from the lower portion of the Tigris-Euphrates river system to the upper portion as irrigated land lower down became unusable for farming. Today, much of the soil is still too salty for cultivation. Recent irrigation schemes during Saddam Hussein's regime have seriously degraded the downstream Iraqi marshes. Less than 10 percent of the marsh wetlands remain, putting over 60 bird species at risk. In addition, the loss of the marshlands has reduced the ability of the marshland to filter the water before it reaches the Persian Gulf, which has led to declines in productivity of the coastal fisheries. The severity of the degradation in the region has been compared with the deforestation of the Amazon.

The lessons of history have not yet been learned. The San Joaquin Valley of California, perhaps the most productive agricultural area in the world, now has a serious salinization problem. One solution in many of the areas of the Great American Desert is to pump water up from underground. Indeed, in many places there is a great deal of water underground. For example, the Ogallala aquifer, which underlies parts of Nebraska, Kansas, Texas, Oklahoma, Colorado, and New Mexico, contains water left from the ice ages. But the pumping solution, if it is a solution, is only a short-term fix, for the huge Ogallala aquifer is also the fastest-disappearing aquifer. The only question is how long it will take to disappear totally.

Too many people raising too many animals can also have serious effects on the environment. We can easily imagine how the possibility of profit might inspire people to try to raise more animals than the land will support. For example, 300 years ago the Great American Desert was a vast grassland. It supported large herds of buffalo, which were all but exterminated by overhunting in the next 200 years. The European-American settlers soon discovered they could raise cattle and sheep on this grassland, but many parts of it were overgrazed. It took the swirling dust storms of the 1930s to make people realize that overgrazing as well as poor farming practices could be disastrous. The problems are not just recent ones. The Norse colonized Greenland and Iceland around A.D. 800; but overgrazing of pasture undoubtedly contributed to soil erosion and the disappearance or decline of the colonies by A.D. 1500.

Are environmental problems associated only with food production? Although food producers may be the worst offenders, there is reason to think that foragers may also have sometimes overfished, overgathered, or overhunted. For example, some scholars suspect that the movement of humans into the New World was mainly responsible for the disappearance of the mammoth. Unfortunately, there is little evidence that humans have been good conservers in the past. That does not mean that humans cannot do better in the future—but they have to want to.

Sources: Curtis et al. 2005; Dirks 2009; *Los Angeles Times* 1994; Hillel 2000; Reisner 1993.

However, Boserup's assumption that more work is required with intensive agriculture has recently been questioned. Comparing horticultural (swidden or shifting) rice production with rice produced on permanent fields using irrigation, Robert Hunt found that *less*, not more, labor is required with irrigation.[37] Still, population increase may generally provide the impetus to intensify production to increase yields to support the additional people.

Intensive agriculture has not yet spread to every part of the world. Horticulture continues to be practiced in certain tropical regions, and there are still some pastoralists and foragers. Some environments may make it somewhat more difficult to adopt certain subsistence practices. For example, intensive agriculture cannot supplant horticulture in some tropical environments without tremendous investments in chemical fertilizers and pesticides, not to mention the additional labor required.[38] And enormous amounts of water may be required to make agriculturalists out of foragers and pastoralists who now exploit semiarid environments. However, difficulty is not impossibility. Anna Roosevelt points out that, although horticulture was a common food-getting strategy in Amazonia in recent times, archaeological evidence indicates that there were complex societies practicing intensive agriculture on raised, drained fields in the past.[39] The physical environment does not completely control what can be done with it.

The Allocation of Resources

Natural Resources: Land

Every society has access to natural resources—land, water, plants, animals, minerals—and every society has cultural rules for determining who has access to particular resources and what can be done with them. In societies like the United States, where land and many other things may be bought and sold, land is divided into precisely measurable units, the borders of which may be visible or invisible. Individuals usually own relatively small plots of land and the resources on them. Large plots of land are generally owned collectively. The owner may be a government agency, such as the National Park Service, which owns land on behalf of the entire population of the United States (referred to as public ownership). Or the owner may be a corporation—a private collective of shareholders. In the United States, property ownership entails a more or less exclusive right to use land or other resources (called *usufruct*) in whatever ways the owner wishes, including the right to withhold or prevent use by others. In the United States and many other societies, property ownership also includes the right to "alienate" property—that is, to sell, give away, bequeath, or destroy the resources owned. This type of property ownership by individuals, families, or private corporations is often referred to as a *private property* system.

Society specifies what is considered property and the rights and duties associated with that property.[40] These specifications are social in nature, for they may be changed over time. For example, France declared all its beaches to be public, thereby stating, in effect, that the ocean shore is not a resource that an individual can own. As a result, all the hotels and individuals that had fenced-off portions of the best beaches for their exclusive use had to remove the barriers. Even in countries with private property, such as the United States, people cannot do anything that they want with their property. Federal, state, and local governments have adopted legislation to prevent the pollution of the air and the water supply. Such regulation may be new, but the rights of ownership in the United States have been limited for some time. For example, government may take land for use in the construction of a highway; compensation is paid, but the individual cannot prevent confiscation. Similarly, people are not allowed to burn their houses or to use them as brothels or munitions arsenals. In short, even with an individualistic system of ownership, property is not entirely private.

Economics

How societies differ in their rules for access to land and other natural resources seems to be related in part to how they differ in food-getting. Let us now examine how foragers, horticulturalists, pastoralists, and intensive agriculturalists structure rights to land in different ways. We look at traditional patterns first. As we shall see later, traditional rights to land have been considerably affected by state societies that have spread to and colonized native societies in the New World, Africa, and Asia.

Foragers Members of food-collecting societies generally do not have private ownership of land. If there is collective ownership, it is always by groups of related people (kinship groups) or by territorial groups (bands or villages). Land is not bought and sold. The reason is probably that land itself generally has no intrinsic value for foragers; what is of value is the presence of game and wild plant life on the land. If game moves away or food resources become less plentiful, the land is less valuable. Therefore, the greater the possibility that the wild food supply in a particular locale will fluctuate, the less desirable it is to parcel out small areas of land to individuals and the more advantageous it is to make land ownership communal. This is not to say that private ownership of land does not exist among foragers. Among foragers heavily dependent on fishing in rivers, individual or family ownership is more common,[41] perhaps because the fishing in rivers is more predictable than other kinds of foraging. And, in some foraging societies, individuals and families have private rights to trees.[42] It is more common in food-collecting societies for a group of individuals, usually kin, to "own" land. To be sure, such ownership is not usually exclusive; typically, some degree of access is provided to members of neighboring bands.[43]

Horticulturalists Like foragers, most horticulturalists do not have individual or family ownership of land. This may be because rapid depletion of the soil necessitates letting some of the land lie fallow for a period of years or abandoning an area after a few years and moving to a new

A Surui village in the Amazon with cleared land for horticulture in the foreground and the surrounding rain forest in the background.

location. There is no reason for individuals or families to claim permanent access to land that, given available technology, is not usable permanently. But, in contrast to foragers, horticulturalists are more likely to allocate particular plots of land to individuals or families for their use, although these individuals or families do not commonly own the land in our sense of potentially permanent ownership. For example, among the Mundurucú of Brazil, the village controls the rights to use land. People in the community can hunt and fish where they like, and they have the right to clear a garden plot wherever land belonging to the community is not being used. Gardens can be cultivated for only 2 years before the soil is exhausted, then the land reverts to the community. The Mundurucú distinguish between the land and the produce on the land, so that a person who cultivates the land owns the produce. Similarly, the person who kills an animal or catches a fish owns it, no matter where it was obtained. But because all food is shared with others, it does not really matter who owns it. Rights to land became more individualized when Mundurucú men began to tap rubber trees for sale. Rights to a particular path in the forest where trees were tapped could not be bought and sold, but the rights could be inherited by a son or son-in-law.[44]

Pastoralists The territory of pastoral nomads usually far exceeds that of most horticultural societies. Because their wealth ultimately depends on mobile herds, uncultivated pasture for grazing, and water for drinking, pastoralists often combine the adaptive potential of both foragers and horticulturalists. Like foragers, they generally need to know the potential of a large area of land. For example, the Basseri of southern Iran moved over an area of 15,000 square miles to obtain supplies of grass and water. And, like horticulturalists, pastoralists must move on when a resource is exhausted (in this case, until grass renews itself). Also like horticulturalists, they depend for subsistence on human manipulation of a natural resource—animals—as opposed to the horticulturalists' land.

Because land is only good if there is sufficient pasture and water, there would be considerable risk to individuals or families to own land that did not predictably have grass and water. So, like most foragers and horticulturalists, community members generally have free access to pasture land.[45] Although grazing land tends to be communally held, it is customary for pastoralist individuals to own animals.[46]

As among hunter-gatherers, pastoralists vary in how much a group actually has ownership rights to the territories through which they move their animals. The Basseri have rights to pass through certain areas, including agricultural areas and even cities, but they do not own the entire territory. The Baluch, another pastoralist group in the border region between Iran, Pakistan, and Afghanistan, claim a "tribal" territory, which they defend by force, if necessary.[47]

Intensive Agriculturalists Individual ownership of land resources—including the right to use the resources and the right to sell or otherwise dispose of them—is common among intensive agriculturalists. The development of such ownership is partly a result of the possibility of using land season after season, which gives the land more or less permanent value. But the concept of individual ownership is also partly a political and social matter. So, for example, the occupation and cultivation of frontier land in the United States was transformed by law into individual ownership. Under the Homestead Act of 1862, if a person cleared a 160-acre piece of land and farmed it for five years, the federal government would consider that person the owner of the land. This practice is similar to the custom in some societies by which a kin group, a chief, or a community is obligated to assign a parcel of land to anyone who wishes to farm it. The difference is that, once the American homesteader had become the owner of the land, the laws of the country gave the homesteader the right to dispose of it at will by selling or giving it away. Once individual ownership of land has become established, property owners may use their economic, and hence political, power to pass laws that favor themselves. In the early years of the United States, only property owners could vote.

Colonialism, the State, and Land Rights Almost universally around the world, colonial conquerors and settlers have taken land away from the natives or aborigines. Even if the natives were given other land in exchange, as in Brazil and the United States, these reservations were often, if not always, poorer in potential than the original land. (If the reservation land hadn't been poorer in quality,

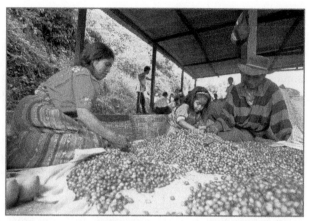

Colonial governments have often taken land away from the natives to establish plantations. A family in Guatemala works on a coffee plantation.

the settlers would have taken it for themselves.)[48] In addition, the new centralized governments often tried to change how the natives owned the land, almost always in the direction of individual or private ownership. If kin groups or larger social entities owned the land, it would be more difficult for the settlers to get the natives to give it up, either by sale or threat. Individual owners could be dispossessed more easily.[49]

This is not to say that native peoples in Africa, Asia, and the New World were never guilty of conquering and exploiting others on their continents or elsewhere. They were. The Aztecs in Mexico and Central America, the native kingdoms in West Africa after about 800 years ago, and the Arabs after the rise of Islam were just some of the expanding state societies of the past, before the rise of the West. Wherever there have been "civilized" (urban) societies, there have been imperialism and colonialism.

The taking of land by state authorities does not just happen with colonialism and imperialism. Indigenous revolutionary movements have collectivized land, as in Russia, or broken up large private landholdings, as in Mexico. Typically, state authorities do not like communal land-use systems. State authorities particularly view mobile pastoralists unfavorably because their mobility makes them difficult to control. Governments usually try to settle pastoralists or break up communally held pasture into small units.[50]

The Conversion of Resources

In all societies, resources have to be transformed or converted through labor into food, tools, and other goods. These activities constitute what economists call *production*. In this section, after briefly reviewing different types of production, we examine how societies divide up the work to be done.

Types of Economic Production

At the times they were first described, most of the societies known to anthropology had a *domestic*—family or kinship—mode of production. People labored to get food and to produce shelter and implements for themselves and their kin. Usually families had the right to exploit productive resources and control the products of their labor. Even part-time specialists, such as potters, could still support themselves without that craft if they needed to. At the other extreme are *industrial* societies, where much of the work is based on mechanized production, as in factories but also in mechanized agriculture. Because machines and materials are costly, only some individuals (capitalists), corporations, or governments can afford the expenses of production. Therefore, most people in industrial societies labor for others as wage earners. Although wages can buy food, people out of work lose their ability to support themselves, unless they are protected by welfare payments or unemployment insurance. Then there is the *tributary* type of production system, found in nonindustrial societies in which most people still produce their own food but an elite or aristocracy controls a portion of production (including the products of specialized crafts). The feudal societies of medieval western Europe were examples of tributary production, as was czarist Russia under serfdom.[51]

Many people have suggested that our own and other developed economies are now moving from *industrialism* to *postindustrialism*. In many areas of commerce, computers have radically transformed the workplace. Computers "drive" machines and robots, and much of the manual work required in industry is disappearing. Businesses are now more knowledge- and service-oriented. Information is more accessible with telecommunication, so much so that *telecommuting* has entered our vocabulary to describe how people can now work (for wages) at home. With inexpensive home computers and speedy data transmission by telephone and other means, more people are able to work at home. In addition, when information and knowledge become more important than capital equipment, more people can own and have access to the productive resources of society.[52]

Forced and Required Labor

Thus far, we have mostly discussed *voluntary labor*—voluntary in the sense that no formal organization within the society compels people to work and punishes them for not working. Social training and social pressure are powerful enough to persuade an individual to perform some useful task. In both food-collecting and horticultural societies, individuals who can stand being the butt of jokes about laziness will still be fed. At most, the other members of the group will ignore them. There is no reason to punish them and no way to coerce them to do the work expected of them.

More complex societies have ways of forcing people to work for the authorities, whether those authorities are kings or presidents. An indirect form of forced labor is taxation. The average tax in the United States (local, state, and federal) is about 33 percent of income, which means that the average person works 4 months out of the year for the various levels of government. If a person decides not to pay the tax, the money will be taken forcibly or the person may be put in prison.

Money is the customary form of tax payment in a commercial society. In a politically complex but nonmonetary society, people may pay their taxes in other ways—by performing a certain number of hours of labor or by giving up a certain percentage of what they produce. The **corvée,** a system of required labor, existed in the Inca Empire in the central Andes before the Spanish conquest. Each male commoner was assigned three plots of land to work: a temple plot, a state plot, and his own plot. The enormous stores of food that went into state warehouses were used to supply the nobles, the army, the artisans, and all other state employees. If labor became overabundant, the people were still kept occupied; it is said that one ruler had a hill moved to keep some laborers busy. In addition to subsistence work for the state, Inca commoners were subject to military service, to duty as personal servants for the nobility, and to other

Economics

"public" service.[53] Elderly villagers in the Chiang Mai area of Thailand describe corvée this way: "Villagers had to work one *rai* [*rai myong* or 0.1 acre] per person for them for nothing. And one had to do it properly. The lord's underlings would take a banana tree trunk and stick it upright in the field after it was plowed. If it fell over, that meant it was well plowed. Otherwise, one would have to keep on plowing until the ground was soft."[54]

Conscription or the draft, or compulsory military service, is also a form of corvée, in that a certain period of service is required, and fail-

The Great Wall of China, like many monumental works in ancient societies, was built with forced labor.

ure to serve can be punished by a prison term or involuntary exile. Emperors of China had soldiers drafted to defend their territory and to build the Great Wall along the northern borders of the empire. The wall extends over 1,500 miles, and thousands were drafted to work on it. Slavery is the most extreme form of forced work, in that slaves have little control over their labor. Because slaves constitute a category or class of people in many societies, slavery should also be studied.

Division of Labor

All societies have some division of labor, some customary assignment of different kinds of work to different kinds of people. Universally, males and females and adults and children do not do the same kinds of work. In a sense, then, division of labor by gender and age is a kind of universal specialization of labor. Many societies known to anthropology divide labor only by gender and age; other societies have more complex specialization.

By Gender and Age All societies make use of gender differences to some extent in their customary assignment of labor.

Age is also a universal basis for division of labor. Clearly, children cannot do work that requires a great deal of strength. But, in many societies, girls and boys contribute much more in labor than do children in our own society. For example, they help in animal tending, weeding, and harvesting and do a variety of domestic chores such as child care, fetching water and firewood, and cooking and cleaning. In agricultural communities in the Ivory Coast, children's tasks mirror the tasks of same-sex adults (see Figure 1). In some societies, a child that is 6 years old is considered old enough to be responsible for a younger sibling for a good part of the day.[55] Animal tending is often important work for children. Children in some societies spend more time at this task than adults.[56]

Beyond Gender and Age In societies with relatively simple technologies, there is little specialization of labor beyond that of gender and age. But as a society's technology becomes more complex and it is able to produce large quantities of food, more of its people are freed from subsistence work to become specialists in some other tasks.

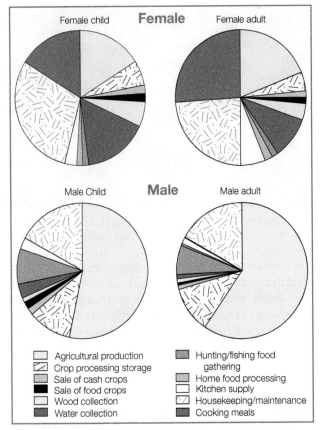

Female

Female child | Female adult

Male

Male Child | Male adult

Agricultural production
Crop processing storage
Sale of cash crops
Sale of food crops
Wood collection
Water collection

Hunting/fishing food gathering
Home food processing
Kitchen supply
Housekeeping/maintenance
Cooking meals

Figure 1 A Comparison of the Proportion of Work Tasks Done by Adults and Children

Source: From James A. Levine, Robert Weisell, Simon Chevassus, Claudio D. Martinez, and Barbara Burlingame, "The Distribution of Work Tasks for Male and Female Children and Adults Separated by Gender," in "Looking at Child Labor," *Science, 296* (May 10, 2002): 1025.

In contrast with foragers, horticultural societies may have some part-time specialists. Some people may devote special effort to perfecting a particular skill or craft—pottery making, weaving, house building, doctoring—and in return for their products or services be given food or other gifts. Among some horticultural groups, the entire village may specialize part time in making a particular product, which can then be traded to neighboring people. With the development of intensive agriculture, full-time specialists—potters, weavers, blacksmiths—begin to appear.

The Distribution of Goods and Services

Goods and services are distributed in all societies by systems that, however varied, can be classified under three general types: reciprocity, redistribution, and market or commercial exchange.[57] The three systems often coexist in a society, but one system usually predominates. The predominant system seems to be associated with the society's food-getting technology and, more specifically, its level of economic development.

Reciprocity

Reciprocity consists of giving and taking without the use of money; it mainly takes the form of gift giving or generalized reciprocity. There may also be exchanges of equal value (barter or nonmonetary trade) or balanced reciprocity, without the use of money.[58]

Generalized Reciprocity When goods or services are given to another, without any apparent expectation of a return gift, we call it **generalized reciprocity.** Generalized reciprocity sustains the family in all societies. Parents give food, clothing, and labor to children because they want to or perhaps feel obliged to, but they do not usually calculate exactly how their children will reciprocate years later. These gifts are one-way transfers. In this sense, all societies have some kind of generalized reciprocity. But some societies depend on it almost entirely to distribute goods and services.

Lorna Marshall recounted how the San in the Nyae Nyae area divided an eland brought to a site where five bands and several visitors were camping—more than 100 people in all. The owner of the arrow that had first penetrated the eland was, by custom, the owner of the meat.

He first distributed the forequarters to the two hunters who had aided him in the kill. After that, the distribution depended on kinship: Each hunter shared with his wives' parents, wives, children, parents, and siblings, and they in turn shared with their kin. Sixty-three gifts of raw meat were recorded, after which further sharing of raw and cooked meat was begun.[59] The Nyae Nyae distribution of large game—clearly, generalized reciprocity—is common among foragers.

Parent–child giving may seem easy to understand, but why do some societies rely more on generalized reciprocity than others, particularly beyond the family? Sharing may be most likely if resources are unpredictable. So a Nyae Nyae band may share its water with other bands because they may have water now but not in the future. A related group of San in the Kalahari, the G//ana,[60] has been observed to share less than other groups. It turns out that the resources available to the G//ana are more predictable, because the G//ana supplement their hunting and gathering with plant cultivation and goat herding. Cultivated melons (which store water) appear to buffer the G//ana against water shortages, and goats buffer them against shortages of game. Thus, whereas the Nyae Nyae distribute the meat right after a kill, the G//ana dry it and then store it in their houses.[61]

Does food-sharing increase the food supply for an individual? Calculations for the Aché of eastern Paraguay, who get most of their food from hunting when they go on food-collecting trips, suggest that the average individual gets more food when food is shared. Even the males who actually do the hunting get more, although the benefits are greater for the females and children on the trip.[62] Mathematically, the risk that an individual food collector will not find enough food on a particular day will be appreciably reduced if at least six to eight adult collectors share the food they collect. Food-collecting bands may often contain only 25–30 people, which is about the size that is needed to ensure that there are six to eight adult collectors.[63]

What happens to a system of generalized reciprocity when resources are scarce because of a drought or other disaster? Does the ethic of giving break down? Evidence from a few societies suggests that the degree of sharing may actually *increase* during the period of food shortage.[64] For example, in describing the Netsilik Inuit, Asen Balikci said, "Whenever game was abundant, sharing among non-relatives was avoided, since every family was supposedly capable of obtaining the necessary catch. In situations of scarcity, however, caribou meat was more evenly distributed throughout camp."[65] Sharing may increase during mild scarcity because people can minimize their deprivation, but generalized reciprocity may be strained by extreme scarcity such as famine.[66]

Researchers generally have difficulty explaining sharing because they assume that, other things being equal, individuals would tend to be selfish. But experimental evidence suggests that sharing is likely even with people who do not know each other or who have no expectation of any return in the future from that person. Experimenters set up "games" in which they can control for or eliminate certain responses. For example, in one game, a particular player is given a certain amount of money and the player decides how much of the money to offer to the second player in the game. The second player can accept or reject the offer. If the division is rejected, no one gets any money. If the division is accepted, both players receive the proposed division. If selfishness were normal, one would expect that the proposer of the division would try to give away as little as possible and the second player should always accept whatever is offered because otherwise nothing is gained. Surprisingly, equal divisions are commonly proposed and low offers are commonly rejected because they are viewed as unfair. If a person views the offer as unfair and forfeits any money, that player seems willing to "punish" the greedy individual. Although such experiments were mostly done at first in Western societies, we now have results from over 15 other societies that largely confirm the earlier results.[67] And there is now evidence suggesting that cooperation may even evoke pleasure. Researchers studying brain activity in women, who are playing a game allowing either cooperative or greedy strategies, found to their surprise that cooperation made certain areas of the brain light up. These areas are normally associated with pleasure, such as when eating desserts. So cooperation may be more "natural" than some people think.[68]

Balanced Reciprocity Balanced reciprocity is explicit and short term in its expectations of return. In contrast to generalized reciprocity or a one-way transfer, which has no expectation of a return, balanced reciprocity involves either an immediate exchange of goods or services or an agreed-upon exchange over a limited period of time. *Barter* is the term used most often for this type of nonmonetary exchange of goods and services. In the 1600s, the Iroquois of the North American Northeast traded deerskin to Europeans for brass kettles, iron hinges, steel axes, woven textiles, and guns.[69] The Iroquois acquired trade goods by balanced reciprocity, but such exchanges were not crucial to their economies.

The Inuit of Baffin Island, Canada are collecting their shares of whale meat. Hunting societies commonly share meat from larger animals.

Sometimes the line between generalized and balanced reciprocity is not so clear. Consider our gift giving at Christmas. Although such gift giving may appear to be generalized reciprocity, and it often is in the case of gift giving from parents to children, there may be strong expectations of balance. Two friends or relatives may try to exchange presents of fairly equal value, based on calculations of what last year's gift cost. If a person receives a $5 present when he or she gave a $25 present, that person may be hurt and perhaps angry. On the other hand, a person who receives a $500 present when he or she gave a $25 present may well also be dismayed.

Redistribution

Redistribution is the accumulation of goods or labor by a particular person, or in a particular place, for the purpose of subsequent distribution. Although redistribution is found in all societies, it becomes an important mechanism only in societies that have political hierarchies—that is, chiefs or other specialized officials and agencies. In all societies, there is some redistribution, at least within the family. Members of the family pool their labor, products, or income for the common good. But in many societies, there is little or no redistribution beyond the family. It seems that redistribution on a territorial basis emerges when there is a political apparatus to coordinate centralized collection and distribution of goods or to mobilize labor for some public purpose.

Why do redistribution systems develop? Elman Service suggested that they develop in agricultural societies that contain subregions suited to different kinds of crops or natural resources. Foragers can take advantage of environmental variation by moving to different areas. With agriculture, the task is more difficult; it might be easier to move different products across different regions.[70] If the demand for different resources or products becomes too great, reciprocity between individuals might become awkward. So it might be more efficient to have someone—a chief, perhaps—coordinate the exchanges.

Marvin Harris agreed that redistribution becomes more likely with agriculture, but for a somewhat different reason. He argued that competitive feasting, as in New Guinea, is adaptive because it encourages people to work harder to produce somewhat more than they need. Why would this feature be adaptive? Harris argued that, with agriculture, people really have to produce more than they need so that they can protect themselves against crises such as crop failure. The groups that make feasts may be indirectly ensuring themselves against crises by storing up social credit with other villages, who will reciprocate by making feasts for them in the future. On the other hand, inducements to collect more than they need may not be advantageous to food-collecting groups, who might lose in the long run by overcollecting.[71]

Market or Commercial Exchange

When we think of markets, we usually think of bustling, colorful places where goods are bought and sold. The exchanges usually involve money. In our own society, we have supermarkets and the stock market and other places for buying and selling that we call shops, stores, and malls. In referring to **market** or **commercial exchange,** economists and economic anthropologists are referring to exchanges or transactions in which the "prices" are subject to supply and demand, whether or not the transactions actually occur in a marketplace.[72] Market exchange involves not only the exchange (buying and selling) of goods but also transactions of labor, land, rentals, and credit.

Kinds of Money Although market exchange need not involve money, most commercial transactions, particularly nowadays, do involve what we call money. Some anthropologists define money according to the functions and characteristics of the **general-purpose money** used in our own and other complex societies, for which nearly all goods, resources, and services can be exchanged. According to this definition, money performs the basic functions of serving as an accepted medium of exchange, a standard of value, and a store of wealth. As a medium of exchange, it allows all goods and services to be valued in the same objective way; we say that an object or service is worth so much money. Also, money is nonperishable, and therefore savable or storable, and almost always transportable and divisible, so transactions can involve the buying and selling of goods and services that differ in value. Money has little or no intrinsic value; rather, it is society that determines its value. In the United States today, paper bills, bank checks, and credit and debit cards are fully accepted as money, and money is increasingly transferred electronically.

The Worldwide Trend Toward Commercialization

Most societies were not commercialized at all, or only barely so, when first described in the ethnographic record by explorers, missionaries, and anthropologists. That is, most societies as first described did not rely on market or commercial exchange to distribute goods and services. But commercial exchange has become the dominant form of distribution in the modern world. Most societies of the ethnographic past are now incorporated into larger nation-states; for example, the Trobriand Islands, where the Trobriand Islanders of Melanesia now live, is now a district in the nation of Papua New Guinea. Selling today goes far beyond the nation-state. The world is now a multinational market.[73]

However, there is considerable variation in the degree to which societies today depend on market or commercial exchange. Many societies still allocate land without purchase and distribute food and other goods primarily by reciprocity and redistribution, participating only peripherally in market exchange. These are societies in transition; their traditional subsistence economies are becoming commercialized.

What anthropologists call *peasant economies* are somewhat more commercialized than transitional subsistence economies. Although **peasants** also produce food largely for their own consumption, they regularly sell part of their surplus (food, other goods, or labor) to others, and land is one of the commodities they buy, rent, and sell. However, although their production is somewhat commercialized, peasants are still not like the fully commercialized farmers in industrialized societies, who rely on the market to exchange all or almost all of their crops for all or almost all of the goods and services they need.

In fully commercialized societies such as our own, market or commercial exchange dominates the economy; prices and wages are regulated, or at least significantly affected, by the forces of supply and demand. A modern industrial or postindustrial economy may involve international as well as national markets in which everything—natural resources, labor, goods, services, prestige items, religious and ceremonial items—has a price, stated in the same money terms. Reciprocity is reserved for family members and friends or remains behind the scenes in business transactions. Redistribution, however, is an important mechanism. It is practiced in the form of taxation and the use of public revenue for transfer payments and other benefits to low-income families—welfare, Social Security, health care, and so on. But commercial exchange is the major way goods and services are distributed.

Many anthropologists have noted that, with the introduction of money, customs of sharing seem to change dramatically. Money, perhaps because it is nonperishable and largely hideable, tends to invoke feelings of not wanting to share. The plight of a man from the central highlands of New Guinea is typical. He agrees that it is not good manners to refuse a request from a relative or village friend; nonetheless, to keep his income from being "eaten," he tries to conceal some of his income. Some of the strategies include opening a savings account into which his pay is deposited, purchasing a semipermanent house, or joining a revolving credit association.[74] A recent series of experiments in the United States, where money has always been fundamental to the economic system, suggests that even the mere reminder of money causes people to behave more independently and to be less helpful to others.[75]

Types of Commercialization

Migratory Labor One way commercialization can occur is for some members of a community to move to a place that offers the possibility of working for wages. This happened in Tikopia, an island near the Solomon Islands in the South Pacific. In 1929, when Raymond Firth first studied the island, its economy was still essentially noncommercial—simple, self-sufficient, and largely self-contained.[76] Some Western goods were available but, with the exception of iron and steel in limited quantities, not sought after. Their possession and use were associated solely with Europeans. This situation changed dramatically with World War II. During the war, military forces occupied neighboring islands, and people from Tikopia migrated to those islands to find employment. In the period following the war, several large commercial interests extended their activities in the Solomons, thus creating a continued demand for labor. As a result, when Firth revisited Tikopia in 1952, he found the economic situation already significantly altered. More than 100 Tikopians had left the island to work for varying periods. The migrants wanted to earn money because they aspired to standards of living previously regarded as appropriate only to Europeans. Already, living conditions on Tikopia were changing. Western cooking and water-carrying utensils, mosquito nets, kerosene storm lamps, and so forth had come to be regarded as normal items in a Tikopia household.

In many areas of the world, the money sent back home has become a major factor in the economy. Often remittances are not sent through the formal banking system, but rather through an informal network of brokers. In the Middle East and South Asia, the system is called *hawala* and is based on an honor system. For instance, the Hazara, the third largest ethnic group in Afghanistan, have migrated throughout the twentieth century to cities in Afghanistan as well as to Pakistan and Iran. The banks in Afghanistan are not functioning and the Hazara often do not have official identification papers, so they use *hawala* brokers to transfer money back home.[77] The money from remittances often far exceeds the money spent by development efforts.[78] But unlike development efforts, usually supported by wealthier countries, money received by remittances can be channeled where families want. Migration becomes part of a family's economic strategy. Of course, not all families can employ that strategy—the poorest families cannot afford the costs of long-distance migration.[79]

Nonagricultural Commercial Production Commercialization can also occur when a self-sufficient society comes to depend more and more on trading for its livelihood. Such a change is exemplified by the Mundurucú of the Amazon Basin, who largely abandoned general horticulture for commercial rubber production.

Navajo women weave rugs for sale.

They did this to obtain other industrially made objects.[80] The primary socioeconomic change that occurred among the Mundurucú and the Montagnais was a shift from cooperative labor and community autonomy to individualized economic activity and a dependence on an external market.

Among the Mundurucú, for example, before close trading links were established, the native population and the Europeans had been in contact for some 80 years without the Mundurucú way of life being noticeably altered. Some trading took place with Brazilians, with the chief acting as agent for the village. Barter was the method of exchange. Traders first distributed their wares, ranging from cheap cottons to iron hatchets, trinkets, and so on; they returned about 3 months later to collect manioc, India rubber, and beans from the Mundurucú. At this time (1860), however, rubber was only a secondary item of commerce.

The rapidly growing demand for rubber from the 1860s onward increased the importance of Mundurucú-trader relationships. Traders now openly began to appoint agents, called *capitoes*, whose job it was to encourage greater rubber production. *Capitoes* were given economic privileges and hence power, both of which began to undercut the position of the traditional chief. In addition, the process of rubber collection itself began to alter Mundurucú social patterns by moving people away from their jungle-based communities. The Mundurucú man who elected to gather rubber had to separate himself from his family for about half the year. The Mundurucú became increasingly dependent on goods the trader supplied. Firearms were useless without regular quantities of gun powder and lead or shot; clothing required needles and thread for repairs. But these items could be earned only through increased rubber production, which in turn led to greater dependency on the outside world. Metal pots took the place of clay ones, and manufactured hammocks replaced homemade ones. Gradually, the village agricultural cycle ceased to be followed by all in the community so that rubber production would not suffer. The authority of the traditional chiefs was weakened as that of the *capitoes* was enhanced.

Apricots laid out in flat baskets are drying in the Himalayan sun and are sold to the world market.

The point of no return was reached when significant numbers of Mundurucú abandoned the villages for permanent settlements near their individual territories of trees. These new settlements lacked the unity, the sense of community, of former village life. Nuclear families held and carefully maintained property in the interest of productivity.

With the discovery of gold, many Mundurucú young men have turned to panning for gold in rivers. The required equipment is simple, and gold is easier to transport and trade than rubber. Because gold can be sold for cash, which is then used for purchases, trading relationships are no longer so important. Cash is now used to buy transistor radios, tape recorders, watches, bicycles, and new kinds of clothing, in addition to firearms, metal pots, and tools. With money as a medium of exchange, the traditional emphasis on reciprocity has declined. Even food may now be sold to fellow Mundurucú, a practice that would have been unthinkable in the 1950s.[81]

Supplementary Cash Crops A third way commercialization occurs is when people cultivating the soil produce a surplus above their subsistence requirements, which is then sold for cash. In many cases, this cash income must be used to pay rent or taxes. Under these circumstances, commercialization may be said to be associated with the formation of a peasantry.

What changes does the development of a peasantry entail? In some respects, there is little disturbance of the cultivator's (now peasant's) former way of life. The peasant still has to produce enough food to meet family needs, to replace what has been consumed, to cover a few ceremonial obligations (e.g., the marriage of a child, village festivals, and funerals). But in other respects, the peasant's situation is radically altered. For, in addition to the traditional obligations—indeed, often in conflict with them—the peasant now has to produce extra crops to meet the requirements of a group of outsiders—landlords or officials of the state. These outsiders expect to be paid rent or taxes in produce or currency, and they are able to enforce their expectations because they control the military and the police.

Introduction of Commercial and Industrial Agriculture Commercialization can come about through the introduction of commercial agriculture, cultivation for sale rather than personal consumption. The system of agriculture may come to be industrialized. In other words, some of the production processes, such as plowing, weeding, irrigation, and harvesting, can be done by machine. Commercial agriculture is, in fact, often as mechanized as any manufacturing industry. Land is worked for the maximum return it will yield, and labor is hired and fired just as impersonally as in other industries.

The introduction of commercial agriculture brings several important social consequences. Gradually, a class polarization develops. Farmers and landlords become increasingly separated from laborers and tenants, just as the employer in town becomes socially separated from the employees. Gradually, too, manufactured items of all sorts are introduced into rural areas.

Laborers migrate to urban centers in search of employment, often meeting even less sympathetic conditions there than exist in the country.

The changeover to commercial agriculture may result in an improved standard of living in the short and long run. But sometimes the switch is followed by a decline in the standard of living if the market price for the commercial crop declines. For example, the changeover of the farmer-herders of the arid *sertão* region of northeastern Brazil after 1940 to the production of sisal (a plant whose fibers can be made into twine and rope) seemed to be a move that could provide a more secure living in their arid environment. But when the world price for sisal dropped and the wages of sisal workers declined, many workers were forced to curtail the caloric intake of their children. The poorer people were obliged to save their now more limited food supplies for the money earners, at the expense of the children.[82]

Commercialization can start in various ways: People can begin to sell and buy because they begin to work near home or away for wages, or because they begin to sell nonagricultural products, surplus food, or **cash crops** (crops grown deliberately for sale). One type of commercialization does not exclude another; all types can occur in any society. However commercialization begins, it seems to have predictable effects on traditional economics. The ethic of generalized reciprocity declines, particularly with respect to giving away money. (Perhaps because it is nonperishable and hideable, money seems more likely than other goods to be kept for one's immediate family rather than shared with others.) Property rights become individualized rather than collective when people begin to buy and sell. Even in societies that were previously egalitarian, commercialization usually results in more unequal access to resources and hence a greater degree of social stratification.

✓●─[Study and **Review** on **myanthrolab.com**

Summary

1. All societies have economic systems, whether or not these involve the use of money. All societies have customs specifying access to natural resources; customary ways of transforming or converting those resources, through labor, into necessities and other desired goods and services; and customs for distributing and perhaps exchanging goods and services.

2. Foraging—hunting, gathering, and fishing—depends on wild plants and animals and is the oldest human food-getting technology. Today, only a small number of societies depend largely on foraging and they tend to inhabit marginal environments.

3. Foragers tend to be nomadic or seminomadic, have low population density, small bands or communities, limited personal possessions, little recognition of individuals' land rights, division of labor along age and gender lines, and no class differences.

4. Beginning about 10,000 years ago, certain peoples in widely separated geographic locations began to make the revolutionary changeover to food production—the cultivation and raising of plants and animals.

5. Horticulturalists farm with relatively simple tools and methods and do not cultivate fields permanently. They generally have larger, more densely populated communities than can be fed by foraging. Their way of life is generally sedentary, although communities may move after some years to farm a new series of plots.

6. Intensive agriculture is characterized by techniques such as fertilization and irrigation that allow fields to be cultivated permanently. In contrast with horticultural societies, intensive agriculturalists are more likely to have towns and cities, a high degree of craft specialization, large differences in wealth and power, and more complex political organization. They are also more likely to face food shortages. In the modern world, intensive agriculture is increasingly mechanized and geared to production for a market.

7. Pastoralism is a subsistence technology involving principally the raising of large herds of animals. It is generally found in low-rainfall areas. Pastoralists tend to be nomadic, to have small communities consisting of related families, and to depend significantly on trade because they do not produce items (including certain types of food) they need.

8. Anthropologists generally agree that the physical environment normally exercises a restraining rather than a determining influence on how people in an area get their food; technology as well as social and political factors may be more important.

9. We see the first evidence of a changeover to food production in the Near East about 8000 B.C. Most archaeologists think that certain conditions must have pushed people to switch from collecting to producing food. Some possible causal factors include (1) population growth in regions of bountiful wild resources, which may have pushed people to move to marginal areas where they tried to reproduce their former abundance; (2) global population growth; and (3) the emergence of hotter and drier summers and colder winters.

10. Individual or private ownership of land—including the right to use its resources and the right to sell or otherwise dispose of them—is common among intensive agriculturalists and is generally lacking amongst foragers, horticulturalists, and pastoralists.

11. Resources are transformed or converted through labor into food, tools, and other goods. Production systems vary from domestic (family and kin), tributary, to industrial and post-industrial systems. More complex societies may have various forms of forced labor.

12. Division of labor by gender is universal.

13. Goods and services are distributed in all societies by systems that can be classified under three types: reciprocity, redistribution, and market or commercial exchange.

14. Redistribution becomes an important mechanism of distribution only in societies with political hierarchies.

15. Market or commercial exchange usually involves an all-purpose medium of exchange— money. Most societies today are at least partly commercialized; the world is becoming a single market system.

16. One of the principal changes resulting from the expansion of Western culture is the increasing dependence of much of the world on commercial exchange.

17. Subsistence economies transition to more commercialization in the following ways: (1) members of the community travel far to engage in migratory work; (2) greater dependence on trading; (3) producing surpluses to sell (in many instances, this cash income must be used to pay rent or taxes; under such circumstances, commercialization may be said to be associated with the formation of a peasantry); and (4) the introduction of commercial agriculture, in which all the cultivated commodities are produced for sale rather than for personal consumption.

Glossary Terms

balanced reciprocity
cash crops
commercialization
corvée
extensive (shifting)
  cultivation
food production
foraging

generalized
  reciprocity
general-purpose
  money
horticulture
hunter-gatherers
intensive agriculture

market or commercial
  exchange
pastoralism
peasants
reciprocity
redistribution
slash-and-burn

Critical Questions

1. Why might meat be valued more than plant foods in many societies?

2. Why might foragers be less likely than intensive agriculturalists to suffer from food shortages?

3. What are the possible effects of a postindustrial economy in which a large proportion of the population has inexpensive access to computers and information?

4. Do you expect any appreciable change in the amount of resources privately owned in the future? State your reasons.

5. We tend to emphasize the negative consequences of the worldwide trend toward commercialization. Have there been any beneficial consequences?

Read the Original Source on myanthrolab.com

Read the chapter by Burton Pasternak, "Han: Pastoralists and Farmers on a Chinese Frontier," on MyAnthroLab and answer the following questions.

1. The Han Chinese traditionally depended on intensive agriculture. The Mongols traditionally depended on pastoralism. What happened to the Han when they moved beyond the Great Wall to a grassland environment?

2. How has the change to more pastoralism affected marriage and family among the Han?

3. How have the Mongols changed?

Photo Credits

Glossary

Balanced reciprocity Giving with the expectation of a straightforward immediate or limited-time trade.

Cash crop A cultivated commodity raised for sale rather than for personal consumption by the cultivator.

Commercial exchange See **Market (or commercial) exchange**.

Commercialization The increasing dependence on buying and selling, with money usually as the medium of exchange.

Corvée A system of required labor.

Extensive (shifting) cultivation A type of horticulture in which the land is worked for short periods and then left to regenerate for some years before being used again. Also called **shifting cultivation**.

Food production The form of subsistence technology in which food-getting is dependent on the cultivation and domestication of plants and animals.

Foraging May be generally defined as a food-getting strategy that obtains wild plant and animal resources through gathering, hunting, scavenging, or fishing; also known as food collection.

Generalized reciprocity Gift giving without any immediate or planned return.

General-purpose money A universally accepted medium of exchange.

Horticulture Plant cultivation carried out with relatively simple tools and methods; nature is allowed to replace nutrients in the soil, in the absence of permanently cultivated fields.

Hunter-gatherers People who collect food from naturally occurring resources, that is, wild plants, animals, and fish. The term *hunter-gatherers* minimizes sometimes heavy dependence on fishing. Also referred to as *foragers* or *food collectors*.

Intensive agriculture Food production characterized by the permanent cultivation of fields and made possible by the use of the plow, draft animals or machines, fertilizers, irrigation, water-storage techniques, and other complex agricultural techniques.

Market or commercial exchange Transactions in which the "prices" are subject to supply and demand, whether or not the transactions occur in a marketplace.

Pastoralism A form of subsistence technology in which food-getting is based directly or indirectly on the maintenance of domesticated animals.

Peasants Rural people who produce food for their own subsistence but who must also contribute or sell their surpluses to others (in towns and cities) who do not produce their own food.

Reciprocity Giving and taking (not politically arranged) without the use of money.

Economics

Redistribution The accumulation of goods (or labor) by a particular person or in a particular place and their subsequent distribution.

Slash-and-burn A form of shifting cultivation in which the natural vegetation is cut down and burned off. The cleared ground is used for a short time and then left to regenerate.

Notes

1. Hitchcock and Beisele 2000, 5.
2. C. R. Ember 1978.
3. Kent 1996.
4. Myers 1988; Schrire 1984a.
5. Morrison and Junker 2002.
6. The discussion of the Australian aborigines is based on R. A. Gould 1969.
7. Burbank 1994, 23; 2009.
8. Data from Textor 1967 and Service 1979.
9. Murdock and Provost 1973, 207.
10. DeVore and Konner 1974; R. B. Lee 1968.
11. C. R. Ember 1978.
12. McCarthy and McArthur 1960.
13. R. B. Lee 1979, 256–58, 278–80.
14. Palsson 1988; Roscoe 2002.
15. Keeley 1991.
16. R. L. Kelly 1995, 293–315.
17. Mitchell 2009; Tollefson 2009.
18. Roscoe 2002.
19. D. Werner 1978.
20. Textor 1967.
21. This section is largely based on Hames 2009.
22. Chagnon 1983, 60.
23. S. S. King 1979.
24. Hickey 1964, 135–65.
25. C. R. Ember 1983, 289.
26. Dirks 2009; Messer 1996, 244; Textor 1967.
27. Finnis 2006.
28. Barlett 1989, 253–91.
29. U.S. Environmental Protection Agency 2009.
30. Salzman 1996.
31. A. L. Johnson 2002; Lees and Bates 1974.
32. Itkonen 1951; Whitaker 1955.
33. Paine 1994.
34. Textor 1967.
35. Dirks 2009.
36. Boserup 1993/1965.
37. R. C. Hunt 2000.
38. Janzen 1973.
39. Roosevelt 1992.
40. Hoebel 1968/1954, 46–63.
41. Pryor 2005, 36.
42. Ibid.
43. Leacock and Lee 1982; Pryor 2005, 36.
44. R. Murphy 1960, 69, 142–43.
45. Salzman 1996.
46. Not all pastoralists have individual ownership. For example, the Tungus of northern Siberia have kin group ownership of reindeer. See Dowling 1975, 422.
47. Salzman 2002.
48. Fratkin 2008, 86–89.

49. Bodley 1990, 77–93; Wilmsen 1989, 1–14.
50. Salzman 1996, 904–05.
51. Plattner 1989, 379–96.
52. Hage and Powers 1992.
53. Steward and Faron 1959, 122–25.
54. Bowie 2006, 251.
55. B. B. Whiting and Edwards 1988, 164.
56. Nag, White, and Peet 1978, 295–96.
57. Polanyi 1957.
58. Sahlins 1972, 188–96.
59. L. Marshall 1961, 239–41.
60. The "//" sign in the name for the G//ana people symbolizes a click sound not unlike the sound we make when we want a horse to move faster.
61. Cashdan 1980, 116–20.
62. H. Kaplan, Hill, and Hurtado 1990.
63. Winterhalder 1990.
64. Mooney 1978.
65. Balikci 1970, quoted in Mooney 1978, 392.
66. Mooney 1978, 392.
67. Ensminger 2002; Fehr and Fischbacher 2003; Henrich et al. 2004, as cited by Ensminger 2002.
68. Angier 2002, F1, F8.
69. Abler 2009.
70. Service 1962, 145–46.
71. M. Harris 1975, 118–21.
72. Plattner 1985, viii.
73. Plattner 1985, xii.
74. Pollier 2000.
75. Vohs, Mead, and Goode 2006.
76. The description of Tikopia is based on Firth 1959, Chapters 5, 6, 7, and 9, passim.
77. Monsutti 2004.
78. Eversole 2005; Monsutti 2004.
79. Eversole 2005.
80. Most of this discussion is based on R. F. Murphy and Steward 1956.
81. Burkhalter and Murphy 1989.
82. Gross and Underwood 1971.

Bibliography

Abler, Thomas S. 2009. Iroquois: The tree of peace and the war kettle. In MyAnthroLibrary, eds. C. R. Ember, M. Ember, and P. N. Peregrine. MyAnthroLibrary.com. Pearson.
Angier, Natalie. 2002. Why we're so nice: We're wired to cooperate. *New York Times,* Science Times, July 23, pp. F1, F8.
Balikci, Asen. 1970. *The Netsilik Eskimo.* Garden City, NY: Natural History Press.
Barlett, Peggy F. 1989. Industrial agriculture. In *Economic anthropology,* ed. S. Plattner. Stanford, CA: Stanford University Press.
Bodley, John H. 1990. *Victims of progress,* 3rd edition. Mountain View CA: Mayfield Publishing Company.
Boserup, Ester. 1993/1965. *The conditions of agricultural growth: The economics of agrarian change under population pressure.* Toronto: Earthscan.
Bowie, Katherine A. 2006. Of corvée and slavery: Historical intricacies of the division of labor and state power in northern Thailand. In *Labor in cross-cultural perspective,* eds. E. Paul Durrenberger and Judith E. Martí, 245–64. Lanham, MD: Roman & Littlefield.
Burbank, Victoria K. 1994. *Fighting women: Anger and aggression in aboriginal Australia.* Berkeley: University of California Press.
Burbank, Victoria K. 2009. Australian Aborigines: An adolescent mother and her family. In MyAnthroLibrary, eds. C. R. Ember, M. Ember, and P. N. Peregrine. MyAnthroLibrary.com. Pearson.
Burkhalter, S. Brian, and Robert F. Murphy. 1989. Tappers and sappers: Rubber, gold and money among the Mundurucú. *American Ethnologist* 16:100–16.
Cashdan, Elizabeth. 1980. Egalitarianism among hunters and gatherers. *American Anthropologist* 82:116–20.
Chagnon, Napoleon. 1983. *Yanomamö: The fierce people.* 3rd ed. New York: Holt, Rinehardt, and Winston.
DeVore, Irven, and Melvin J. Konner. 1974. Infancy in hunter-gatherer life: An ethological perspective. In *Ethology and psychiatry,* ed. N. F. White. Toronto: Ontario Mental Health Foundation and University of Toronto Press.
Dirks, Robert. 2009. Hunger and famine. In MyAnthroLibrary, eds. C. R. Ember, M. Ember, and P. N. Peregrine. MyAnthroLibrary.com. Pearson.

Economics

Dowling, John H. 1975. Property relations and productive strategies in pastoral societies. *American Ethnologist* 2:419–26.

Ember, Carol R. 1978. Myths about hunter-gatherers. *Ethnology* 17:439–48.

Ember, Carol R. 1983. The relative decline in women's contribution to agriculture with intensification. *American Anthropologist* 85:285–304.

Ensminger, Jean. 2002. Experimental economics: A powerful new method for theory testing in anthropology. In *Theory in economic anthropology,* ed. J. Ensminger, 59–78. Walnut Creek, CA: AltaMira Press.

Eversole, Robyn. 2005. "Direct to the poor": Revisited: Migrant remittances and development assistance. In *Migration and economy: Global and local dynamics,* ed. Lillian Trager, 289–322. Walnut Creek, CA: AltaMira Press.

Fehr, Ernst, and Urs Fischbacher. 2003. The nature of human altruism. *Nature* (October 23):785–91.

Finnis, Elizabeth. 2006. Why grow cash crops? Subsistence farming and crop commercialization in the Kolli Hills, South India. *American Anthropologist* 108:363–69.

Firth, Raymond. 1959. *Social change in Tikopia.* New York: Macmillan.

Fratkin, Elliot. 2008. Pastures lost: The decline of mobile pastoralism among Maasai and Rendille in Kenya, East Africa. In *Economies and the transformation of landscape,* eds. Lisa Cliggett and Christopher A. Pool, 149–68. Lanham, MD: AltaMira Press.

Gould, Richard A. 1969. *Yiwara: Foragers of the Australian desert.* New York: Scribner's.

Gross, Daniel R., and Barbara A. Underwood. 1971. Technological change and caloric costs: Sisal agriculture in northeastern Brazil. *American Anthropologist* 73:725–40.

Hage, Jerald, and Charles H. Powers. 1992. *Post-industrial lives: Roles and relationships in the 21st century.* Newbury Park, CA: Sage.

Hames, Raymond. 2009. Yanomamö: Varying adaptations of foraging horticulturalists. In MyAnthroLibrary, eds. C. R. Ember, M. Ember, and P. N. Peregrine. MyAnthroLibrary.com. Pearson.

Harris, Marvin. 1975. *Cows, pigs, wars and witches: The riddles of culture.* New York: Random House, Vintage.

Henrich, Joseph, Robert Boyd, Samuel Bowles, Colin Camerer, Ernst Fehr, and Herbert Gintis, eds. 2004. *Foundations of human sociality: Economic experiments and ethnographic evidence from fifteen small-scale societies.* Oxford, UK: Oxford University Press.

Hickey, Gerald Cannon. 1964. *Village in Vietnam.* New Haven, CT: Yale University Press.

Hitchcock, Robert K. and Megan Biesele. 2000. Introduction. In *Hunters and gatherers in the modern world: Conflict, resistance, and self-determinations,* eds. P. P. Schweitzer, M. Biesele, and R. K. Hitchcock, 1–27. New York: Berghahn Books.

Hoebel, E. Adamson. 1968/1954. *The law of primitive man.* New York: Atheneum.

Hunt, Robert C. 2000. Labor productivity and agricultural development: Boserup revisited. *Human Ecology* 28:251–77.

Itkonen, Toivo I. 1951. The Lapps of Finland. *Southwestern Journal of Anthropology* 7:32–68.

Janzen, Daniel H. 1973. Tropical agroecosystems. *Science* 182 (December 21):1212–19.

Johnson, Amber Lynn. 2002. Cross-cultural analysis of pastoral adaptations and organizational states: A preliminary study. *Cross-Cultural Research* 36:151–80.

Kaplan, Hillard, Kim Hill, and A. Magdalena Hurtado. 1990. Risk, foraging and food sharing among the Aché. In *Risk and uncertainty in tribal and peasant economies,* ed. E. Cashdan. Boulder, CO: Westview Press.

Keeley, Lawrence H. 1991. Ethnographic models for late glacial hunter-gatherers. In *The late glacial in north-west Europe: Human adaptation and environmental change at the end of the Pleistocene,* eds. N. Barton, A. J. Roberts, and D. A. Roe. London: Council for British Archaeology. *CBA Research Report* 77:179–90.

Kelly, Robert L. 1995. *The foraging spectrum: Diversity in hunter-gatherer lifeways.* Washington, DC: Smithsonian Institution Press.

Kent, Susan, ed. 1996. *Cultural diversity among twentieth-century foragers: An African perspective.* Cambridge, UK: Cambridge University Press.

King, Seth S. 1979. Some farm machinery seems less than human. *New York Times,* April 8, p. E9.

Leacock, Eleanor, and Richard Lee. 1982. Introduction. In *Politics and history in band societies,* eds. E. Leacock and R. Lee. Cambridge, UK: Cambridge University Press.

Lee, Richard B. 1968. What hunters do for a living, or, how to make out on scarce resources. In *Man the hunter,* eds. R. B. Lee and I. DeVore. Chicago: Aldine.

Lee, Richard B. 1979. *The !Kung San: Men, women, and work in a foraging society.* Cambridge, UK: Cambridge University Press.

Lees, Susan H., and Daniel G. Bates. 1974. The origins of specialized nomadic pastoralism: A systemic model. *American Antiquity* 39:187–93.

Marshall, Lorna. 1961. Sharing, talking and giving: Relief of social tensions among !Kung Bushmen. *Africa* 31:239–42.

McCarthy, Frederick D., and Margaret McArthur. 1960. The food quest and the time factor in Aboriginal economic life. In *Records of the Australian-American scientific expedition to Arnhem Land,* ed. C. P. Mountford, vol. 2: *Anthropology and Nutrition.* Melbourne: Melbourne University Press.

Messer, Ellen. 1996. Hunger vulnerability from an anthropologist's food system perspective. In *Transforming societies, transforming anthropology,* ed. E. F. Moran. Ann Arbor: University of Michigan Press.

Mitchell, Donald. 2009. Nimpkish: Complex foragers on the northwest coast of North America. In MyAnthroLibrary, eds. C. R. Ember, M. Ember, and P. N. Peregrine. MyAnthroLibrary.com. Pearson.

Monsutti, Alessandro. 2004. Cooperation, remittances, and kinship among the Hazaras. *Iranian Studies* 37:219–40.

Mooney, Kathleen A. 1978. The effects of rank and wealth on exchange among the coast Salish. *Ethnology* 17:391–406.

Morrison, Kathleen D., and Laura L. Junker. 2002. *Forager-traders in South and Southeast Asia: Long-term histories.* Cambridge, UK: Cambridge University Press.

Murdock, George P., and Caterina Provost. 1973. Factors in the division of labor by sex: A cross-cultural analysis. *Ethnology* 12:203–25.

Murphy, Robert F. 1960. *Headhunter's heritage: Social and economic change among the Mundurucú.* Berkeley: University of California Press.

Murphy, Robert F., and Julian H. Steward. 1956. Tappers and trappers: Parallel process in acculturation. *Economic Development and Cultural Change* 4 (July):335–55.

Myers, Fred R. 1988. Critical trends in the study of hunter-gatherers. *Annual Review of Anthropology* 17:261 82.

Nag, Moni, Benjamin N. F. White, and R. Creighton Peet. 1978. An anthropological approach to the study of the economic value of children in Java and Nepal. *Current Anthropology* 19:293–301.

Paine, Robert. 1994. *Herds of the tundra.* Washington, DC: Smithsonian Institution Press.

Palsson, Gisli. 1988. Hunters and gatherers of the sea. In *Hunters and gatherers. 1. History, evolution and social change,* eds. T. Ingold, D. Riches, and J. Woodburn. New York: St. Martin's Press.

Plattner, Stuart, ed. 1985. *Markets and marketing.* Monographs in Economic Anthropology, No. 4. Lanham, MD: University Press of America.

Economics

Plattner, Stuart. 1989. Marxism. In *Economic anthropology*, ed. S. Plattner. Stanford, CA: Stanford University Press.

Polanyi, Karl. 1957. The economy as instituted process. In *Trade and market in the early empires*, eds. K. Polanyi, C. M. Arensberg, and H. W. Pearson. New York: Free Press.

Pollier, Nicole. 2000. Commoditization, cash, and kinship in postcolonial Papua New Guinea. In *Commodities and globalization: Anthropological perspectives*, eds. Angelique Haugerud, M. Priscilla Stone, and Peter D. Little, 197–217. Lanham, MD: Rowman & Littlefield.

Pryor, Frederic L. 2005. *Economic systems of foraging, agricultural, and industrial societies*. Cambridge, UK: Cambridge University Press.

Roosevelt, Anna C. 1992. Secrets of the forest. *The Sciences* (November/December):22–28.

Roscoe, Paul. 2002. The hunters and gatherers of New Guinea. *Current Anthropology* 43:153–62.

Sahlins, Marshall D. 1972. *Stone Age economics*. Chicago: Aldine.

Salzman, Philip Carl. 1996. Pastoralism. In *Encyclopedia of cultural anthropology*, vol. 3, eds. D. Levinson and M. Ember, 899–905. New York: Henry Holt.

Salzman, Philip Carl. 2002. Pastoral nomads: Some general observations based on research in Iran. *Journal of Anthropological Research* 58:245–64.

Schrire, Carmel, ed. 1984a. *Past and present in hunter-gatherer studies*. Orlando, FL: Academic Press.

Service, Elman R. 1962. *Primitive social organization: An evolutionary perspective*. New York: Random House.

Service, Elman R. 1979. *The hunters*. 2nd ed. Upper Saddle River, NJ: Prentice Hall.

Steward, Julian H., and Louis C. Faron. 1959. *Native peoples of South America*. New York: McGraw-Hill.

Textor, Robert B., comp. 1967. *A cross-cultural summary*. New Haven, CT: HRAF Press.

Tollefson, Kenneth D. 2009. Tlingit: Chiefs past and present. In MyAnthroLibrary, eds. C. R. Ember, M. Ember, and P. N. Peregrine. MyAnthroLibrary.com. Pearson.

U.S. Environmental Protection Agency. 2009. http://epa.gov/oecaagct/ag101/demographics.html (accessed October 15, 2009).

Vohs, Kathleen D., Nicole L. Mead, and Miranda R. Goode. 2006. The psychological consequences of money. *Science* 314 (November 17):1154–56.

Werner, Dennis. 1978. Trekking in the Amazon forest. *Natural History* (November):42–54.

Whitaker, Ian. 1955. *Social relations in a nomadic Lappish community*. Oslo: Utgitt av Norsk Folksmuseum.

Whiting, Beatrice B., and Carolyn Pope Edwards (in collaboration with Carol R. Ember, Gerald M. Erchak, Sara Harkness, Robert L. Munroe, Ruth H. Munroe, Sara B. Nerlove, Susan Seymour, Charles M. Super, Thomas S. Weisner, and Martha Wenger). 1988. *Children of different worlds: The formation of social behavior*. Cambridge, MA: Harvard University Press.

Wilmsen, Edwin N., ed. 1989. *We are here: Politics of Aboriginal land tenure*. Berkeley: University of California Press.

Winterhalder, Bruce. 1990. Open field, common pot: Harvest variability and risk avoidance in agricultural and foraging societies. In *Risk and uncertainty in tribal and peasant economies*, ed. E. Cashdan. Boulder, CO: Westview Press.

Language and Communication

From Chapter 4 of *Human Culture*, Second Edition. Carol R. Ember, Melvin Ember. Copyright © 2012 by Pearson Education, Inc. All rights reserved.

Language and Communication

Language and Communication

((•—|Listen to the **Chapter Audio** on **myanthrolab.com** |□•|—|Read on **myanthrolab.com**

Few of us can remember when we first became aware that words signified something. Yet that moment was a milestone for us, not just in the acquisition of language but in becoming acquainted with all the complex, elaborate behavior that constitutes our culture. Without language, the transmission of complex traditions would be virtually impossible, and each person would be trapped within his or her own world of private sensations.

Helen Keller, left deaf and blind by illness at the age of 19 months, gives a moving account of the afternoon she first established contact with another human being through words:

[My teacher] brought me my hat, and I knew I was going out into the warm sunshine. This thought, if a wordless sensation may be called a thought, made me hop and skip with pleasure.

We walked down the path to the well house, attracted by the fragrance of the honeysuckle with which it was covered. Someone was drawing water and my teacher placed my hand under the spout. As the cool stream gushed over one hand she spelled into the other the word water, first slowly, then rapidly. Suddenly I felt a misty consciousness as of something forgotten—a thrill of returning thought; and somehow the mystery of language was revealed to me. I knew then that w-a-t-e-r meant the wonderful cool something that was flowing over my hand. That living word awakened my soul, gave it light, hope, joy, set it free! There were barriers still, it is true, barriers that could in time be swept away.

I left the well house eager to learn. Everything had a name, and each name gave birth to a new thought. As we returned to the house every object which I touched seemed to quiver with life. That was because I saw everything with the strange, new sight that had come to me.[1]

Communication

Against all odds, Helen Keller had come to understand the essential function that language plays in all societies—namely, that of communication. The word *communicate* comes from the Latin verb *communicare,* "to impart," "to share," "to make *common.*" We communicate by agreeing, consciously or unconsciously, to call an object, a movement, or an abstract concept by a common name. For example, speakers of English have agreed to call the color of grass *green,* even though we have no way of comparing precisely how two people actually experience this color. What we share is the agreement to call similar sensations *green.* Any system of language consists of publicly accepted symbols by which individuals try to share private experiences. Spoken or vocal language is probably the major transmitter of culture, allowing us to share and pass on our complex configuration of attitudes, beliefs, and patterns of behavior.

Nonverbal Human Communication

As we all know from experience, the spoken word does not communicate all that we know about a social situation. We can usually tell when someone says, "It was good to meet you," whether he or she really means it. We can tell if people are sad from their demeanor, even if they just say, "I'm fine," in response to the question "How are you?"

Obviously, our communication is not limited to spoken language. We communicate directly through facial expression, body stance, gesture, and tone of voice and indirectly through systems of signs and symbols, such as writing, algebraic equations, musical scores, dancing, painting, code flags, and road signs. As Anthony Wilden put it, "every act, every pause, every movement in living and social systems is also a message; silence is communication; short of death it is impossible for an organism or person not to communicate."[2] How can silence be a communication? Silence may reflect companionship, as when two people work side by side on a project, but silence can also communicate unfriendliness. An anthropologist can learn a great deal from what people in a society do not talk about. For example, in India, sex is not supposed to be talked about. HIV infection is spreading very fast in India, so the unwillingness of people to talk about sex makes it extraordinarily difficult for medical anthropologists and health professionals to do much to reduce the rate of spread.[3]

Some nonverbal communication appears to be universal in humans. For example, humans the world over appear to understand facial expression in the same way; that is, they are able to recognize a happy, sad, surprised, angry, disgusted, or afraid face. How the face is represented in art appears to evoke similar feelings in many different cultures. Masks intended to be frightening have sharp, angular features and inward- and downward-facing eyes and eyebrows.

Nonverbal communication is also culturally variable. For instance, the distance between people standing together is culturally variable. In the realm of facial expression, different cultures have different rules about the emotions that are acceptable to express. One study compared how Japanese and Americans express emotion. Individuals from both groups were videotaped while they were shown films intended to evoke feelings of fear and disgust. When the subjects saw the films by themselves, without other people present, they showed the same kinds of facial expressions of fear and disgust. But there was a cultural effect too. When an authority figure was present during the videotaping, the Japanese subjects tried to mask their negative feelings with a half-smile more often than did the Americans.[4] Many gestures are culturally variable. In some cultures, an up-and-down nod of the head means "yes," in others it means "no."

Nonverbal communication can even involve the voice. Consider how we might know that a person is not fine even though she just said "I'm fine." We can tell a lot by tone of voice. A depressed person might speak very quietly and use a flat tone of voice. If a person thought about explaining what was really wrong but thought better of it, a significant pause or silence might come before the words, "I'm fine." Even a person's **accent** (differences in pronunciation) can tell a lot about the person's background, such as place of origin and education. There are also nonverbal (nonword) sounds that people make—grunts, laughs, giggles, moans, and sighs.

Nonhuman Communication

Systems of communication are not unique to human beings, nor is communication by sound. Other animal species communicate in a variety of ways. One way is by sound. A bird may communicate by a call that "this is my territory"; a squirrel may utter a cry that leads other squirrels to flee from danger. Another means of animal communication is odor. An ant releases a chemical when it dies, and its fellows then carry it away to the compost heap. Apparently the communication is highly effective; a healthy ant painted with the death chemical will be dragged to the funeral heap again and again. Bees use another means of communication, body movement, to convey the location of food sources. Karl von Frisch discovered that the black Austrian honeybee—by choosing a round dance, a wagging dance, or a short, straight run—can communicate not only the precise direction of the source of food but also its distance from the hive.[5]

One of the biggest scholarly debates is the degree to which nonhuman animals, particularly nonhuman primates, differ from humans in their capacity for language. Some scholars see so much discontinuity that they postulate that humans must have acquired (presumably through mutation) a specific genetic capability for language. Others see much more continuity between humans and nonhuman primates and point to research that shows much more cognitive capacity in nonhuman primates than previously thought possible. They point out that the discontinuity theorists are constantly raising the standards for the capacities thought necessary for language.[6] For example, in the past, only human communication was thought to be symbolic. But recent research suggests that some monkey and ape calls in the wild are also symbolic.

When we say that a call, word, or sentence is **symbolic communication,** we mean at least two things. First, the communication has meaning even when its *referent* (whatever is referred to) is not present. Second, the meaning is arbitrary; the receiver of the message could not guess its meaning just from the sound(s) and does not know the meaning instinctively. In other words, symbols have to be learned. There is no compelling or "natural" reason that the word *dog* in English should refer to a smallish four-legged omnivore.

Vervet monkeys in Africa are not as closely related to humans as are African apes. Nevertheless, scientists who have observed vervet monkeys in their natural environment consider at least three of their alarm calls to be symbolic because each of them *means* (refers to) a different kind of predator—eagles, pythons, or leopards—and monkeys react differently to each call. For example, they look up when they hear the "eagle" call. Experimentally, in the absence of the referent, investigators have been able to evoke the normal reaction to a call by playing it back electronically. Another indication that the vervet alarm calls are symbolic is that infant vervets appear to need some time to learn the referent for each. When they are very young, infants apply a particular call to more animals than adult vervets apply the call to. So, for example, infant vervets will often make the eagle warning call when they see any flying bird. The infants learn the appropriate referent apparently through adult vervets' repetition of infants' "correct" calls; in any case, the infants gradually learn to restrict the call to eagles.

How is human vocalization different? All of the nonhuman vocalizations we have described so far enable individual animals to convey messages. The sender gives a signal that is received and "decoded" by the receiver, who usually responds with a specific action or reply. How is human vocalization different? Because monkeys and apes appear to use symbols at least some of the time, it is not appropriate to emphasize symbolism as the distinctive feature of human language. However, there is a significant quantitative difference between human language and other primates' systems of vocal communication. All human languages employ a much larger set of symbols.

Another often-cited difference between human and nonhuman vocalizations is that the other primates' vocal systems are *closed*—that is, different calls are not combined to produce new, meaningful utterances. In contrast, human languages are *open* systems, governed by

Apes lack the human capacity for speech, so researchers have explored the capacity of chimpanzees and other apes to communicate with hand gestures. Researcher Joyce Butler teaches Nim, a chimpanzee, a sign for "drink." A family employs sign language to communicate with a deaf child.

complex rules about how sounds and sequences of sounds can be combined to produce an infinite variety of meanings.[7] For example, an English speaker can combine *care* and *full* (*careful*) to mean one thing, then use each of the two elements in other combinations to mean different things. *Care* can be used to make *carefree, careless,* or *caretaker; full* can be used to make *powerful* or *wonderful.* And because language is a system of shared symbols, it can be reformed into an infinite variety of expressions and be understood by all who share these symbols. In this way, for example, T. S. Eliot could form a sentence never before formed—"In the room the women come and go/talking of Michelangelo"[8]—and all speakers of English could understand the sense of his sentence, though not necessarily his private meaning.

Although no primatologist disputes the complexity and infinite variety with which human languages can combine sounds, other primates (cotton-top tamarins, pygmy marmosets, capuchin monkeys, and rhesus macaques) also combine calls in orderly sequences,[9] but not nearly as much as humans do.

Another trait thought to be unique to humans is the ability to communicate about past or future events. But Sue Savage-Rumbaugh has observed wild bonobos leaving what appear to be messages to other bonobos to follow a trail. They break off vegetation where trails fork and point the broken plants in the direction to follow.

Perhaps most persuasive are the successful attempts to teach apes to communicate with humans and with each other using human-created signs. These successes have led many scholars to question the traditional assumption that the gap between human and other animal communication is enormous. Even a parrot, which has a small brain, has been taught to communicate with a human trainer in ways once thought impossible. Alex (a parrot) could correctly answer questions in English about what objects were made of, how many objects of a particular type there were, and even what made two objects the same or different.[10] When he was not willing to continue a training session, Alex said, "I'm sorry . . . Wanna go back."[11] Chimpanzees Washoe and Nim and the gorilla Koko were taught hand signs based on American Sign Language (ASL; used by the hearing impaired in the United States).

Some of the best examples of linguistic ability come from a chimpanzee named Kanzi. In contrast to other apes, Kanzi initially learned symbols just by watching his mother being taught, and he spontaneously began using the computer symbols to communicate with humans, even indicating his intended actions. Kanzi did not need rewards or to have his hands put in the right position. And he understood a great deal of what was spoken to him in English. For example, when he was 5 years old, Kanzi heard someone talk about throwing a ball in the river, and he turned around and did so. Kanzi has come close to having a primitive English grammar when he strings symbols together.[12] If chimpanzees and other primates have the capacity to use nonspoken language and even to understand spoken language, then the difference between humans and nonhumans may not be as great as people used to think.

Are these apes really using language in some minimal way? Many investigators do agree about one thing—nonhuman primates have the ability to "symbol," to refer to something (or a class of things) with an arbitrary "label" (gesture or sequence of sounds).[13] For example, Washoe originally learned the sign *dirty* to refer to feces and other soil and then began to use it insultingly, as in "dirty Roger," when her trainer Roger Fouts refused to give her things she wanted.

When we discuss the structure of sounds (phonology) later in this chapter, we will see that every human language has certain ways of combining sounds and ways of not combining those sounds. Apes do not have anything comparable to linguistic rules for allowed and disallowed combinations of sounds. In addition, humans have many kinds of discourse. We make lists and speeches, tell stories, argue, and recite poetry. Apes do none of these things.[14] But apes do have at least some of the capacities for language. Therefore, understanding their capacities may help us better understand the evolution of human language.

The Origins of Language

How long humans have had spoken language is not known. Some think that the earliest *Homo sapiens,* perhaps 100,000 years ago, may have had the beginnings of language. Others believe that language developed only after 100,000 years ago, with the emergence of modern humans. Because the only unambiguous remains of language are found on written tablets, and the earliest stone tablets date back only about 5,000 years,[15] pinpointing the emergence of the earliest languages remains speculative. Theories about when language developed are based on nonlinguistic information such as when cranial capacity expanded dramatically, when complex technology and symbolic artifacts (such as art) started to be made, and when the anatomy of the throat, as inferred from fossil remains, began to resemble what we see in modern humans.

Noam Chomsky and other theoreticians of grammar suggest that there is an innate *language-acquisition device* in the human brain, as innate to humans as call systems are to other animals.[16] If humans are unique in having an innate capacity for language, then some mutation or series of mutations had to be favored in human evolution, not before the human line separated from apes. Whether such a mechanism in fact exists is not clear. But we do know that the actual development of individual language is not completely biologically determined; if it were, all human beings would speak the same brain-generated language. Instead, about 4,000–5,000 mutually unintelligible languages have been identified. More than 2,000 of them were still spoken as of recently, most by peoples who did not traditionally have a system of writing.

Can we learn anything about the origins of language by studying the languages of nonliterate (without writing) and technologically simpler societies? The answer is no, because such languages are not simpler or less developed than ours. The sound systems, vocabularies, and grammars of technologically simpler peoples are in no way inferior to those of peoples with more complex technology.[17] Of course, people in other societies, and even some people in our own society, will not be able to name the sophisticated machines used in our society. All languages, however, have the potential for doing so. As we will see later in this chapter, all languages possess the amount of vocabulary their speakers need, and all languages expand in response to cultural changes. A language that lacks terminology for some of our conveniences may have a rich vocabulary for events or natural phenomena that are of particular importance to the people in that society.

If there are no primitive languages, and if the earliest languages have left no traces that would allow us to reconstruct them, does that mean we cannot investigate the origins of language? Some linguists think that understanding the way children acquire language, which we discuss shortly, can help us understand the origins of language. Other linguists have suggested that an understanding of how creole languages develop will also tell us something about the origins of language.

Pidgin and Creole Languages

In many contact situations where one group is much more powerful than the other, people shift to the dominant language, and their native language gradually becomes lost. However, some contact situations led to a different result—the development of a new language, different from the dominant language or the previous native languages.

Some languages developed where European colonial powers established commercial enterprises that relied on imported labor, generally slaves. The laborers in one place often came from many different societies and, in the beginning, would speak with their masters and with each other in some kind of simplified way, using linguistic features of one or more of the languages. Often, most of the vocabulary is drawn from the masters' language.[18] These *pidgin languages* become a new way of communicating. Pidgins are simplified languages and lack many of the building blocks found in the languages of whole societies, building blocks such as prepositions (*to, on,* and so forth) and auxiliary verbs (designating future and other tenses). Many pidgin languages developed into and were replaced by so-called *creole languages,* which incorporate much of the vocabulary of another language (often the masters' language) but also have a grammar that differs from it and from the grammars of the laborers' native languages.[19]

Derek Bickerton argues that there are striking grammatical similarities in creole languages throughout the world. This similarity, he thinks, is consistent with the idea that some grammar is inherited by all humans. Creole languages, therefore, may resemble early human languages. All creoles use intonation instead of a change in word order to ask a question. The creole equivalent of the question "Can you fix this?" would be "You can fix this?" The creole version puts a rising inflection at the end; in contrast, the English version reverses the subject and verb without much inflection at the end. All creoles express the future and the past in the same grammatical way, by the use of particles (such as the English *shall*) between subject and verb, and they all employ double negatives, as in the Guyana English Creole "Nobody no like me."[20]

It is possible that many other things about language are universal, that all languages are similar in many respects, because of the way humans are "wired" or because people in all societies have similar experiences. For example, names for frogs may usually contain *r* sounds because frogs make them.[21]

Children's Acquisition of Language

Apparently a child is equipped from birth with the capacity to reproduce all the sounds used by the world's languages and to learn any system of grammar. Research on 6-month-old infants finds that they can distinguish sounds of approximately 600 consonants and 200 vowels—all the sounds of all the languages of the world. But, by about the time of their first birthdays, babies become better at recognizing the salient sounds and sound clusters of their parents or caretakers and become less adept at distinguishing those of other languages.[22]

Children's acquisition of the structure and meaning of language has been called the most difficult intellectual achievement in life. If that is so, it is pleasing to note that they accomplish it with relative ease and vast enjoyment. As we have noted, many believe that this "difficult intellectual achievement" may in reality be a natural response to the capacity for language that is one of humans' genetic characteristics. All over the world, children begin to learn language at about the same age, and in no culture do children wait until they are 7 or 10 years old. By 12 or 13 months of age, children are able to name a few objects and actions, and by 18–20 months, they can make one key word stand for a whole sentence: "Out!" for "Take me out for a walk right now"; "Juice!" for "I want some juice now." Evidence suggests that children acquire the concept of a word as a whole,

A lot of language instruction occurs by pointing to something and saying what it is called.

learning sequences of sounds that are stressed or at the ends of words (e.g., "raffe" for giraffe). Even children with hearing impairments who are learning signs in ASL tend to acquire and use signs in a similar fashion.[23]

Children the world over tend to progress to two-word sentences at about 18–24 months of age. In their sentences, they express themselves in "telegraph" form—using nounlike words and verblike words but leaving out the seemingly less important words. So a two-word sentence such as "Shoes off" may stand for "Take my shoes off," or "More milk" may stand for "Give me more milk, please."[24] They do not utter their two words in random order, sometimes saying "off" first, other times saying "shoes" first. If children say, "Shoes off," then they will also say, "Clothes off" and "Hat off." They seem to select an order that fits the conventions of adult language, so they are likely to say, "Daddy eat," not "Eat Daddy." In other words, they tend to put the subject first, as adults do. And they tend to say "Mommy coat" rather than "Coat Mommy" to indicate "Mommy's coat."[25] Adults do not utter sentences such as "Daddy eat," so children seem to know a lot about how to put words together with little or no direct teaching from their caretakers.

If there is a basic grammar imprinted in the human mind, we should not be surprised that children's early and later speech patterns seem to be similar in different languages. We might also expect children's later speech to be similar to the structure of creole languages. And it is, according to Derek Bickerton.[26] The "errors" children make in speaking are consistent with the grammar of creoles. For example, English-speaking children 3–4 years old tend to ask questions by intonation alone, and they tend to use double negatives, such as "I don't see no dog," even though the adults around them do not speak that way and consider the children's speech "wrong."

But some linguists argue that the evidence for an innate grammar is weak because children the world over do not develop the same grammatical features at similar ages. For example, word order is a more important determinant of meaning in English than in Turkish; the endings of words are more important in Turkish. The word at the beginning of the sentence in English is likely to be the subject. The word with a certain ending in Turkish is the likely subject. Consistent with this difference, English-speaking children learn word order earlier than Turkish children do.[27]

Future research on children's acquisition of language and on the structure of creole languages may bring us closer to an understanding of the origins of human language. But, even if much of grammar is universal, we still need to understand how and why the thousands of languages in the world vary, which brings us to the conceptual tools linguists have had to invent to study languages.

Descriptive Linguistics

In every society, children do not need to be taught "grammar" to learn how to speak. They begin to grasp the essential structure of their language at a very early age, without direct instruction. If you show English-speaking children a picture of one "gork" and then a picture of two of these creatures, they will say there are two "gorks." Somehow they know that adding an s to a noun means more than one. But they do not know this consciously, and adults may not either. One of the most surprising features of human language is that meaningful sounds and sound sequences are combined according to rules that the speakers often do not consciously know.

These rules should not be equated with the "rules of grammar" you were taught in school so that you would speak "correctly." Rather, when linguists talk about rules, they are referring to the patterns of speaking that are discoverable in actual speech. Needless to say, there is some overlap between the actual rules of speaking and the rules taught in school. But there are rules that children never hear about in school, because their teachers are not linguists and are not aware of them. When linguists use the term *grammar*, they are *not* referring to the prescriptive rules that people are supposed to follow in speaking. Rather, *grammar* to the linguist consists of the actual, often unconscious principles that predict how most people talk. As we have noted, young children may speak two-word sentences that conform to a linguistic rule, but their speech is hardly considered "correct."

Discovering the mostly unconscious rules operating in a language is a very difficult task. Linguists have had to invent special concepts and methods of transcription (writing) to permit them to describe: (1) the rules or principles that predict how sounds are made and how they are used (slightly varying sounds are often used interchangeably in words without creating a difference in meaning—this aspect of language is called **phonology**); (2) how sound sequences (and sometimes even individual sounds) convey meaning and how meaningful sound sequences are strung together to form words (this aspect is called **morphology**); and (3) how words are strung together to form phrases and sentences (this aspect is called **syntax**).

Phonology

Most of us have had the experience of trying to learn another language and finding that some sounds are exceedingly difficult to make. Although the human vocal tract theoretically can make a very large number of different sounds—**phones,** to linguists—each language uses only some of them. It is not that we cannot make the sounds that are strange to us; we just have not acquired the habit of making those sounds. And until the sounds become habitual for us, they continue to be difficult to make.

Finding it difficult to make certain sounds is only one of the reasons we have trouble learning a "foreign" language. Another problem is that we may not be used to combining certain sounds or making a certain sound in a particular position in a word. Thus, English speakers find it difficult to combine *z* and *d*, as Russian speakers often do (because we never do so in English), or to pronounce words in Samoan, a South Pacific language, that begin with the sound English speakers write as *ng*, even though we have no trouble putting that sound at the end of words, as in the English *sing* and *hitting.*

To study the patterning of sounds, linguists who are interested in *phonology* have to write down speech utterances as sequences of sound. This task would be almost impossible if linguists were restricted to using their own alphabet (say, the one we use to write English), because other languages use sounds that are difficult to represent with the English alphabet or because the alphabet we use in English can represent a particular sound in different ways. (English writing represents the sound *f* by *f* as in *food,* but also as *gh* in *tough* and *ph* in *phone.*) In addition, in English, different sounds may be represented by the same letter. English has 26 letters but more than 40 significant sounds (sounds that can change the meaning of a word).[28] To overcome these difficulties in writing sounds with the letters of existing writing systems, linguists have developed systems of transcription with special alphabets in which each symbol represents only one particular sound.

Once linguists have identified the sounds or phones used in a language, they try to identify which sounds affect meaning and which sounds do not. One way is to start with a simple word like *lake* and change the first sound to *r* to make the word *rake*. A linguist will ask if this new combination of sounds means the same thing. An English speaker would say *lake* means something completely different from *rake.* These minimal contrasts enable linguists to identify a **phoneme** in a language—a sound or set of sounds that makes a difference in meaning in that language.[29] So the sound *l* in *lake* is different phonemically from the sound *r* in *rake.* The ways in which sounds are grouped together into phonemes vary from language to language. We are so used to phonemes in our own language that it may be hard to believe that the contrast between *r* and *l* may not make a difference in meaning in some languages. For example, in Samoan, *l* and *r* can be used interchangeably in a word without changing the meaning (therefore, these two sounds belong to the same phoneme in Samoan). So Samoan speakers may say "Leupena" sometimes and "Reupena" at other times when they are referring to someone who in English would be called "Reuben."

English speakers may joke about languages that "confuse" *l* and *r*, but they are not usually aware that we do the same thing with other sets of sounds. For example, in English, the word we spell *and* may be pronounced quite differently by two different English speakers without changing the meaning, and no one would think that a different word was spoken. We can pronounce the *a* in *and* as in the beginning of the word *air*, or we can pronounce it as the *a* in *bat*. If you say those varying *a* sounds and try to think about how you are forming them in your mouth, you will realize that they are two different sounds. English speakers might recognize a slight difference in pronunciation but pay little or no attention to it because the two ways to pronounce the *a* in *and* do not change the meaning. Now think about *l* and *r*. If you form them in your mouth, you will notice that they are only slightly different with respect to how far the tongue is from the ridge behind the upper front teeth. As early as 6 months of age, infants "ignore" sound shifts within the same phoneme of their own language, but they "hear" a sound shift within the phoneme of another language.[30] Languages do tend to consider sounds that are close as belonging to the same phoneme, but why they choose some sounds and not others to group together is not yet fully understood.

Why, for example, are two or more consonants strung together in some languages, whereas in other languages, vowels are *almost* always put between consonants? The Samoan language now has a word for "Christmas" borrowed from English, but the borrowed word has been changed to fit the rules of Samoan. In the English word, two consonants come first, *k* and *r*, which we spell as *ch* and *r*. The Samoan word is *Kerisimasi* (pronounced as if it were spelled Keh-ree-see-mah-see). It has a vowel after each consonant, or five consonant–vowel syllables.

Why do some languages like Samoan alternate consonants and vowels more or less regularly? Recent cross-cultural research suggests three predictors of this variation. One predictor is a warmer climate. Where people live in warmer climates, the typical syllable is more likely to be a consonant–vowel syllable. Linguists have found that consonant–vowel syllables provide the most contrast in speech. Perhaps when people converse outdoors at a distance, which they are likely to do in a warmer climate, they need more contrast between sounds to be understood. A second predictor of consonant–vowel alternation is literacy. Languages that are written have fewer consonant–vowel syllables. If communication is often in written form, meaning does not have to depend so much on contrast between adjacent sounds. A third (indeed the strongest) predictor of consonant–vowel alternation is the degree to which babies are held by others. Societies with a great deal of baby-holding have a lot of consonant–vowel syllables. Elsewhere, you might read about research that relates baby-holding to a societal preference for regular rhythm in music. The theory is that, when babies are held on a person much of the day, they begin to associate regular rhythm with pleasurable experiences. The baby senses the regular rhythm of the caretaker's heartbeats or the caretaker's rhythmic work, and the reward value of that experience generalizes to a preference for all regular rhythms in adult life, including apparently a regular consonant–vowel alternation in adult speech. Compare the rhythm of the Samoan word *Kerisimasi* with the English word *Christmas*.[31]

Morphology

A phoneme in a language usually does not mean something by itself. Usually phonemes are combined with other phonemes to form a meaningful sequence of sounds. *Morphology* is the study of sequences of sounds that have meaning. Often these meaningful sequences of sounds make up what we call *words,* but a word may be composed of a number of smaller meaningful units. We take our words so much for granted that we do not realize how complicated it is to say what words are. People do not usually pause very much between words when they speak; if we did not know our language, a sentence would seem like a continuous stream of sounds. This is how we first hear a foreign language. Only when we understand the language and write down what we say do we separate (by spaces) what we call words. But a word is really only an arbitrary sequence of sounds that has a meaning; we would not "hear" words as separate units if we did not understand the language spoken.

Because anthropological linguists traditionally investigated unwritten languages, sometimes without the aid of interpreters, they had to figure out which sequences of sounds conveyed meaning. And because words in many languages can often be broken down into smaller meaningful units, linguists had to invent special words to refer to those units. Linguists call the smallest unit of language that has a meaning a **morph.** Just as a phoneme may have one or more phones, one or more morphs with the same meaning may make up a **morpheme.** For example, the prefix *in-,* as in *indefinite,* and the prefix *un-,* as in *unclear,* are morphs that belong to the morpheme meaning *not.* Although some words are single morphs or morphemes (e.g., *for* and *giraffe* in English), many words are a combination of morphs, generally prefixes, roots, and suffixes. Thus *cow* is one word, but the word *cows* contains two meaningful units—a root (*cow*) and a suffix (pronounced like *z*) meaning more than one. The **lexicon** of a language, which a dictionary approximates, consists of words and morphs and their meanings.

In English, the meaning of an utterance (containing a subject, verb, object, and so forth) usually depends on the order of the words. "The dog bit the child" is different in meaning from "The child bit the dog." But in many other languages, the grammatical meaning of an utterance does not depend much, if at all, on the order of the words. Rather, meaning may be determined by how the morphs in a word are ordered. For example, in Luo, a language of East Africa, the same bound morpheme may mean the subject or object of an action. If the morpheme is the prefix to a verb, it means the subject; if it is the suffix to a verb, it means the object. Another way that grammatical meaning may be conveyed is by altering or adding a bound morpheme to a word to indicate what part of speech it is. For example, in Russian, when the subject of a sentence, the word for *mail* is pronounced something like *pawchtah.* When *mail* is used as the object of a verb, as in "I gave her the mail," the ending of the word changes to *pawchtoo.* And if I say, "What was in the mail?" the word becomes *pawchtyeh.*

Some languages have so many bound morphemes that they might express as a complex but single word what is considered a sentence in English. For example, the English sentence, "He will give it to you" can be expressed in Wishram, a Chinookan dialect that was spoken along the Columbia River in the Pacific Northwest, as *acimluda* (a-c-i-m-l-ud-a, literally "will-he-him-thee-to-give-will"). Note that the pronoun *it* in English is gender-neutral; Wishram requires that *it* be given a gender, in this case, "him."[32]

Syntax

Because language is an open system, we can make up meaningful utterances that we have never heard before. We are constantly creating new phrases and sentences. Just as they do for morphology, speakers of a language seem to have an intuitive grasp of *syntax*—the rules that predict how phrases and sentences are generally formed. These "rules" may be partly learned in school, but children know many of them even before they get to school. In adulthood, our understanding of morphology and syntax is so intuitive that we can even understand a nonsense sentence, such as this famous one from Lewis Carroll's *Through the Looking-Glass:*

> *'Twas brillig, and the slithy toves*
> *Did gyre and gimble in the wabe*

Simply from the ordering of the words in the sentence, we can surmise which part of speech a word is, as well as its function in the sentence. *Brillig* is an adjective; *slithy,* an adjective; *toves,* a noun and the subject of the sentence; *gyre* and *gimble,* verbs; and *wabe,* a noun and the object of a prepositional phrase. Of course, an understanding of morphology helps too. The *-y* ending in *slithy* is an indication that the latter is an adjective, and the *-s* ending in *toves* tells us that we most probably have more than one of these creatures. In addition to producing and understanding an infinite variety of sentences, speakers of a language can tell when a sentence is not "correct" without consulting grammar books. For example, an English speaker can tell that "Child the dog the hit" is not an acceptable sentence but "The child hit the dog" is fine. There must, then, be a set of rules underlying how phrases and sentences are constructed in a language.[33] Speakers of a language know these implicit rules of syntax but are not usually consciously aware of them. The linguist's description of the syntax of a language tries to make these rules explicit.

Historical Linguistics

The field of **historical linguistics** focuses on how languages change over time. Written works provide the best data for establishing such changes. For example, the following brief passage from Chaucer's *Canterbury Tales,* written in the English of the fourteenth century, has recognizable elements but is different enough from modern English to require a translation.

> *A Frere ther was, a wantowne and a merye,*
> *A lymytour, a ful solempne man.*
> *In alle the ordres foure is noon that kan*
> *So muche of daliaunce and fair language.*
> *He hadde maad ful many a mariage*
> *Of yonge wommen at his owene cost.*

> *A Friar there was, wanton and merry,*
> *A limiter [a friar limited to certain districts], a very important man.*
> *In all the orders four there is none that knows*
> *So much of dalliance [flirting] and fair [engaging] language.*
> *He had made [arranged] many a marriage*
> *Of young women at his own cost.*[34]

In this passage, we can recognize several changes. Many words are spelled differently today, and in some cases, meaning has changed: *Full,* for example, would be translated today as *very.* What is less evident is that changes in pronunciation have occurred. For example, the *g* in *mariage* (marriage) was pronounced *zh,* as in the French from which it was borrowed, whereas now it is usually pronounced like either *g* in *George.*

An illustration accompanies the ornate script text on a page from Chaucer's famed *The Canterbury Tales.*

Because languages spoken in the past leave no traces unless they were written, and most of the languages known to anthropology were not written by their speakers, you might think that historical linguists can study linguistic change only by studying written languages such as English. But that is not the case. Linguists can reconstruct changes that have occurred by comparing contemporary languages that are similar. Such languages show phonological, morphological, and syntactical similarities because they usually derive from a common ancestral language. For example, Romanian, Italian, French, Spanish, and Portuguese have many similarities. On the basis of these similarities, linguists can reconstruct what the ancestral language was like and how it changed into what we call the Romance languages. Of course, these reconstructions can easily be tested and confirmed because we know from many surviving writings what the ancestral language, Latin, was like; we also know from documents how Latin diversified as the Roman Empire expanded. Thus, common ancestry is frequently the reason why neighboring, and sometimes even separated, languages show patterns of similarity.

But languages can be similar for other reasons too. Contact between speech communities, often with one group dominant over another, may lead one language to borrow from the other. For example, English borrowed a lot of vocabulary from French after England was conquered by the French-speaking Normans in A.D. 1066. Languages may also show similarities even though they do not derive from a common ancestral language and even though there has been no contact or borrowing between them. Such similarities may reflect common or universal features of human cultures or human brains or both. (As we noted earlier, the grammatical similarities exhibited by creole languages may reflect how the human brain is "wired.") Finally, even unrelated and separated languages may show some similarities because of the phenomenon of convergence; similarities can develop because some processes of linguistic change may have only a few possible outcomes.

Language Families and Culture History

Latin is the ancestral language of the Romance languages. We know this from documentary (written) records. But if the ancestral language of a set of similar languages is not known from written records, linguists still can reconstruct many features of that language by comparing the derived languages. (Such a reconstructed language is called a **protolanguage.**) That is, by comparing presumably related languages, linguists can become aware of the features that many of them have in common, features that were probably found in the common ancestral language. The languages that derive from the same protolanguage are called a *language family.* The language family that English belongs to is called *Indo-European* because it includes most of the languages of Europe and some of the languages of India. (Persian, spoken in Iran, and Kurdish also belong to this family.) About 50 percent of the world's population (now more than 6 billion people) speak Indo-European languages.[35] Another very large language family, now spoken by more than a billion people, is Sino-Tibetan, which includes the languages of northern and southern China as well as those of Tibet and Burma.[36]

The field of historical linguistics got its start in 1786, when a British scholar living in India, Sir William Jones, noticed similarities between Sanskrit, a language spoken and written in ancient India, and classical Greek, Latin, and more recent European languages.[37] In 1822, Jakob Grimm, one of the brothers Grimm of fairy tale fame, formulated rules to describe the sound shifts that had occurred when the various Indo-European languages diverged from each other. So, for example, in English and the other languages in the Germanic branch of the Indo-European family, *d* regularly shifted to *t* (compare the English *two* and *ten* with the Latin *duo* and *decem*), and *p* regularly shifted to *f* (compare the English *father* and *foot* to Latin's *pater* and *pes*). Scholars generally agree that the Indo-European languages derive from a language spoken 5,000–6,000 years ago.[38] The ancestral Indo-European language, many of whose features have now been reconstructed, is called *proto-Indo-European.*

The Bantu languages in Africa (spoken by perhaps 100 million people) form a subfamily of the larger Niger-Congo family of languages. Bantu speakers currently live in a wide band across the center of Africa and down the eastern and western sides of southern Africa. All of the Bantu languages presumably derive from people who spoke proto-Bantu. But where was their homeland? Most historical linguists now agree with Joseph Greenberg's suggestion that the origin of Bantu was in what is now the Middle Benue area of eastern Nigeria.[39] The point of origin is presumably where there is the greatest diversity of related languages and *dialects* (varying forms of a language); it is assumed that the place of origin has had the most time for linguistic diversity to develop, compared with an area only recently occupied by a related language. For example, England has more dialect diversity than New Zealand or Australia.

Why were the Bantu able to spread so widely over the last few thousand years? Anthropologists have only begun to guess.[40] Initially, the Bantu probably kept goats and practiced some form of agriculture and thereby were able to spread, displacing hunter-gatherers in the area. As the Bantu speakers expanded, they began to cultivate certain cereal crops and herd sheep and cattle. Around this time, after 1000 B.C., they also began to use and make iron tools, which may have given them significant advantages. In any case, by 1,500–2,000 years ago, Bantu speakers had spread throughout central Africa and into the northern reaches of southern Africa. But speakers of non-Bantu languages still live in eastern, southern, and southwestern Africa.

The Processes of Linguistic Divergence

Historical or comparative linguists hope to do more than record and date linguistic divergence. Just as physical anthropologists may attempt to develop explanations for human variation, so linguists investigate the possible causes of linguistic variation. Some of the divergence undoubtedly comes about gradually. When groups of people speaking the same language lose communication with one another because they become separated, either physically or socially, they begin to accumulate small changes in phonology, morphology, and syntax (which occur continuously in any language). These variant forms of language are considered **dialects** when the differences in phonology, morphology, and syntax are not great enough to produce unintelligibility. Eventually, if the separation continues, the former dialects of the same language will become separate languages; that is, they will become mutually unintelligible, as German and English now are. Just as culture change originates from individual changes, language change originates from individual speakers, either from spontaneous innovation or from borrowing. Only when innovative speech patterns are picked up by others does linguistic change occur.[41]

Geographic barriers, such as large bodies of water, deserts, and mountains, may separate speakers of what was once the same language, but distance by itself can also produce divergence. For example, if we compare dialects of English in the British Isles, it is clear that the regions farthest away from each other are the most different linguistically (compare the northeast of Scotland and London).[42]

Whereas isolation brings gradual divergence between speech communities, contact results in greater resemblance. This effect is particularly evident when contact between mutually unintelligible languages introduces borrowed words, which usually name some new item borrowed from the other culture—*tomato, canoe, sushi,* and so on. Bilingual groups within a culture may also introduce foreign words, especially when the mainstream language has no real equivalent. Thus, *salsa* has come into English, and *le weekend* into French.

Conquest and colonization often result in extensive and rapid borrowing, if not linguistic replacement. The Norman conquest of England introduced French as the language of the new aristocracy. It was 300 years before the educated classes began to write in English. During this time, the English borrowed words from French and Latin, and the two languages—English and French—became more alike than they would otherwise have been. About 50 percent of the English general vocabulary originated in French. In those 300 years of extensive contact, the grammar of English remained relatively stable. English lost most of its inflections or case endings, but it adopted little of the French grammar. In general, the borrowing of words, particularly free morphemes,[43] is much more common than the borrowing of grammar.[44] As we might expect, borrowing by one language from another can make the borrowing language more different from its *sibling languages* (those derived from a common ancestral language) than it would otherwise be. Partly as a result of the French influence, the English vocabulary looks

The Fledermaus cabaret bar in Vienna uses some English words in its sign out front.

quite different from the languages to which it is actually most similar in terms of phonology and grammar—German, Dutch, and the Scandinavian languages.

Relationships Between Language and Culture

Some attempts to explain the diversity of languages have focused on the possible interactions between language and other aspects of culture. On the one hand, if it can be shown that a culture can affect the structure and content of its language, then it would follow that linguistic diversity derives at least in part from cultural diversity. On the other hand, the direction of influence between culture and language might work in reverse: Linguistic features and structures might affect other aspects of the culture.

Cultural Influences on Language

One way a society's language may reflect its corresponding culture is in **lexical content,** or vocabulary. Which experiences, events, or objects are singled out and given words may be a result of cultural characteristics.

Basic Words for Colors, Plants, and Animals Early in the twentieth century, many linguists pointed to the lexical domain (vocabulary) of color words to illustrate the supposed truth that languages vary arbitrarily or without apparent reason. Different languages not only had different numbers of basic color words (from 2 to 12 or so; for example, the words *red, green,* and *blue* in English), but they also, it was thought, had no consistency in the way they classified or divided the colors of the spectrum. But findings from a comparative (cross-linguistic) study contradicted these traditional presumptions about variation in the number and meaning of basic color words. On the basis of their study of at first 20 and later over 100 languages, Brent Berlin and Paul Kay found that languages did not encode color in completely arbitrary ways.[45]

Although different languages do have different numbers of basic color words, most speakers of any language are very likely to point to the same color chips as the best representatives of particular colors. For example, people the world over mean more or less the same color when they are asked to select the best "red." Moreover, there appears to be a nearly universal sequence by which basic color words are added to a language.[46] If a language has just two basic color words, its speakers will always refer to "black" (or dark) hues and "white" (or light) hues. If a language has three basic color words, the third word will nearly always be "red." The next category to appear is either "yellow" or "grue" (green/blue), then different words for green and blue, and so on. To be sure, we usually do not see the process by which basic color words are added to a language. But we can infer the usual sequence because, for example, if a language has a word for "yellow," it will almost always have a word for "red," whereas having a word for "red" does not mean that the language will have a word for "yellow."

What exactly is a *basic* color word? All languages, even the ones with only two basic color terms, have many different ways of expressing how color varies. For example, in English, we have words such as *turquoise, blue-green, scarlet, crimson,* and *sky blue.* Linguists do not consider these to be basic color words. In English, the basic color words are *white, black, red, green, yellow, blue, brown, pink, purple, orange,* and *gray.* One feature of a basic color word is that it consists of a single morph; it cannot include two or more units of meaning. This feature eliminates combinations such as *blue-green* and *sky blue.* A second feature of a basic color word is that the color it represents is not generally included in a higher-order color term. For example, scarlet and crimson are usually considered variants of red, turquoise a variant of blue. A third feature is that basic terms tend to be the first-named words when people are asked for color words. Finally, for a word to be considered a basic color word, many individual speakers of the language have to agree on the central meaning (in the color spectrum) of the word.[47]

Why do different societies (languages) vary in number of basic color terms? Berlin and Kay suggest that the number of basic color terms in a language increases with technological specialization as color is used to decorate and distinguish objects.[48] There may also be many basic color terms because of a biological factor.[49] Peoples with darker (more pigmented) eyes seem to have more trouble distinguishing colors at the dark (blue-green) end of the spectrum than do peoples with lighter eyes. It might be expected, then, that peoples who live nearer the equator (who tend to have darker eyes, presumably for protection against damaging ultraviolet radiation) would tend to have fewer basic color terms. And they do.[50] Moreover, it seems that both cultural and biological factors are required to account for cross-linguistic variation in the number of basic color terms. Societies tend to have six or more such terms (with separate terms for blue and green) only when they are relatively far from the equator and only when their cultures are more technologically specialized.[51]

Cecil Brown has found what seem to be developmental sequences in other lexical domains. Two such domains are general, or *life-form*, terms for plants and for animals. Life-form terms are higher-order classifications. All languages have lower-order terms for specific plants and animals. For example, English has words such as *oak, pine, sparrow,* and *salmon.* English speakers make finer distinctions too—*pin oak, white pine, white-throated sparrow,* and *red salmon.* But why, in some languages, do people have a larger number of general terms such as *tree, bird,* and *fish?* It seems that these general terms show a universal developmental sequence too. That is, general terms seem to be added in a somewhat consistent order. After "plant" comes a term for "tree"; then one for "grerb" (small, green, leafy, nonwoody plant); then "bush" (for plants between tree and grerb in size); then "grass"; then "vine."[52] The life-form terms for animals also seem to be added in sequence; after "animal" comes a term for "fish," then "bird," then "snake," then "wug" (for small creatures other than fish, birds, and snakes—for example, worms and bugs), then "mammal."[53]

More complex societies tend to have a larger number of general, or life-form, terms for plants and animals than do simpler societies, just as they tend to have a larger number of basic color terms. Do all realms or domains of vocabulary increase in size as social complexity increases? If we look at the total vocabulary of a language (as can be counted in a dictionary), more complex societies do have larger vocabularies.[54] But if we look instead at the nonspecialist, **core vocabulary** of languages, it seems that all languages have a core vocabulary of about the same size.[55] Indeed, although some domains increase in size with social complexity, some remain the same and still others decrease. An example of a smaller vocabulary domain in complex societies is that of specific names for plants. Urban North Americans may know general terms for plants, but they know relatively few names for specific plants. The typical individual in a small-scale society can commonly name 400–800 plant species; a typical person in our own and similar societies may be able to name only 40–80.[56] The number of life-form terms is larger in societies in which ordinary people know less about particular plants and animals.[57]

The evidence now available strongly supports the idea that the vocabulary of a language reflects the everyday distinctions that are important in the society. Those aspects of environment or culture that are of special importance will receive greater attention in the language. For example, many languages lack the possessive transitive verb we write as *have,* as in "I have." Instead, the language may say something such as "it is to me." A cross-cultural study has suggested that a language may develop the verb *have* after the speakers of that language have developed a system of private property or personal ownership of resources.[58]

Linguistic Influences on Culture: The Sapir-Whorf Hypothesis

There is general agreement that culture influences language. But there is less agreement about the opposite possibility—that language influences other aspects of culture. Edward Sapir and Benjamin Lee Whorf suggested that language is a force in its own right, that it affects how individuals in a society perceive and conceive reality. This suggestion is known as the *Sapir-Whorf hypothesis*.[59] In comparing the English language with Hopi, Whorf pointed out that English-language categories convey discreteness with regard to time and space, but Hopi does not. English has a discrete past, present, and future, and things occur at a definite time. Hopi expresses things with more of an idea of ongoing processes without time being apportioned into fixed segments. According to Ronald Wardhaugh, Whorf believed that these language differences lead Hopi and English speakers to see the world differently.[60]

As intriguing as that idea is, the relevant evidence is mixed. Linguists today do not generally accept the view that language coerces thought, but some suspect that particular features of language may facilitate certain patterns of thought.[61] The influences may be clearest in poetry and metaphors, where words and phrases are applied to other than their ordinary subjects, as in "all the world's a stage."[62] One of the serious problems in testing the Sapir-Whorf hypothesis is that researchers need to figure out how to separate the effects of other aspects of culture from the effects of language.

One approach that may reveal the direction of influence between language and culture is to study how children in different cultures (speaking different languages) develop concepts as they grow up. If language influences the formation of a particular concept, we might expect that children will acquire that concept earlier in societies where the languages emphasize that concept. For example, some languages make more of gender differences than others. Do children develop gender identity earlier when their language emphasizes gender? (Very young girls and boys seem to believe they can switch genders by dressing in opposite-sex clothes, suggesting that they have not yet developed a stable sense that they are unchangeably girls or boys.) Alexander Guiora and his colleagues have studied children growing up in Hebrew-speaking homes (Israel), English-speaking homes (the United States), and Finnish-speaking homes (Finland). Hebrew has the most gender emphasis of the three languages; all nouns are either masculine or feminine, and even second-person and plural pronouns are differentiated by gender. English emphasizes gender less, differentiating by gender only in the third-person singular (*she* or *her* or *hers; he* or *him* or *his*). Finnish emphasizes gender the least; although some words, such as *man* and *woman*, convey gender, differentiation by gender is otherwise lacking in the language. Consistent with the idea that language may influence thought, Hebrew-speaking children acquire the concept of stable gender identity the earliest on the average, Finnish-speaking children the latest.[63]

Another approach is to predict from language differences how people may be expected to perform in experiments. Comparing the Yucatec Mayan language and English, John Lucy predicted that English speakers might recall the *number* of things presented more than Yucatec Mayan speakers. For most classes of nouns, English requires a linguistic way of indicating whether something is singular or plural. You cannot say "I have dog" (no indication of number), but must say "I have a dog," "I have dogs," or "I have one (two, three, several, many) dogs." Yucatec Maya, like English, can indicate a plural, but allows the noun to be neutral with regard to number. For example, the translated phrase there-is-dog-over-there (*yàan pèek té'elo'*) can be left ambiguous about whether there is one or more than one dog. In English, the same ambiguity would occur in the sentence "I saw deer over there," but English does not often allow ambiguity for animate or inanimate nouns.[64] In a number of experiments, Yucatec Mayan and American English speakers were equally likely to recall the objects in a picture, but they differed in how

NEW PERSPECTIVES ON GENDER

Does the English Language Promote Sexist Thinking?

Does English promote sexist thinking, or does the language merely reflect gender inequalities that already exist? For those who wish to promote gender equality, the answers to these questions are important because, if language influences thought (along the lines put forward by Edward Sapir and Benjamin Whorf), then linguistic change will be necessary to bring about change in the culture of gender. If it is the other way around, that is, if language reflects inequality, then social, economic, and political changes have to come before we can expect substantial linguistic change to occur.

Leaving aside for the moment which changes first, how does English represent gender inequity? Consider the following written by Benjamin Lee Whorf: "Speech is the best show man puts on. . . . Language helps man in his thinking." Although *man* in English technically refers to all humans and *his* technically refers to the thinking of a single person of either gender, the frequent use of such words could convey the idea that males are more important. Similarly, do the words *chairman, policeman, businessman,* and *salesman* convey that males are supposed to have those jobs? What is conveyed when there are two words for the two genders, as in *actor* and *actress* and *hero* and *heroine*? Usually the base word is male and the suffix is added for the female form. Does the suffix convey that the female form is an afterthought or less important?

It is not just the structure of the language that may convey gender inequality. How come in the pairs *sir/madam, master/mistress, wizard/witch,* the female version has acquired negative connotations? Men might be called animal names, such as wolves, rats, or pigs. But more animal images seem to be applied to women. They can be *chicks, henpeckers, cows, dogs, bitches, kittens,* or *birds.* Coming back to the original question, how would we know whether language promotes sexism or sexism influences language? One way to find out is to do experimental studies, such as the one conducted by Fatemeh Khosroshashi. Some individuals were asked to read texts written with *man, he,* and *his* referring to people; others were asked to read texts with more gender-neutral phrasing. Individuals were subsequently asked to draw pictures to go with the texts. The

ones who read the texts with more male terminology drew more accompanying pictures of men, strongly suggesting that the use of the terms *man, he,* and *his* conveyed the thought that the people in the text were men, not women, *because* of the vocabulary used. We need more such studies to help address the intellectual question of which comes first, linguistic or nonlinguistic culture.

It would be important to know whether societies with more "male-oriented" language are more male-dominated than are societies without such distinctions. We don't have that kind of comparative research yet. But one study by Robert and Ruth Munroe looked at the *proportion* of female and male nouns in 10 languages (six Indo-European, four other than Indo-European) in which nouns have gender. Although none of those societies could be described as having a female bias, the Munroes were able to ask whether those societies with less male bias in social customs (e.g., all children are equally likely to inherit property) have a higher proportion of female nouns than male nouns (more female than male nouns). The answer appears to be yes. Although this study does not reveal what came first, studies like it are important if we want to discover how language differences may be related to other aspects of culture. If male-oriented languages are not related to male dominance, then it is not likely that sexist thinking is a consequence of language.

On the assumption that language may influence thought, many are pushing for changes in the way English is used, if not structured. It is hard to get English speakers to adopt a gender-neutral singular pronoun to replace *he.* Attempts to do so go back to the eighteenth century and include suggestions of *tey, thon, per,* and *s/he.* Although these efforts have not succeeded, the way English is written and spoken has begun to change. Words or phrases such as *chair* (or *chairperson*), *police officer,* and *sales assistant* (*salesperson*) have begun to replace their former *man* versions. If Whorf were writing his sentence now, it probably would be written: "Speech is the best show humans put on. . . . Language helps people think."

Sources: Holmes 2001, 305–16; Khosroshashi 1989; Lakoff 1973; Munroe and Munroe 1969; Romaine 1994, 105–16; Wardhaugh 2002, 317.

often they described the number of a particular object in the picture. Yucatec Mayan speakers did so less often, consistent with their language's lack of insistence on indicating number.[65] So the salience of number in the experiments was probably a consequence of how the languages differ.

The Ethnography of Speaking

Many are concerned with the *ethnography of speaking*—that is, with cultural and subcultural patterns of speech variation in different social contexts.[66] The sociolinguist might ask, for example, what kinds of things one talks about in casual conversation with a stranger. A foreigner may know English vocabulary and grammar well but may not know that one typically chats with a stranger about the weather or where one comes from, and not about what one ate that day or how much money one earns. A foreigner may be familiar with much of the culture of a North American city, but if that person divulges the real state of his or her health and feelings to the first person who says, "How are you?" he or she has much to learn about "small talk" in North American English.

Similarly, North Americans tend to get confused in societies where greetings are quite different from ours. People in some other societies may ask as a greeting, "Where are you going?" or "What are you cooking?" Some Americans may think such questions are rude; others may try to answer in excruciating detail, not realizing that only vague answers are expected, just as we don't really expect a detailed answer when we ask people how they are.

Social Status and Speech

That a foreign speaker of a language may know little about the small talk of that language is but one example of the sociolinguistic principle that what we say and how we say it are not wholly predictable by the rules of our language. Who we are socially and whom we are talking to may greatly affect what we say and how we say it.

In a study interviewing children in a New England town, John Fischer noted that, in formal interviews, children were likely to pronounce the ending in words such as *singing* and *fishing,* but in

Strangers shake hands when they meet; friends may touch each other more warmly. How we speak to others also differs according to the degree of friendship.

informal conversations, they said *singin'* and *fishin'*. Moreover, he noted that the phenomenon also appeared to be related to social class; children from higher-status families were less likely to drop the ending than were children from lower-status families. Subsequent studies in English-speaking areas tend to support Fischer's observations with regard to this speech pattern.[67]

Status relationships between people can also influence the way they speak to each other. Terms of address are a good example. In English, forms of address are relatively simple. One is called either by a first name or by a title (such as *Doctor, Professor, Ms.,* or *Mister*) followed by a last name. A study by Roger Brown and Marguerite Ford indicates that terms of address in English vary with the nature of the relationship between the speakers.[68] The reciprocal use of first names generally signifies an informal or intimate relationship between two people. A title and last name used reciprocally usually indicates a more formal or businesslike relationship between individuals who are roughly equal in status. Nonreciprocal use of first names and titles in English is reserved for speakers who recognize a marked difference in status between them. This status difference can be a function of age, as when a child refers to her mother's friend as Mrs. Miller and is in turn addressed as Sally, or can be due to occupational hierarchy, as when a person refers to his boss as Ms. Ramirez and is in turn addressed as Joe.

Gender Differences in Speech

In many societies, the speech of men differs from the speech of women. The variation can be slight, as in our own society, or more extreme, as with the Carib Indians in the Lesser Antilles of the West Indies, among whom women and men use different words for the same concepts.[69] In Japan, males and females use entirely different words for numerous concepts (e.g., the male word for water is *mizu*; the female version is *ohiya*), and females often add the polite prefix *o-* (females will tend to say *ohasi* for chopsticks; males will tend to say *hasi*).[70] In the United States and other Western societies, there are differences in the speech of females and males, but they are not as dramatic as in the Carib and Japanese cases. For example, earlier we noted the tendency for the *g* to be dropped in words such as *singing* when the situation is informal and when the social class background is lower. But there is also a gender difference. Gender differences occur in intonation and in phrasing of sentences as well. Robin Lakoff found that, in English, women tend to answer questions with sentences that have rising inflections at the end instead of a falling intonation associated with a firm answer. Women also tend to add questions to statements, such as "They caught the robber last week, didn't they?"[71]

One explanation for the gender differences, particularly with regard to pronunciation, is that women in many societies may be more concerned than men with being "correct."[72] In societies with social classes, what is considered more correct by the average person may be what is associated with the upper class. In other societies, what is older may be considered more correct. Gender differences in speech may parallel some of the gender differences noted in other social behavior: Girls are more likely than boys to behave in ways that are acceptable to adults.

There are not enough studies to know just how common it is for women to exhibit more linguistic "correctness." We do know of some instances where it is not the case. For example, in a community in Madagascar where people speak Merina, a dialect of Malagasy, it is considered socially correct to avoid explicit directives. So, instead of directly ordering an action, a Merina speaker will try to say it indirectly. Also, it is polite to avoid negative remarks, such as expressing anger toward someone. In this community, however, women, not men, often break the rules; women speak more directly and express anger more often.[73] This difference may be related to the fact that women are more involved in buying and selling in the marketplace.

Men and women typically differ in what they talk about, or do not talk about. Deborah Tannen offers some examples. When women hear about someone else's troubles, they are likely to express understanding of the other's feelings; in contrast, men are likely to offer solutions. Men tend not to ask for directions; women do. Women tend to talk a lot in private settings; men talk more in public settings. These and other differences can cause friction and misunderstanding between the genders. When women express their troubles and men offer solutions, women feel that their feelings are not understood; men are frustrated that the women do not take their solutions seriously. Men may prefer to sit at home quietly and feel put upon to have to engage in conversation; women feel slighted when men avoid extended conversations with them. Why these differences? Tannen suggests that misunderstanding between men and women arises because boys and girls grow up in somewhat different cultures. Girls typically play in small groups, talk frequently, and are intimate with others. Boys more often play in large groups in which jockeying for status and attention are more of a concern. Higher-status individuals give directions and solutions; they do not seek directions or solutions. So asking for directions is like acknowledging lower status. But large play groups resemble public settings, and so later in life, men feel more comfortable speaking in public. Women, in contrast, are more comfortable speaking in small, intimate groups.[74]

Multilingualism and Code-Switching

For many people, the ability to speak more than one language is a normal part of life. One language may be spoken at home and another in school, the marketplace, or government. Or more than one language may be spoken at home if family members come from different cultures and still other languages are spoken outside. Some countries explicitly promote multilingualism. For example, Singapore has four official languages—English, Mandarin (one of the Chinese languages), Tamil, and Malay. English is stressed for trade, Mandarin as the language of communication with most of China, Malay as the language of the general region, and Tamil as the language of an important ethnic group. Moreover, most of the population speaks Hokkien, another Chinese language. Education is likely to be in English and Mandarin.[75]

What happens when people who know two or more languages communicate with each other? Very often you find them **code-switching,** using more than one language in the course of conversing.[76] Switching can occur in the middle of a Spanish–English bilingual sentence, as in "No van a bring it up in the meeting" ("They are not going to bring it up in the meeting").[77] Or switching can occur when the topic or situation changes, such as from social talk to schoolwork. Why do speakers of more than one language sometimes switch? Although speakers switch for a lot of different reasons, what is clear is that the switching is not a haphazard mix that comes from laziness or ignorance. Code-switching involves a great deal of knowledge of two or more languages and an awareness of what is considered appropriate or inappropriate in the community. For example, in the Puerto Rican community in New York City, code-switching within the same sentence seems to be common in speech among friends, but if a stranger who looks like a Spanish speaker approaches, the language will shift entirely to Spanish.[78]

Code-switching may need to be understood in terms of the broader political and historical context. For example, German speakers in Transylvania, where Romanian is the national language, hardly ever code-switch to Romanian. Perhaps the reason is that, before the end of World War II, German speakers were a privileged economic group who looked down upon landless Romanians and their language. Under socialism, the German speakers lost their economic privilege, but they continued to speak German among themselves. In the rare cases that Romanian is used among German speakers, it tends to be associated with low-status speech, such as singing bawdy songs. The opposite situation occurred in a Hungarian region of German-speaking Austria. The people of this agricultural region, annexed to Austria in 1921, were fairly poor peasant farmers. After World War II, business expansion began to attract labor from rural areas, so many Hungarians eagerly moved into jobs in industry. Younger generations saw German as a symbol of higher status and upward mobility; not surprisingly, code-switching between Hungarian and German became part of their conversations. Indeed, in the third generation, German has become the language of choice, except when speaking to the oldest Hungarians. The Hungarian–Austrian situation is fairly common in many parts of the world, where the language of the politically dominant group ends up being "linguistically dominant."[79]

Writing and Literacy

Most of us have come to depend on writing for so many things that it is hard to imagine a world without it. Yet humans spent most of their history on earth without written language and many, if not most, important human achievements predate written language. Parents and other teachers passed on their knowledge by oral instruction and demonstration. Stories, legends, and myths abounded—the stuff we call oral literature—even in the absence of writing. This is not to say that writing is not important. Far more information and far more literature can be preserved for a longer period of time with a writing system. The earliest writing systems are only about 6,000 years old and are associated with early cities and states. Early writing is associated with systematic record-keeping—keeping of ledgers for inventorying goods and transactions. In early times, probably only the elite could read and write—indeed only recently has universal literacy (the ability to read and write) become the goal of most countries. But in most countries, the goal of universal literacy is far from achieved. Even in countries with universal education, the quality of education and the length of education varies considerably between subcultures and genders. Just as some ways of speaking are considered superior to others, a high degree of literacy is usually considered superior to illiteracy.[80] But literacy in what language or languages? Recent efforts to preserve languages have encouraged writing of texts in languages that were only spoken previously. Obviously, there will be few texts in those languages; other languages have vast numbers of written texts. As more accumulated knowledge is written and stored in books, journals, and databases, attainment of literacy in those written languages will be increasingly critical to success. And texts do not only convey practical knowledge—they may also convey attitudes, beliefs, and values that are characteristic of the culture associated with the language in which the texts are written.

Children do not need help learning the language spoken in their homes. However, reading and writing cannot usually be learned without instruction. Nowadays, children in most cultures are expected to learn to read and write in school. These Trobriand children from Papua New Guinea are allowed to wear their traditional clothes to school once a week.

Language and Communication

✔•—[Study and **Review** on **myanthrolab.com**

Summary

1. The essential function language plays in all societies is that of communication. Although human communication is not limited to spoken language, such language is of overriding importance because it is the primary vehicle through which culture is shared and transmitted.

2. Systems of communication are not unique to humans. Other animal species communicate in a variety of ways—by sound, odor, body movement, and so forth. The ability of chimpanzees and gorillas to learn and use sign language suggests that symbolic communication is not unique to humans. Still, human language is distinctive as a communication system in that its spoken and symbolic nature permits an infinite number of combinations and recombinations of meaning.

3. Nonverbal human communication includes posture, mannerisms, body movement, facial expressions, and signs and gestures. Nonverbal human communication also includes tone of voice, accent, nonword sounds, and all the optional vocal features that communicate meaning apart from the language itself.

4. Descriptive (or structural) linguists try to discover the rules of phonology (the patterning of sounds), morphology (the patterning of sound sequences and words), and syntax (the patterning of phrases and sentences) that predict how most speakers of a language talk.

5. By comparing related languages, historical linguists try to reconstruct the features of the protolanguage, the linguistic changes over time (such as sound shifts), how the offspring languages separated from the protolanguage or from each other, and to establish the approximate dates of such separations.

6. When two groups of people speaking the same language lose communication with each other because they become separated either physically or socially, they begin to accumulate small changes in phonology, morphology, and syntax. If the separation continues, the two former dialects of the same language will eventually become separate languages—that is, they will become mutually unintelligible.

7. Whereas isolation brings about divergence between speech communities, contact results in greater resemblance. This effect is particularly evident when contact between people who speak mutually unintelligible languages introduces borrowed words, most of which name some new item borrowed from the other culture.

8. Some attempts to explain the diversity of languages have focused on the possible interaction between language and other aspects of culture. On the one hand, if it can be shown that a culture can affect the structure and content of its language, then it would follow that linguistic diversity derives at least in part from cultural diversity. On the other hand, the direction of influence between culture and language might work in reverse; the linguistic structures might affect other aspects of the culture.

9. In recent years, some linguists have begun to study variations in how people actually use language when speaking. This type of linguistic study, called sociolinguistics, is concerned with the ethnography of speaking—that is, with cultural and subcultural patterns of speaking in different social contexts.

10. In bilingual or multilingual populations, code-switching (using more than one language in the course of conversing) has become increasingly common.

11. Written language dates back only about 6,000 years, but writing and written records have become increasingly important; literacy is now a major goal of most countries.

Glossary Terms

accent	lexicon	phonology
code-switching	morph	protolanguage
core vocabulary	morpheme	syntax
dialects	morphology	symbolic communication
historical linguistics	phoneme	
lexical content	phones	

Critical Questions

1. Why might natural selection have favored the development of true language in humans but not in apes?

2. Would the world be better off with many different languages spoken or with just one universal language? Why do you think so?

3. How does some aspect of your speech differ from your parents or others of the previous generation? Why do you think it has changed?

Read the Original Source on myanthrolab.com

Read the chapter by Jane H. Hill, "Do Apes Have Language?" on MyAnthroLab and answer the following questions.

1. Jane Hill raises the question of whether apes have language. Briefly, what is her answer to the question?

2. Chimpanzees have learned signs from American Sign Language but they have not been able to learn to speak words. Why not?

Photo Credits

Credits are listed in order of appearance.

Anthony Bannister; Gallo Images/Corbis; (left): Susan Kuklin/Photo Researchers, Inc.; (right): Ellen Senisi/The Image Works; Roy Morsch/Corbis; Lebrecht Music & Arts Photo Library; Peter Wilson/DK Images; (left): RAYES/Photodisc/Thinkstock; (right): diego_cervo/iStockphoto; Caroline Penn/Corbis.

Helen Keller, "The Story of My Life." New York, NY: Random House, Inc., 1974. Lewis Carroll, "Through the Looking Glass and What Alice Found There." Philadelphia: Henry Altemus Company, 1897. From Chaucer, Canterbury Tales. From Chaucer, Geoffrey. 1926. The prologue to the Canterbury Tales, the Knights Tale, the Nonnes Prestes Tale, ed. Mark H. Liddell. New York: Macmillan.

Glossary

Accent Differences in pronunciation characteristic of a group.

Code-switching Using more than one language in the course of conversing.

Core vocabulary Nonspecialist vocabulary.

Dialect A variety of a language spoken in a particular area or by a particular social group.

Historical linguistics The study of how languages change over time.

Lexical content Vocabulary or lexicon.

Lexicon The words and morphs, and their meanings, of a language; approximated by a dictionary.

Morph The smallest unit of a language that has a meaning.

Morpheme One or more morphs with the same meaning.

Morphology The study of how sound sequences convey meaning.

Phone A speech sound in a language.

Phoneme A sound or set of sounds that makes a difference in meaning to the speakers of the language.

Phonology The study of the sounds in a language and how they are used.

Protolanguage A hypothesized ancestral language from which two or more languages seem to have derived.

Symbolic communication An arbitrary (not obviously meaningful) gesture, call, word, or sentence that has meaning even when its *referent* is not present.

Syntax The ways in which words are arranged to form phrases and sentences.

Notes

1. Keller 1974/1902, 34.
2. Wilden 1987, 124, referred to in Christensen, Hockey, and James 2001.
3. Lambert 2001.
4. Ekman and Keltner 1997, 32.
5. von Frisch 1962.
6. Gibson and Jessee 1999, 189–90; King 1999.

7. Hockett and Ascher 1964; the vervet monkey example is described in Seyfarth, Cheney, and Marler 1980.
8. T. S. Eliot 1963.
9. Snowdon 1999, 81.
10. Pepperberg 1999.
11. Mukerjee 1996, 28.
12. Savage-Rumbaugh 1992, 138–41.
13. J. H. Hill 1978, 94; 2009.
14. Ibid.
15. Senner 1989.
16. Chomsky 1975.
17. Southworth and Daswani 1974, 312. See also Boas 1911/1964, 121–23.
18. Akmajian et al. 2001, 296.
19. Bickerton 1983.
20. Ibid., 122.
21. B. Berlin 1992; Hays 1994.
22. G. Miller 2004.
23. Blount 1981; Gleitman and Wanner 1982.
24. R. Brown 1980, 93–94.
25. de Villiers and de Villiers 1979, 48; see also Wanner and Gleitman 1982.
26. Bickerton 1983, 122.
27. E. Bates and Marchman 1988, as referred to by Snowdon 1999, 88–91.
28. Crystal 1971, 168.
29. Ibid., 100–01.
30. Barinaga 1992, 535.
31. M. Ember and C. R. Ember 1999; R. L. Munroe, Munroe, and Winters 1996. The theory about the effect of baby-holding on consonant–vowel alternation is an extension of the theory that regular baby-holding encourages a preference for regular rhythm in music; see Ayres 1973.
32. Sapir and Swadesh 1964, 103.
33. Akmajian et al. 2001, 149–54.
34. Chaucer 1926, 8. Our modern English translation is based on the glossary in this book.
35. Katzner 2002, 10.
36. Akmajian et al. 2001, 334.
37. Baldi 1983, 3.
38. Ibid., 12.
39. Greenberg 1972; see also Phillipson 1976, 71.
40. Phillipson 1976, 79.
41. Holmes 2001, 194–95.
42. Trudgill 1983, 34.
43. Weinreich 1968: 31.
44. But see Thomason and Kaufman (1988) for a discussion of how grammatical changes due to contact may be more important than was previously assumed.
45. Berlin and Kay 1969.
46. Ibid.
47. Ibid., 5–6.
48. Ibid., 104; Witkowski and Brown 1978.
49. Bornstein 1973, 41–101.
50. M. Ember 1978, 364–67.
51. Ibid.
52. C. H. Brown 1977.
53. C. H. Brown 1979.
54. Witkowski and Burris 1981.
55. Ibid.
56. C. H. Brown and Witkowski 1980, 379.
57. C. H. Brown 1984, 106.
58. Webb 1977, 42–49; see also Rudmin 1988.
59. Sapir 1931, 578; see also J. B. Carroll 1956.
60. Wardhaugh 2002, 222.
61. Denny 1979, 97.
62. Friedrich 1986.
63. Guiora et al. 1982.
64. Lucy 1992, 46.
65. Ibid., 85–148.
66. Hymes 1974, 83–117.

67. Fischer 1958; Wardhaugh 2002, 160–88.
68. R. Brown and Ford 1961.
69. Wardhaugh 2002, 315.
70. Shibamoto 1987, 28.
71. Lakoff 1973; 1990.
72. Holmes 2001, 158–59; Trudgill 1983, 87–88; Wardhaugh 2002, 328.
73. Keenan 1989.
74. Tannen 1990, 49–83.
75. Wardhaugh 2002, 100.
76. Heller 1988, 1.
77. Pfaff 1979.
78. Wardhaugh 2002, 108.
79. Gal 1988, 249–55.
80. Collins and Blot 2003, 1–3.

Bibliography

Akmajian, Adrian, Richard A. Demers, Ann K. Farmer, and Robert M. Harnish. 2001. *Linguistics: An introduction to language and communication.* Cambridge, MA: MIT Press.
Ayres, Barbara C. 1973. Effects of infant carrying practices on rhythm in music. *Ethos* 1:387–404.
Baldi, Philip. 1983. *An introduction to the Indo-European languages.* Carbondale: Southern Illinois University Press.
Barinaga, Maria. 1992. Priming the brain's language pump. *Science* 255 (January 31):535.
Bates, Elizabeth, and V. A. Marchman, 1988. What is and is not universal in language acquisition. In *Language, communication, and the brain,* ed. F. Plum, 19–38. New York: Raven Press.
Berlin, Brent. 1992. *Ethnobiological classification: Principles of categorization of plants and animals in traditional societies.* Princeton, NJ: Princeton University Press.
Berlin, Brent, and Paul Kay. 1969. *Basic color terms: Their universality and evolution.* Berkeley: University of California Press.
Bickerton, Derek. 1983. Creole languages. *Scientific American* (July):116–22.
Blount, Ben G. 1981. The development of language in children. In *Handbook of cross-cultural human development,* eds. R. H. Munroe, R. L. Munroe, and B. B. Whiting. New York: Garland.
Boas, Franz. 1964/1911. On grammatical categories. In *Language in culture and society,* ed. D. Hymes. New York: Harper & Row.
Bornstein, Marc H. 1973. The psychophysiological component of cultural difference in color naming and illusion susceptibility. *Behavior Science Notes* 8:41–101.
Brown, Cecil H. 1977. Folk botanical life-forms: Their universality and growth. *American Anthropologist* 79:317–42.
Brown, Cecil H. 1979. Folk zoological life-forms: Their universality and growth. *American Anthropologist* 81:791–817.
Brown, Cecil H. 1984. World view and lexical uniformities. *Reviews in Anthropology* 11:99–112.
Brown, Cecil H., and Stanley R. Witkowski. 1980. Language universals. In *Toward explaining human culture,* eds. D. Levinson and M. J. Malone, Appendix B. New Haven, CT: HRAF Press.
Brown, Roger. 1980. The first sentence of child and chimpanzee. In *Speaking of apes,* eds. T. A. Sebeok and J. Umiker-Sebeok. New York: Plenum Press.
Brown, Roger, and Marguerite Ford. 1961. Address in American English. *Journal of Abnormal and Social Psychology* 62:375–85.
Carroll, John B., ed. 1956. *Language, thought, and reality: Selected writings of Benjamin Lee Whorf.* New York: Wiley.
Chaucer, Geoffrey. 1926. *The prologue to the Canterbury Tales, the Knights Tale, the Nonnes Prestes Tale,* ed. Mark H. Liddell. New York: Macmillan.
Chomsky, Noam. 1975. *Reflections on language.* New York: Pantheon.
Christensen, Pia, Jenny Hockey, and Allison James, 2001. Talk, silence and the material world: Patterns of indirect communication among agricultural farmers in northern England. In *An anthropology of indirect communication,* eds. J. Hendry and C. W. Watson, 68–82. London: Routledge.
Collins, James, and Richard Blot. 2003. *Literacy and literacies.* Cambridge, UK: Cambridge University Press.
Crystal, David. 1971. *Linguistics.* Middlesex, UK: Penguin.
de Villiers, Peter A., and Jill G. de Villiers. 1979. *Early language.* Cambridge, MA: Harvard University Press.
Denny, J. Peter. 1979. The "extendedness" variable in classifier semantics: Universal features and cultural variation. In *Ethnolinguistics,* ed. M. Mathiot. The Hague: Mouton.
Ekman, Paul, and Dachner Keltner. 1997. Universal facial expressions of emotion: An old controversy and new findings. In *Nonverbal communication: Where nature meets culture,* eds. U. Segerstrale and P. Molnar. Mahwah, NJ: Erlbaum.
Eliot, Thomas Sterns. 1963. The love song of J. Alfred Prufrock. In *Collected poems, 1909–1962.* New York: Harcourt, Brace & World.
Ember, Melvin. 1978. Size of color lexicon: Interaction of cultural and biological factors. *American Anthropologist* 80:364–67.
Ember, Melvin, and Carol R. Ember. 1999. Cross-language predictors of consonant-vowel syllables. *American Anthropologist* 101:730–42.
Friedrich, Paul. 1986. *The language parallax.* Austin: University of Texas Press.
Gal, Susan. 1988. The political economy of code choice. In *Codeswitching,* ed. M. Heller, 245–64. Berlin: Mouton de Gruyter.
Gibson, Kathleen R., and Stephen Jessee. 1999. Language evolution and expansions of multiple neurological processing areas. In *The origins of language,* ed. B. J. King, 189–227. Santa Fe, NM: School of American Research Press.

Language and Communication

Gleitman, Lila R., and Eric Wanner. 1982. Language acquisition: The state of the state of the art. In *Language acquisition,* eds. E. Wanner and L. R. Gleitman. Cambridge, UK: Cambridge University Press.

Greenberg, Joseph H. 1972. Linguistic evidence regarding Bantu origins. *Journal of African History* 13:189–216.

Guiora, Alexander Z., Benjamin Beit-Hallahmi, Risto Fried, and Cecelia Yoder. 1982. Language environment and gender identity attainment. *Language Learning* 32:289–304.

Hays, Terence E. 1994. Sound symbolism, onomatopoeia, and New Guinea frog names. *Journal of Linguistic Anthropology* 4:153–74.

Heller, Monica, ed. 1988. *Codeswitching: Anthropological and sociolinguistic perspectives.* Berlin: Mouton de Gruyter.

Hill, Jane H. 1978. Apes and language. *Annual Review of Anthropology* 7:89–112.

Hill, Jane H. 2009. Do apes have language? In MyAnthroLibrary, eds. C. R. Ember, M. Ember, and P. N. Peregrine. MyAnthroLibrary.com. Pearson.

Hockett, Charles F., and R. Ascher. 1964. The human revolution. *Current Anthropology* 5:135–68.

Holmes, Janet. 2001. *An introduction to sociolinguistics.* 2nd ed. London: Longman.

Hymes, Dell. 1974. *Foundations in sociolinguistics: An ethnographic approach.* Philadelphia: University of Pennsylvania Press.

Katzner, Kenneth. 2002. *Languages of the world.* London: Routledge.

Keenan, Elinor. 1989. Norm-makers, norm-breakers: Uses of speech by men and women in a Malagasy community. In *Explorations in the ethnography of speaking.* 2nd ed. eds. R. Bauman and J. Sherzer. New York: Cambridge University Press.

Keller, Helen. 1974/1902. *The story of my life.* New York: Dell.

King, Barbara J. 1999. Introduction. In *The origins of language,* ed. B. J. King, 3–19. Santa Fe, NM: School of American Research Press.

Lakoff, Robin. 1973. Language and woman's place. *Language in Society* 2:45–80.

Lakoff, Robin. 1990. Why can't a woman be less like a man? In *Talking power,* ed. R. Lakoff. New York: Basic Books.

Lambert, Helen. 2001. Not talking about sex in India: Indirection and the communication of bodily intention. In *An anthropology of indirect communication,* eds. J. Hendry and C. W. Watson, 51–67. London: Routledge.

Lucy, John A. 1992. *Grammatical categories and cognition: A case study of the linguistic relativity hypothesis.* Cambridge, UK: Cambridge University Press.

Miller, Greg. 2004. Listen, baby. *Science* 306 (November 12):1127.

Mukerjee, Madhusree. 1996. Field notes: Interview with a parrot. *Scientific American* (April):28.

Munroe, Robert L., Ruth H. Munroe, and Stephen Winters. 1996. Cross-cultural correlates of the consonant-vowel (cv) syllable. *Cross-Cultural Research* 30:60–83.

Pepperberg, Irene Maxine. 1999. *The Alex studies: Cognitive and communicative abilities of grey parrots.* Cambridge, MA: Harvard University Press.

Pfaff, Carol. 1979. Constraints on language mixing. *Language* 55:291–318, as cited in *An introduction to sociolinguistics.* 2nd ed. ed. R. Wardhaugh. Oxford, UK: Blackwell.

Phillipson, David W. 1976. Archaeology and Bantu linguistics. *World Archaeology* 8:65–82.

Rudmin, Floyd Webster. 1988. Dominance, social control, and ownership: A history and a cross-cultural study of motivations for private property. *Behavior Science Research* 22:130–60.

Sapir, Edward. 1931. Conceptual categories in primitive languages. Paper presented at the autumn meeting of the National Academy of Sciences, New Haven, CT. Published in *Science* 74.

Sapir, Edward, and M. Swadesh. 1964. American Indian grammatical categories. In *Language in culture and society,* ed. D. Hymes. New York: Harper & Row.

Savage-Rumbaugh, E. Sue. 1992. Language training of apes. In *The Cambridge encyclopedia of human evolution,* eds. S. Jones, R. Martin, and D. Pilbeam. New York: Cambridge University Press.

Senner, Wayne M. 1989. Theories and myths on the origins of writing: A historical overview. In *The origins of writing,* ed. W. M. Senner. Lincoln: University of Nebraska Press.

Shibamoto, Janet S. 1987. The womanly woman: Japanese female speech. In *Language, gender, and sex in comparative perspective,* eds. S. U. Philips, S. Steele, and C. Tanz. Cambridge, UK: Cambridge University Press.

Snowdon, Charles T. 1999. An empiricist view of language evolution and development. In *The origins of language,* ed. B. J. King, 79–114. Santa Fe, NM: School of American Research Press.

Southworth, Franklin C., and Chandler J. Daswani. 1974. *Foundations of linguistics.* New York: Free Press.

Tannen, Deborah. 1990. *You just don't understand: Women and men in conversation.* New York: William Morrow.

Thomason, Sarah Grey, and Terrence Kaufman. 1988. *Language contact, creolization, and genetic linguistics.* Berkeley: University of California Press.

Trudgill, Peter. 1983. *Sociolinguistics: An introduction to language and society.* Rev. ed. New York: Penguin.

von Frisch, Karl. 1962. Dialects in the language of the bees. *Scientific American* (August):78–87.

Wanner, Eric, and Lila R. Gleitman, eds. 1982. *Language acquisition: The state of the art.* Cambridge, UK: Cambridge University Press.

Wardhaugh, Ronald. 2002. *An introduction to sociolinguistics.* 4th ed. Oxford, UK: Blackwell.

Webb, Karen E. 1977. An evolutionary aspect of social structure and a verb "have." *American Anthropologist* 79:42–49.

Weinreich, Uriel. 1968. *Languages in contact.* The Hague: Mouton.

Wilden, Anthony. 1987. *The rules are no game: The strategy of communication.* London: Routledge and Kegan Paul.

Witkowski, Stanley R., and Cecil H. Brown. 1978. Lexical universals. *Annual Review of Anthropology* 7:427–51.

Witkowski, Stanley R., and Harold W. Burris. 1981. Societal complexity and lexical growth. *Behavior Science Research* 16:143–59.

Global Problems

Global Problems

Global Problems

The news on television and in the newspapers makes us aware every day that terrible social problems threaten people around the world. War, crime, family violence, natural disasters, poverty, famine—all these and more are the lot of millions of people in many places. And now there is an increasing threat of terrorism. Can anthropological and other research help us solve these global social problems? Many anthropologists and other social scientists think so.

High-tech communications have increased our awareness of problems all over the world, and we seem to be increasingly more aware of, and bothered by, problems in our own society. For these two reasons, and perhaps also because we know much more than we used to about human behavior, we may be more motivated now to try to solve those problems. We call them "social problems" not just because a lot of people worry about them but also because they have social causes and consequences, and treating or solving them requires changes in social behavior. Even AIDS is partly a social problem. It may be caused by a virus, but it is mostly transmitted by social (sexual) contact with another person. And the main ways to avoid it—abstinence and "safe" sex—require changes in social behavior.

The idea that we can solve social problems, even the enormous ones such as war and family violence, is based on two assumptions. First, we have to assume that it is possible to discover the causes of a problem. And two, we have to assume that we may be able to do something about the causes, once they are discovered, and thereby eliminate or reduce the problem. Not everyone would agree with these assumptions. Some would say that our understanding of a social problem cannot ever be sufficient to suggest a solution guaranteed to work. To be sure, no understanding in science is perfect or certain; there is always some probability that even a well-supported explanation is wrong or incomplete. But the uncertainty of knowledge does not rule out the possibility of application. With regard to social problems, the possible payoff from even incomplete understanding could be a better and safer world. This possibility is what motivates many researchers who investigate social problems. After all, the history of the various sciences strongly supports the belief that scientific understanding can often allow humans to control nature, not just predict and explain it. Why should human behavior be any different?

So what do we know about some of the global social problems, and what policies or solutions are suggested by what we know?

Natural Disasters and Famine

Natural events such as floods, droughts, earthquakes, and insect infestations are usually but not always beyond human control, but their effects are not.[1] We call such events accidents or emergencies when only a few people are affected, but we call them disasters when large numbers of people or large areas are affected. The harm caused is not just a function of the magnitude of the natural event. Between 1960 and 1980, 43 natural disasters in Japan killed an average of 63 people per disaster. During the same period, 17 natural disasters in Nicaragua killed an average of 6,235 people per disaster. In the United States, between 1960 and 1976, the average flood or other environmental disturbance killed just one person, injured a dozen, and destroyed fewer than five buildings. These comparative figures demonstrate that climatic and other events in the physical environment become disasters because of events or conditions in the social environment.

If people live in houses that are designed to withstand earthquakes—if governing bodies require such construction and the economy is developed enough so that people can afford such construction—the effects of an earthquake will be minimized. If poor people are forced to live in deforested floodplains to be able to find land to farm (as in coastal Bangladesh), if the poor

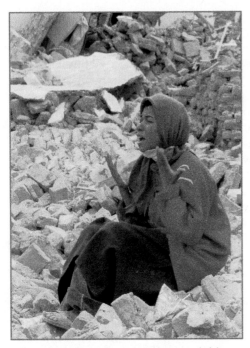

Although earthquakes are not preventable, collapse of houses is mostly preventable by building houses to withstand earthquakes. In Bam, Iran, 20,000 people were killed during a 2003 earthquake and most of the houses collapsed. This woman sits amid the ruins of her house.

are forced to live in shanties built on precarious hillsides (like those of Rio de Janeiro), the floods and landslides that follow severe hurricanes and rainstorms can kill thousands and even hundreds of thousands.

Thus, natural disasters can have greater or lesser effects on human life, depending on social conditions. And therefore disasters are also social problems, problems that have social causes and possible social solutions. Legislating safe construction of a house is a social solution. The 1976 earthquake in Tangsham, China, killed 250,000 people, mostly because they lived in top-heavy adobe houses that could not withstand severe shaking, whereas the 1989 Loma Prieta earthquake in California, which was of comparable intensity, killed 65 people.

One might think that floods, of all disasters, are the least influenced by social factors. After all, without a huge runoff from heavy rains or snow melt, there cannot be a flood. But consider why so many people have died from Hwang River floods in China. (One such flood, in 1931, killed nearly 4 million people, making it the deadliest single disaster in history.) The floods in the Hwang River basin have occurred mostly because the clearing of nearby forests for fuel and farmland has allowed enormous quantities of silt to wash into the river, raising the riverbed and increasing the risk of floods that burst the dams that normally would contain them. The risk of disastrous flooding would be greatly reduced if different social conditions prevailed—if people were not so dependent on firewood for fuel, if they did not have to farm close to the river, or if the dams were higher and more numerous.

Famines, episodes of severe starvation and death, often appear to be triggered by physical events such as a severe drought or a hurricane that kills or knocks down food trees and plants. But famines do not inevitably follow such an event. Social conditions can prevent a famine or increase the likelihood of one. Consider what is likely to happen in Samoa after a hurricane.[2] Whole villages that have lost their coconut and breadfruit trees, as well as their taro patches, pick up and move for a period of time to other villages where they have relatives and friends. The visitors stay and are fed until some of their cultivated trees and plants start to bear food again, at which point they return home. This kind of intervillage reciprocity probably could occur only in a society that has relatively little inequality in wealth. Nowadays, the central government or international agencies may also help out by providing food and other supplies.

Researchers point out that famine rarely results from just one bad food production season. During one bad season, people can usually cope by getting help from relatives, friends, and neighbors or by switching to less desirable foods. The 1974 famine in the African Sahel occurred after 8 years of bad weather; a combination of drought, floods, and a civil war in 1983–1984 contributed to the subsequent famine in the Sahel, Ethiopia, and Sudan.[3] Famine almost always has some social causes. Who has rights to the available food, and do those who have more food distribute it to those who have less? Cross-cultural research suggests that societies with individual property rights rather than shared rights are more likely to suffer famine.[4] Nonetheless, government assistance can lessen the risk of famine in societies with individual property.

Relief provided by government may not always get to those who need it the most. In India, for example, the central government provides help in time of drought to minimize the risk of famine. But the food and other supplies provided to a village may end up being unequally distributed, following the rules of social and gender stratification. Members of the local elite arrange to function as distributors and find ways to manipulate the relief efforts to their advantage. Lower-class and lower-caste families still suffer the most. Within the family, biases against females, particularly young girls and elderly women, translate into their getting less food. It is no wonder, then, that in times of food shortage and famine, the poor and other socially disadvantaged people are especially likely to die.[5]

Thus, the people of a society may not all be equally at risk in case of disaster. In socially stratified societies, the poor particularly suffer. They are likely to be forced to overcultivate, overgraze, and deforest their land, making it more susceptible to degradation. A society most helps those it values the most.

People in the past, and even recently in some places, viewed disasters as divine retribution for human immorality. For example, the great flood described in the Old Testament was understood to be God's doing. But scientific research increasingly allows us to understand the natural causes of disasters, and particularly the social conditions that magnify or minimize their effects. To reduce the impact of disasters, then, we need to reduce the social conditions that magnify the effects of disasters. If humans are responsible for those social conditions, humans can change them. If earthquakes destroy houses that are too flimsy, we can build stronger houses. If floods caused by overcultivation and overgrazing kill people directly (or indirectly by stripping their soils), we can grow new forest cover and provide new job opportunities to floodplain farmers. If prolonged natural disasters or wars threaten famine, social distribution systems can lessen the risk. In short, we may not be able to do much about the weather or other physical causes of disasters, but we can do a lot—if we want to—about the social factors that make disasters disastrous.

Inadequate Housing and Homelessness

In most nations, those who are poor typically live in inadequate housing, in areas we call *slums*. The magnitude of the problem is made clear in some statistics. As of the 2000s, 32 percent of the population of urban areas live in slums, most of them in developing countries. In developing countries only 15 percent of the urban households have sewers, 37 have piped water, and 60 percent have electricity.[6]

In many of the developing nations, where cities are growing very rapidly, squatter settlements emerge as people build dwellings (often makeshift) that are typically declared illegal, either because the land is illegally occupied or because the dwellings violate building codes. Squatter settlements are often located in degraded environments that are subject to flooding and mudslides or have inadequate or polluted water.

But contrary to what some people have assumed, not all dwellers in illegal settlements are poor; all but the upper-income elite may be found in such settlements.[7] Moreover, although squatter settlements have problems, they are not chaotic and unorganized places that are full of crime. Most of the dwellers are employed, aspire to get ahead, live in intact nuclear families, and help each other.[8] People live in such settlements because they cannot find affordable housing and they house themselves as best they can. Many researchers think that such self-help tendencies should be assisted to improve housing because governments in developing countries can seldom afford costly public housing projects. But they could invest somewhat in infrastructure—sewers, water supplies, roads—and provide construction materials to those who are willing to do the work required to improve their dwellings.[9]

Housing in slum areas or shantytowns does provide shelter, minimal though it may be. But many people in many areas of the world have no homes at all. Even in countries such as the United States, which are affluent by world standards, large numbers of people are homeless. They sleep in parks, over steam vents, in doorways, subways, and cardboard boxes. Homelessness is difficult to measure. In 1987, more than 1 million people were estimated to be homeless in the United States.[10] Homelessness has increased in the last few decades. About 3.5 million people experienced homelessness in 2000, almost 40 percent of them children.[11]

Who are the homeless, and how did they get to be homeless? We have relatively little research on these questions, but what we do have suggests differences in the causes of homelessness in different parts of the world. In the United States, unemployment and the shortage of decent low-cost housing appear to be at least partly responsible for the large number of homeless people.[12] But there is also another factor: the deliberate policy to reduce the number of people hospitalized for mental illness and other disabilities. For example, from the mid-1960s to the mid-1990s, New York State released thousands of patients from mental hospitals. Many of these ex-patients had to live in cheap hotels or poorly monitored facilities with virtually no support network. With very little income, they found it especially hard to cope with their circumstances. Ellen Baxter and Kim Hopper, who studied the homeless in New York City, suggest that one event is rarely sufficient to render a person homeless. Rather, poverty and disability (mental or physical) seem to lead to one calamity after another and, finally, homelessness.[13]

Many people cannot understand why homeless individuals do not want to go to municipal shelters. But observations and interviews with the homeless suggest that violence pervades the municipal shelters, particularly the men's shelters. Many feel safer on the streets. Some private charities provide safe shelters and a caring environment. These shelters are filled, but the number of homeless they can accommodate is small.[14] Even single-room-occupancy hotels are hardly better. Many of them are infested with vermin, the common bathrooms are filthy, and they, like the shelters, are often dangerous.[15]

Some poor individuals may be socially isolated, with few or no friends and relatives and little or no social contact. But a society with many such individuals does not necessarily have much homelessness. Socially isolated individuals, even mentally ill individuals, could still have housing, or so the experience of Melbourne, Australia, suggests. Universal health insurance there pays for health care as well as medical practitioners' visits to isolated and ill individuals, wherever they live. Disabled individuals receive a pension or sickness benefits sufficient to allow them to live in a room or apartment. And there is still a considerable supply of cheap housing in Melbourne. Research in Melbourne suggests that a severe mental disorder often precedes living in marginal accommodations—city shelters, commercial shelters, and cheap single rooms. About 50 percent of the people living in such places were diagnosed as previously having some form of mental illness; this percentage is similar to what seems to be the case for homeless people and people living in marginal accommodations in the United States.

The contrast between the United States and Australia makes it clear that social and political policies cause homelessness. Individuals with similar characteristics live in both Australia and the United States, but a larger percentage of them are homeless in the United States.[16]

Because homelessness cannot occur if everybody can afford housing, some people would say that homelessness can happen only in a society with great extremes in income. Statistics on income distribution in the United States clearly show that, since the 1970s, the rich have gotten much richer and the poor have gotten much poorer.[17] The United States now has more income inequality than any country in western Europe and more than most high-income countries. In fact, the profile of inequality in the United States more closely resembles that of developing countries, such as Cambodia and Morocco[18]

A homeless boy in Calcutta, India, with his belongings.

In the United States and many other countries, most homeless people are adults. Whereas adults are "allowed" to be homeless, public sensibilities in the United States appear to be outraged by the sight of children living in the streets; when authorities discover homeless children, they try to find shelters or foster homes for them. But many countries have "street children." In the late 1980s, 80 million of the world's children lived in the streets: 40 million in Latin America, 20 million in Asia, 10 million in Africa and the Middle East, and 10 million elsewhere.[19] In the 2000s, the estimated number grew to about 150 million worldwide.[20]

Lewis Aptekar, who studied street children in Cali, Colombia, reported some surprises.[21] Whereas many of the homeless in the United States and Australia are mentally disabled, the street children in Cali, ranging in age from 7 to 16, are mostly free of mental problems; by and large, they also test normally on intelligence tests. In addition, even though many street children come from abusive homes or never had homes, they usually seem happy and enjoy the support and friendship of other street children. They cleverly and creatively look for ways to get money, frequently through entertaining passersby.

Although observers might think that the street children must have been abandoned by their families, most of them in actuality have at least one parent they keep in touch with. Street life begins slowly, not abruptly; children usually do not stay on the streets full time until they are about 13 years old. Though street children in Cali seem to be in better physical and mental shape than their siblings who stay at home, they often are viewed as a "plague." The street children come from poor families and cope with their lives as best they can, so why are they not viewed with pity and compassion? Aptekar suggests that well-off families see the street children as a threat because a life independent of family may appeal to children, even those from well-off families, who wish to be free of parental constraint and authority.

Whether people become homeless, whether they have shantytowns, seems to depend on a society's willingness to share wealth and help those in need. The street children of Cali may remind us that children as well as adults need companionship and care. Addressing physical needs without responding to emotional needs may get people off the streets, but it won't get them a "home."

Family Violence and Abuse

In U.S. society, we hear regularly about the abuse of spouses and children, which makes us think that such abuse is increasing—but is it? This seems to be a simple question, but it is not so simple to answer. We have to decide what we mean by *abuse.*

Is physical punishment of a child who does something wrong child abuse? Not so long ago, teachers in public schools in the United States were allowed to discipline children by hitting them with rulers or paddles, and many parents used switches or belts. Many would consider these practices to be child abuse, but were they abusive when they were generally accepted? Some would argue that abuse is going beyond what a culture considers appropriate behavior. Others would disagree and would focus on the violence and severity of parents' or teachers' behavior, not the cultural judgment of appropriateness. And abuse need not involve physical violence. It could be argued that verbal aggression and neglect may be just as harmful as physical aggression. Neglect presents its own problems of definition. People from other cultures might argue that we act abusively when we put an infant or child alone in a room to sleep.[22] Few would disagree about severe injuries that kill a child or spouse or require medical treatment, but other disciplinary behaviors are more difficult to judge.

To avoid having to decide what is or is not abuse, many researchers focus their studies on variation in the frequencies of specific behaviors. For example, one can ask which societies have physical punishment of children without calling physical punishment abusive.

According to four national interview surveys of married or cohabiting couples in the United States conducted from 1975 to 1995, physical violence against children appears to have decreased in frequency over time, as did serious assaults by husbands against wives. But serious assaults by wives on husbands did not decrease.[23] The decreasing rates of abuse may be mostly due to reporting differences: wife and child beating is less acceptable now. For example, men report dramatically fewer assaults on their wives, but wives report only slight declines.[24] However, the United States remains a society with a lot of physical violence in families. In 1992 alone, one out of 10 couples had a violent assault episode and one out of 10 children was severely assaulted by a parent.[25] A survey conducted in the mid-1990s found that about 75 percent of the violence against women comes from a male intimate partner, such as a husband. In contrast, most of the violence men experience comes from strangers and acquaintances. Just as women face more risk from those close to them, so do children. When a child is the target of violence, it usually comes from the birth mother.[26]

Cross-culturally, if one form of family violence occurs, others are also likely. So, for example, wife beating, husband beating, child punishment, and fighting among siblings are all significantly associated with each other. But the relationships between these types of family violence are not that strong, which means that they cannot be considered as different facets of the same phenomenon. Indeed, somewhat different factors seem to explain different forms of family violence.[27] We focus here on two forms of violence that are most prevalent cross-culturally: violence against children and violence against wives.

Violence against Children

Cross-culturally, many societies practice and allow infanticide. Frequent reasons for infanticide include illegitimacy, deformity of the infant, twins, too many children, or that the infant is unwanted. Infanticide is usually performed by the mother, but this does not mean that she is uncaring; it may mean that she cannot adequately feed or care for the infant or that it has a poor chance to survive. The reasons for infanticide are similar to those given for abortion. Therefore, it seems that infanticide may be performed when abortion does not work or when unexpected qualities of the infant (e.g., deformity) force the mother to reevaluate her ability to raise the child.[28]

Physical punishment of children occurs at least sometimes in over 70 percent of the world's societies.[29] And physical punishment is frequent or typical in 40 percent of the world's societies. The finding that societies with class stratification and political hierarchy, either native or introduced (colonialism), are very likely to practice corporal punishment of children[30] suggests that parents are consciously or unconsciously preparing their children for a life of power inequality. Research in the United States is consistent with the cross-cultural finding: Those at the bottom of the socioeconomic hierarchy are more likely than those at the top to practice corporal punishment of children.[31] Unfortunately, parents probably do not realize that physical punishment may produce more violent behavior in their children, an outcome they probably do not want or intend.

Violence against Wives

Cross-culturally, wife beating is the most common form of family violence; it occurs at least occasionally in about 85 percent of the world's societies. In about half the societies, wife beating is sometimes serious enough to cause permanent injury or death.[32] It is often assumed that wife beating is common in societies in which males control economic and political resources. In a cross-cultural test of this assumption, David Levinson found that not all indicators of male dominance predict wife beating, but many do. Specifically, wife beating is most common when men control the products of family labor, when men have the final say in decision making in the home, when divorce is difficult for women, when remarriage for a widow is controlled by the husband's kin, and when women do not have any female work groups.[33] Similarly, in the United States, the more one spouse in the family makes the decisions and has the power, the more physical violence occurs in the family. Wife beating is even more likely when the husband controls the household and is out of work.[34]

Wife beating appears to be related to broader patterns of violence. Societies that have violent methods of conflict resolution within communities, physical punishment of criminals, high frequency of warfare, and cruelty toward enemies generally have more wife beating.[35] Corporal punishment of children may be related to wife beating. Research in the United States supports the idea that individuals (males and females) who were punished corporally as adolescents are more likely to approve of marital violence and are more likely to commit it.[36]

Reducing the Risk

What can be done to minimize family violence? First, we have to recognize that probably nothing can be done as long as people in a society do not acknowledge that a problem exists. If severe child punishment and wife beating are perfectly acceptable by almost everyone in a society, they are unlikely to be considered social problems that need solutions. In our own society, many programs are designed to take abused children or wives out of the family situation or to punish the abuser. (Of course, in these situations, the violence has already occurred and was serious enough to have been noticed.) Cross-culturally, at least with respect to wife beating, intervention by others seems to be successful only if the intervention occurs before violence gets serious. As one would expect, however, those societies most prone to a high rate of wife beating are the

MIGRANTS AND IMMIGRANTS

Refugees Are a Global Social Problem

The continuing turmoil in many countries throughout the world has created a flow of refugees that is much larger than ever before in world history. Refugees have become a worldwide social problem; their numbers are high. In the past, thousands of people might have had to flee persecution and war. Now the refugees number in the millions. They flee to other parts of the country, to neighboring countries, and to countries on the other side of the world. As many as an estimated 140 million people became refugees in the twentieth century. For example, the refugees from the civil wars in Somalia are not unusual; 10 percent of the Somali population is now living outside of Somalia, perhaps a million people altogether.

Conceivably, the problem could be handled with less suffering if countries were willing to accept any and all refugees. Shouldn't governments accept them for humanitarian reasons, just because the refugees could die otherwise? Or does there have to be an acknowledged or felt need in the accepting country for cheap labor? There is a fine line between people who want to migrate to have a better or safer life, and people who have to migrate because they would be killed if they don't flee. Refugees are a problem not just because they are suffering, and the world should do something. They are also a problem because countries may refuse to accept them, because their numbers are so large. Governments and charitable agencies have to provide support until the refugees acquire the skills for making a living on their own.

Compare how we think of refugees from different places. Some are accepted (however grudgingly), whereas others are not. The United States only half-heartedly tries to prevent poor Mexicans from entering the country. But people from Africa who are threatened with genocide are rejected much more. Why? Is it because Mexicans and others from Latin America have skills that we need, and they are willing to take jobs that no one else wants because the pay is low and the benefits nil? Who benefits from this state of affairs? Too many! Think of the employers who would otherwise have to pay their workers more or invest in labor-saving machinery. Think of the Chinese "coolies" who were brought in 150 years ago to build the railroads that linked the eastern and western United States. And, of course, think of the refugee laborers. If they didn't "cross the border" looking for work, their children left at home would suffer or even die from malnutrition and other consequences of poverty.

So, what are countries to do? Should they throw open their doors to everyone who wants to come in? Humanitarians might say yes. But this too would make for problems. Some would say that we should not accept and support refugees when we already have lots of poor people. Don't we owe them more than we owe poor people from somewhere else? Shouldn't our tax money go to improve the lives of people already here? What are taxes for, anyway?

How to help refugees is clearly a complex issue. But if we don't do anything to help them, is that ethical? Refugees are the consequences of social inequality and persecution. They are a global social problem that won't go away, as long as the world contains governments that persecute their own citizens, or allow some groups to persecute others. If the solution is not to rely on those governments because they are not likely to change what they are doing, it would seem that we will have to rely for the near future on international organizations (like the United Nations and charitable foundations) if we want to reduce or eliminate the worldwide problem of refugees.

Sources: Harrell-Bond 1996; Van Hear 2004.

least likely to practice immediate intervention. More helpful perhaps, but admittedly harder to arrange, is the promotion of conditions of life that are associated with low family violence. Research so far suggests that promoting the equality of men and women and the sharing of childrearing responsibilities may go a long way toward lessening incidents of family violence.[37] And reducing the risk of corporal punishment of children may reduce the risk of violence when they have families.

Crime

What is a crime in one society is not necessarily a crime in another. Just as it is difficult to decide what constitutes abuse, it is difficult to define *crime.* In one society, it may be a crime to walk over someone's land without permission; in another, there might not be any concept of personal ownership, and therefore no concept of trespassing. In seeking to understand variation in crime, many researchers have not surprisingly preferred to compare those behaviors that are more or less universally considered crimes and that are reliably reported. For example, in a large-scale comparison of crime in 110 nations over a span of 70 years, Dane Archer and Rosemary Gartner concentrated on homicide rates. They argued that homicide is harder for the public to hide and for officials to ignore than are other crimes. A comparison of interviews about crime with police records suggests that homicide is the most reliably reported crime in official records.[38]

One of the clearest findings to emerge from comparative studies of crime is that war is associated with higher rates of homicide. Archer and Gartner compared changes in homicide rates of nations before and after major wars. Whether a nation is defeated or victorious, homicide rates tend to increase after a war. This result is consistent with the idea that a society or nation legitimizes violence during wartime. That is, during wartime, societies approve of killing the enemy; afterward, homicide rates may go up because inhibitions against killing have been relaxed.[39] Ted Gurr suggested that the long-term downtrend in crime in Western societies seems to be consistent with an increasing emphasis on humanistic values and nonviolent achievement of goals. But such goals may be temporarily suspended during wartime. In the United States, for example, surges in violent crime rates occurred during the 1860s and 1870s (during and after the Civil War), after World War I, after World War II, and during the Vietnam War.[40] Recently, however, the homicide rate in the United States has declined.[41]

In the types of societies that anthropologists have typically studied, homicide statistics were not usually available; so cross-cultural studies of homicide usually measure homicide rates by comparing and rank-ordering ethnographers' statements about the frequency of homicide. For example, the statement that murder is "practically unheard of" is taken to mean that the murder rate is lower than where it is reported that "homicide is not uncommon." Despite the fact that the data on cultural homicide rates are not quantitative, the cross-cultural results are consistent with the cross-national results; more war is usually associated with more homicide and assault, as well as with socially approved aggressive behaviors (as in aggressive games) and severe physical punishment for wrongdoing.[42] A cross-cultural study suggests that the more war a society has, the more the society socializes or trains boys in aggression, and such socialization strongly predicts higher rates of homicide and assault.[43]

Capital punishment—execution of criminals—is severe physical punishment for wrongdoing. It is commonly thought that the prospect of capital punishment deters would be murderers. Yet, cross-national research suggests otherwise. More countries show murder rates going down rather than up after capital punishment was abolished.[44] Capital punishment may legitimize violence rather than deter it.

Research conducted in the United States suggests that juvenile delinquents (usually boys) are likely to come from broken homes, with the father absent for much of the time the boy is growing up. The conclusion often drawn is that father absence somehow increases the likelihood of delinquency and adult forms of physical violence. But other conditions that may cause delinquency are also associated with broken homes, conditions such as the stigma of not having a "regular" family and the generally low standard of living of such families. It is therefore important to conduct research in other societies, in which father absence does not occur in concert with these other factors, to see if father absence by itself is related to physical violence.

For example, in many polygynous societies, children grow up in a mother–child household; the father lives separately and is seldom around the child. Does the father absence explanation of delinquency and violence fit such societies? The answer is apparently yes: Societies in which children are reared in mother–child households or the father spends little time caring for the child tend to have more physical violence by males than do societies in which fathers spend time with children.[45] The rate of violent crime is also more frequent in nations that have more women than men, which is consistent with the theory that father absence increases violence.[46]

More research is needed to discover exactly what accounts for these relationships. It is possible, as some suggest, that boys growing up without fathers are apt to act "supermasculine," to show how "male" they are. But it is also possible that mothers who rear children alone have more frustration and more anger, and therefore are likely to provide an aggressive role model for the child. In addition, high male mortality in war predicts polygyny, therefore, boys in polygynous societies are likely to be exposed to a warrior tradition.[47]

Trying to act supermasculine, however, may be likely to involve violence only if aggression is an important component of the male gender role in society. If men were expected by society to be sensitive, caring, and nonviolent, boys who grew up without fathers might try to be supersensitive and supercaring. So society's expectations for males probably shape how growing up in a mother–child household affects behavior in adolescence and later.[48] The media may also influence the expectations for males. Numerous studies in the United States show that, even controlling for other factors like parental neglect, family income, and mental illness, more television watching in childhood and adolescence predicts more overt aggression later. Estimates show that an hour of prime-time television depicts three to five violent acts, and an hour of children's television depicts 20 to 25 violent acts.[49]

One widely held idea is that poor economic conditions increase the likelihood of crime, but the relationship does not appear to be strong. Also, the findings are somewhat different for different types of crime. For example, hundreds of studies in this and other countries do not show a clear relationship between changes in economic well-being as measured by unemployment rates and changes in violent crime as measured by homicide. The rate of homicide does not appear to increase in bad times. Property crimes, however, do increase with increases in unemployment. Violent crime does appear to be associated with one economic characteristic: Homicide is usually highest in nations or societies with high income inequality.[50] Why income inequality predicts homicide but downturns in the economy do not is something of a puzzle.[51]

The fact that property crime is linked to unemployment is consistent with the cross-cultural finding that theft (but not violent crime) tends to occur less often in egalitarian societies than in stratified ones. Societies with equal access to resources usually have distribution mechanisms that offset any differences in wealth. Hence, theft should be less of a temptation and therefore less likely in an egalitarian society. Theft rates are higher in socially stratified societies despite the fact that

Evidence indicates that violence on TV encourages violence in real life.

they are more likely than egalitarian societies to have police and courts to punish crime. Societies may try to deter property and other crimes when the rates of such are high, but we do not know that these efforts actually reduce the rates.

So what does the available research suggest about how we might be able to reduce crime? The results so far indicate that homicide rates are highest in societies that socialize their boys for aggression. Such socialization is linked to war and other forms of socially approved violence—capital punishment, television and movie violence by heroes, violence in sports. The statistical evidence suggests that war encourages socialization for aggression, which in turn results unintentionally in high rates of violence. The policy implication of these results is that, if we can reduce socialization for aggression by reducing the risk of war and therefore the necessity to produce effective warriors, and if we can reduce other forms of socially approved violence, we may thereby reduce the rates of violent crime. The reduction of inequalities in wealth may also help to reduce crime, particularly theft. And although it is not yet clear why, it appears that raising boys with a male role model around may reduce the likelihood of male violence in adulthood.

War

War is an unfortunate fact of life in most societies known to anthropology. Almost every society had at least occasional wars when it was first described, unless it had been pacified (usually by Western colonial powers).[52] Since the Civil War, the United States has not had any wars on its territory, but it is unusual in that respect. Before pacification, most societies in the ethnographic record had frequent armed combat between communities or larger units that spoke the same language. That is, most warfare was internal to the society or language group. Even some wars in modern times involved speakers of the same language; recall the wars between Italian states before the unification of Italy and many of the "civil" wars of the last two centuries. Although people in some societies might fight against people in other societies, such "external" wars were usually not organized on behalf of the entire society or even a major section of it.[53] That is, warfare in the ethnographic record did not usually involve politically unified societies. The absolute numbers of people killed may have been small, but this does not mean that warfare in nonindustrial societies was a trivial matter. Indeed, it appears that nonindustrial warfare may have been even more lethal *proportionately* than modern warfare, judging by the fact that wars killed 25–30 percent of the males in some nonindustrial societies.[54]

Although warfare has occurred frequently in societies at all levels of complexity, changes over time tell us that war is not inevitable. For example, Norway is one of the world's most peaceful countries. The Viking age, as shown in this reenactment, was an era of militarism.

It is possible that people in nonindustrial societies go to war mostly out of fear, particularly a fear of expectable but unpredictable natural disasters (droughts, floods, hurricanes, among others) that destroy food supplies.[55] People with more of a history of such disasters have more war. It seems as if people go to war to protect themselves ahead of time from disasters, inasmuch as the victors in war almost always take resources (land, animals, other things) from the defeated, even when the victors have no current resource problems. Another factor apparently making for more war is teaching children to mistrust others. People who grow up to be mistrustful of others may be more likely to go to war than to negotiate or seek conciliation with "enemies." Mistrust or fear of others seems to be partly caused by threat or fear of disasters.[56]

Is warfare in and between modern state societies explainable in much the same way that nonindustrial warfare seems to be explainable? If the answer to that question turns out to be yes, it will certainly be a modified yes, because the realities of industrialized societies require an expanded conception of disasters. In the modern world, with its complex economic and political dependencies among nations, we may not be worried only about weather or pest disasters that could curtail food supplies. Possible curtailments of other resources, particularly oil, may also scare us into going to war. According to some commentators, the decision in 1991 to go to war against Iraq after it invaded Kuwait fits this theory of war.

But even if the "threat-to-resources" theory is true, we may be coming to realize (since the end of the Cold War) that war is not the only way to ensure access to resources. There may be a better way in the modern world, a way that is more cost-effective as well as more preserving of human life. If it is true that war is most likely when people fear unpredictable disasters of any kind, the risk of war should lessen when people realize that the harmful effects of disasters could be reduced or prevented by international cooperation. Just as we have the assurance of disaster relief within our country, we could have the assurance of disaster relief worldwide. That is, the fear of unpredictable disasters and the fear of others, and the consequent risk of war, could be reduced by the assurance ahead of time that the world would help those in need in case of disaster. Instead of going to war out of fear, we could go to peace by agreeing to share. The certainty of international cooperation could compensate for the uncertainty of resources.

Consider how Germany and Japan have fared in the years since their "unconditional surrender" in World War II. They were forbidden to participate in the international arms race and could rely on others, particularly the United States, to protect them. Without a huge burden of armaments, Germany and Japan thrived. But countries that competed militarily, particularly the United States and the Soviet Union at the height of the Cold War, experienced economic difficulties. Doesn't that scenario at least suggest the wisdom of international cooperation, particularly the need for international agreements to ensure worldwide disaster relief? Compared with going to war and its enormous costs, going to peace would be a bargain!

Recent research in political science and anthropology suggests an additional way to reduce the risk of war. Among the societies known to anthropology, studies indicate that people in more participatory—that is, more "democratic"—political systems rarely go to war with each other.[57] Thus, if authoritarian governments were to disappear from the world because the powerful nations of the world stopped supporting them militarily and otherwise, the world could be more peaceful for this reason too.

Although democratically governed states rarely go to war with each other, it used to be thought that they are not necessarily more peaceful in general, that they are as likely to go to war as are other kinds of political systems, but not so much with each other. For example, the United States has gone to war with Grenada, Panama, and Iraq—all authoritarian states—but not with democratic Canada, with which the United States has also had disputes. But now a consensus is emerging among political scientists that democracies are not only unlikely to go to war with each other, they are also less warlike in general.[58] The theory suggested by the cross-national and cross-cultural results is that democratic conflict resolution within a political system generalizes to democratic conflict resolution between political systems, particularly if the systems are both democratic. If our participatory institutions and perceptions allow us to resolve our disputes peacefully, internally and externally, we may think that similarly governed people would also be disposed to settle things peacefully. Therefore, disputes between participatory political systems should be unlikely to result in war.

The understanding that participatory systems rarely fight each other, and knowing why they do not, would have important consequences for policy in the contemporary world. The kinds of military preparations believed necessary and the costs people would be willing to pay for them might be affected. On the one hand, understanding the relationship between democracy and peace might encourage war making against authoritarian regimes to overturn them—with enormous costs in human life and otherwise. On the other hand, understanding the consequences of democracy might encourage us to assist the emergence and consolidation of more participatory systems of government in the countries of eastern Europe, the former Soviet Union, and elsewhere. In any case, the relationship between democracy and peace strongly suggests that it is counterproductive to support any undemocratic regimes, even if they happen to be enemies of our enemies, if we want to minimize the risk of war in the world. The latest cross-national evidence suggests that extending democracy around the world would minimize the risk of war. Encouraging nations to be more interdependent economically, and encouraging the spread of international nongovernmental organizations (like professional societies and trade associations) to provide informal ways to resolve conflicts, would also minimize the risk of war, judging by results of recent research by political scientists.[59]

Terrorism

Ever since September 11, 2001, when terrorists crashed airliners into the World Trade Center towers in New York City and into the Pentagon in Arlington, Virginia, people all over the world realize that terrorism has become a social problem globally. It is now painfully clear that organized groups of terrorists can train their people to kill themselves and thousands of others half a world away, not only by hijacking airliners and flying them into skyscrapers, but also by using easily transported explosives and biological weapons. Social scientists are now actively trying to understand terrorism, in the hope that research may lead to ways to minimize the likelihood of future attacks. But there are lots of questions to answer. What is terrorism and how shall it be defined? How long has terrorist activity been around? What are the causes of terrorism? What kind of people are likely to become terrorists? And what are the consequences of terrorism?

Answering these questions is not so simple. Most people can point to instances that hardly anyone would have trouble calling terrorism—spraying nerve gas in a Japanese subway, Palestinian suicide bombers targeting Israeli civilians, and Ku Klux Klan members lynching African Americans.[60] It is harder to identify the boundaries between terrorism, crime, political repression, and warfare.[61] Most researchers agree that terrorism involves the threat or use of violence

A candlelight vigil after the terrorist attack in 2008 on the Taj Mahal Hotel in Mumbai, India.

against civilians. Terrorism is usually also politically or socially organized, in contrast to most crimes, which are usually perpetrated by individuals acting on their own. (To be sure, crime can be socially organized too, as, for example, in what we call "organized crime.") One marker of the difference between most crime and terrorism is that criminals rarely take public credit for their activities because they want to avoid being caught. In terrorism, the perpetrators usually proclaim their responsibility. In terrorism also, the violence is directed mostly at unarmed people, including women and children. It is intended to frighten the "enemy," to *terrorize* them, to scare them into doing something that the terrorists want to see happen. Generally, then, **terrorism** may be defined as the use or threat of violence to create terror in others, usually for political purposes.[62] Some define terrorism as perpetrated by groups that are not formal political entities. However, this criterion presents some difficulty. What are we to call it when governments support death squads and genocide against their own civilians? Some scholars call this "state terror."[63] And what are we to call the activities of some governments that support secret operations against other countries (often referred to as "state-sponsored terrorism")? Finally, although some nations conducting war explicitly try to avoid civilian casualties and focus primarily on combatants (armed soldiers), their weapons, and resources or "assets" such as factories, air strips, and fuel depots, many attacks in wartime throughout history have purposefully targeted civilians (e.g., the United States dropped atomic bombs on Hiroshima and Nagasaki to persuade the Japanese to end World War II).

One thing is certain about terrorism: It is not a new development. Some of the words we use for terrorists—for example, "zealots" and "assassins"—derive from terrorist movements in the past. The Zealots, Jewish nationalists who revolted against the Romans occupying Judea in the first century, would hide in crowds and stab officials and priests as well as soldiers. In the eleventh and twelfth centuries in southwest Asia, the Fedayeen (a group of Muslim Isma'ili Shi'ites) undertook to assassinate Sunni rulers despite the almost certainty of their own capture or death. The rulers said that the Fedayeen were under the influence of hashish and called them

"Hashshashin," which is the root of the later term *assassin*.[64] In the late eighteenth and early nineteenth centuries, the "reign of terror" occurred during and after the French Revolution. In the early and middle twentieth century, dictator Joseph Stalin ordered the execution of many millions of people who were considered enemies of the Soviet state. Six million Jews and millions of other innocents were exterminated by the German Third Reich in the 1930s and 1940s.[65] And many Latin American regimes, such as that in Argentina, terrorized and killed dissidents in the 1970s and 1980s.[66] Now there is a heightened fear of terrorists who may have access to weapons of mass destruction. In a world made smaller by global transportation, cell phones, and the Internet, terrorism is a greater threat than ever before.

We still lack systematic research that explains why terrorism occurs and why people are motivated to become terrorists. But there is a good deal of research about state terrorism. Political scientist R. J. Rummel estimates that governments have killed nearly 262 million people in the twentieth century (he calls this kind of terrorism "democide"). State terrorism has been responsible for four times more deaths than all the wars, civil and international, that occurred in the twentieth century. Regimes in the Soviet Union (1917–1987), China (1923–1987), and Germany (1933–1945) were responsible for killing more than a total of 190 million civilians. Proportionately the Khmer Rouge regime in Cambodia topped them all, killing over 30 percent of its population from 1975 to 1978.[67] What predicts state terrorism against one's own people? Rummel finds one clear predictor: totalitarian governments. By far, they have the highest frequencies of domestic state terrorism, controlling for factors such as economic wealth, type of religion, and population size. As Rummel puts it, "Power kills; absolute power kills absolutely."[68] Democratic countries are less likely to practice state terrorism, but when they do, it occurs during or after a rebellion or a war.[69]

We know relatively little so far about what predicts who will become a terrorist. We do know that terrorists often come from higher social statuses and generally have more education than the average person.[70] If state terrorism is more likely to occur in totalitarian regimes, terrorists and terrorist groups may be more likely to occur in such societies. If so, the spread of democracy may be our best hope of minimizing the risk of terrorism in the world, just as the spread of democracy seems to minimize the likelihood of war between countries.

Making the World Better

Many social problems afflict our world, not just the ones discussed here.[71] We don't have the space to discuss the international trade in drugs and how it plays out in violence, death, and corruption. We haven't talked about the negative effects of environmental degradations such as water pollution, ozone depletion, and destruction of forests and wetlands. We haven't said much, if anything, about overpopulation, the energy crisis, and a host of other problems we should care and do something about, if we hope to make this a safer world. But we have tried to encourage positive thinking about global social problems; we have suggested how the results of past and future scientific research could be applied to solving some of those problems.

We may know enough now that we can do something about our problems, and we will discover more through future research. Social problems are mostly of human making and are therefore susceptible to human unmaking. There may be obstacles on the road to solutions, but we can overcome them if we want to. So let's go for it!

Global Problems

Summary

1. We may be more motivated now to try to solve social problems because worldwide communication has increased our awareness of them elsewhere, because we seem to be increasingly bothered by problems in our own society, and because we know more than we used to about various social problems that afflict our world.

2. The idea that we can solve global social problems is based on two assumptions. We have to assume that it is possible to discover the causes of a problem, and we have to assume that we will be able to do something about the causes once they are discovered and thereby eliminate or reduce the problem.

3. Disasters such as earthquakes, floods, and droughts can have greater or lesser effects on human life, depending on social conditions. Therefore, disasters are partly social problems, with partly social causes and solutions.

4. Whether people become homeless, whether they have shantytowns, seems to depend on a society's willingness to share wealth and to help those in need.

5. Promoting the equality of men and women and the sharing of childrearing responsibilities may reduce family violence.

6. We may be able to reduce rates of violent crime if we can reduce socialization and training for aggression. To do that, we would have to reduce the likelihood of war, the high likelihood of which predicts more socialization for aggression and other forms of socially approved aggression. The reduction of inequalities in wealth may also help to reduce crime, particularly theft. And raising boys with a male role model around may reduce the likelihood of male violence in adulthood.

7. People seem to be most likely to go to war when they fear unpredictable disasters that destroy food supplies or curtail the supplies of other necessities. Disputes between more participatory (more "democratic") political systems are unlikely to result in war. Therefore, the more democracy spreads in the world, and the more people all over the world are assured of internationally organized disaster relief, the more they might go to peace rather than to war to solve their problems.

8. Terrorism has occurred throughout history. State terrorism has killed more than all wars in the twentieth century and seems to be predicted mostly by totalitarianism.

Glossary Term

terrorism

Critical Questions

1. What particular advantages do anthropologists have in trying to solve practical problems?
2. Select one of the social problems discussed in this text and suggest what you think could be done to reduce or eliminate it.
3. Do global problems require solutions by global agencies? If so, which?

📖—**Read** the **Original Source** on **myanthrolab.com**

Read the chapter by Paul C. Rosenblatt titled "Human Rights Violations" on MyAnthroLab. Answer the following questions.

1. Rosenblatt states that human rights may be enhanced by "promoting more respectful, peaceful, and nonexploitive relations among different groups within countries." Explain why he thinks so.
2. Why does he say that "saints can be sinners and sinners can be saints"?
3. Rosenblatt asks: "Is it moral for the United States and a handful of other powerful nations to impose their will on other nations?" What do you think, and why do you think so?

Photo Credits

Credits are listed in order of appearance.

David Greedy/Newsmakers/Getty Images News/Getty Images; Shamil Zhumatov/Reuters/Corbis; Sucheta Das/Reuters/Corbis Wire/Corbis; Edouard Berne/Stone/Getty Images; E&E Image Library/H. Collection: Heritage/Age Fotostock; epa/Corbis.

Glossary

Terrorism The use or threat of violence to create terror in others, usually for political purposes.

Notes

1. The discussion in this section draws extensively from Aptekar 1994.
2. Information collected during Melvin Ember's fieldwork in American Samoa, 1955–1956.
3. Mellor and Gavian 1987.
4. Dirks 1993.
5. Torry 1986.

6. United Nations Human Settlements Programme 2003, xi, 16, 59.
7. Rodwin and Sanyal 1987.
8. Mangin 1967.
9. Rodwin and Sanyal 1987; for a critique of self-help programs, see Ward 1982.
10. A. Cohen and Koegel 2009.
11. National Coalition for the Homeless 2008.
12. A. Cohen and Koegel 2009.
13. Baxter and Hopper 1981, 30–33, 50–74.
14. Ibid.
15. A. Cohen and Koegel 2009.
16. H. Herrman 1990.
17. Barak 1991, 63–65.
18. World Bank 2004.
19. Aptekar 1991, 326.
20. UN Works n.d.
21. Aptekar 1988; 1991, 326–49.
22. Korbin 1981, 4.
23. Straus 2001, 195–96.
24. Straus and Kantor 1994.
25. Straus 1995, 30–33; Straus and Kantor 1995.
26. Straus 1991; U.S. Department of Justice 1988; 1994; 2000.
27. Levinson 1989, 11–12, 44.
28. Minturn and Stashak 1982. Using a sociobiological orientation, a study by Daly and Wilson (1988, 43–59) also suggests that infanticide is largely due to the difficulty of raising the infant successfully.
29. Levinson 1989, 26–28.
30. C. R. Ember and Ember 2005; see also Petersen, Lee, and Ellis 1982, as cited in Levinson 1989, 63.
31. Lareau 2003, 230.
32. Levinson 1989, 31.
33. Ibid., 71.
34. Gelles and Straus 1988, 78–88.
35. Erchak 2009; Levinson 1989, 44–45.
36. Straus and Yodanis 1996.
37. Levinson 1989, 104–07.
38. Archer and Gartner 1984, 35.
39. Archer and Gartner 1984, 63–97.
40. Gurr 1989, 47–48.
41. U.S. Department of Justice n.d.
42. Eckhardt 1975; Russell 1972; Sipes 1973.
43. C. R. Ember and Ember 1994.
44. Archer and Gartner 1984, 118–39.
45. Bacon, Child, and Barry 1963; Barry 2007; B. B. Whiting 1965.
46. Barber 2000.
47. C. R. Ember and Ember 1994, 625.
48. C. R. Ember and Ember 1993, 227.
49. C. A. Anderson and Bushman 2002, 2377; J. G. Johnson et al. 2002.
50. In preindustrial societies, homicide and assault are similarly predicted by the presence of indigenous money, almost always associated with wealth concentration—see Barry 2007.
51. Gartner 2009; Krahn, Hartnagel, and Gartrell 1986, as referred to in Daly and Wilson 1988, 287–88; Loftin, McDowall, and Boudouris 1989.
52. C. R. Ember and Ember 1997.
53. Most of the discussion in this section comes from C. R. Ember and M. Ember 1992, 204–06.
54. Gat 1999, 563–83; Meggitt 1977, 201.
55. Data from Korea is consistent with this explanation of war: More environmental stress strongly predicts higher frequencies of warfare in Korea between the 1st century B.C. and the 8th century A.D. See B. W. Kang 2000, 878.
56. For the cross-cultural results suggesting the theory of war described here, see C. R. Ember and M. Ember 1992.
57. For the results on political participation and peace in the ethnographic record, see C. R. Ember, M. Ember, and Russett 1992. For the results on political participation and peace in the modern world, see Russett and Oneal 2001.
58. Russett and Oneal 2001, 49.
59. Ibid., 125ff.
60. Some of these examples are from Henderson 2001.
61. See the discussions in Ibid., 3–9, and S. K. Anderson and Sloan 2002, 1–5.
62. S. K. Anderson and Sloan 2002, 465.
63. This definition is adapted from Chomsky, who is quoted in Henderson 2001, 5.

64. S. K. Anderson and Sloan 2002, 6–7.
65. Ibid., 6–8.
66. Suárez-Orozco 1992.
67. R. J. Rummel 2002a.
68. R. J. Rummel 2002c.
69. R. J. Rummel 2002d.
70. S. K. Anderson and Sloan 2002, 422.
71. *Scientific American*, Crossroads for Planet Earth 2005.

Bibliography

Anderson, Craig A., and Brad J. Bushman. 2002. The effects of media violence on society. *Science* 295 (March 29):2377–79.

Anderson, Sean K., and Stephen Sloan. 2002. *Historical dictionary of terrorism.* 2nd ed. Lanham, MD: Scarecrow Press.

Aptekar, Lewis. 1988. *Street children of Cali.* Durham, NC: Duke University Press.

Aptekar, Lewis. 1991. Are Colombian street children neglected? The contributions of ethnographic and ethnohistorical approaches to the study of children. *Anthropology and Education Quarterly* 22:326–49.

Aptekar, Lewis. 1994. *Environmental disasters in global perspective.* New York: G. K. Hall/Macmillan.

Archer, Dane, and Rosemary Gartner. 1984. *Violence and crime in cross-national perspective.* New Haven, CT: Yale University Press.

Bacon, Margaret, Irvin L. Child, and Herbert Barry III. 1963. A cross-cultural study of correlates of crime. *Journal of Abnormal and Social Psychology* 66:291–300.

Barak, Gregg. 1991. *Gimme shelter: A social history of homelessness in contemporary America.* New York: Praeger.

Barber, Nigel. 2000. The sex ratio as a predictor of cross-national variation in violent crime. *Cross-Cultural Research* 34:264–82.

Barry, Herbert III. 2007. Wealth concentration associated with frequent violent crime in diverse communities. *Social Evolution and History* 6:29–38.

Baxter, Ellen, and Kim Hopper. 1981. *Private lives/public spaces: Homeless adults on the streets of New York City.* New York: Community Service Society of New York.

Cohen, Alex, and Paul Koegel. 2009. Homelessness. In MyAnthroLibrary, eds. C. R. Ember, M. Ember, and P. N. Peregrine. MyAnthro-Library.com. Pearson.

Daly, Martin, and Margo Wilson. 1988. *Homicide.* New York: Aldine.

Dirks, Robert. 1993. Starvation and famine. *Cross-Cultural Research* 27:28–69.

Eckhardt, William. 1975. Primitive militarism. *Journal of Peace Research* 12:55–62.

Ember, Carol R., and Melvin Ember. 1993. Issues in cross-cultural studies of interpersonal violence. *Violence and Victims* 8:217–33.

Ember, Carol R., and Melvin Ember. 1994. War, socialization, and interpersonal violence: A cross-cultural study. *Journal of Conflict Resolution* 38:620–46.

Ember, Carol R., and Melvin Ember. 1997. Violence in the ethnographic record: Results of cross-cultural research on war and aggression. In *Troubled times,* eds. D. Martin and D. Frayer. Langhorn, PA: Gordon and Breach.

Ember, Carol R., and Melvin Ember. 2005. Explaining corporal punishment of children: A cross-cultural study. *American Anthropologist* 107:609–19.

Ember, Carol R., Melvin Ember, and Bruce Russett. 1992. Peace between participatory polities: A cross-cultural test of the "democracies rarely fight each other" hypothesis. *World Politics* 44:573–99.

Erchak, Gerald M. 2009. Family violence. In MyAnthroLibrary, eds. C. R. Ember, M. Ember, and P. N. Peregrine. MyAnthroLibrary .com. Pearson.

Gat, Azar. 1999. The pattern of fighting in simple, small-scale, prestate societies. *Journal of Anthropological Research* 55:563–83.

Gartner, Rosemary. 2009. Crime variations across cultures and nations. In MyAnthroLibrary, eds. C. R. Ember, M. Ember, and P. N. Peregrine. MyAnthroLibrary.com. Pearson.

Gelles, Richard J., and Murray A. Straus. 1988. *Intimate violence.* New York: Simon & Schuster.

Gurr, Ted Robert. 1989. Historical trends in violent crime: Europe and the United States. In *Violence in America,* vol. 1: *The history of crime,* ed. T. R. Gurr. Newbury Park, CA: Sage.

Henderson, Harry. 2001. *Global terrorism: The complete reference guide.* New York: Checkmark Books.

Herrman, Helen. 1990. A survey of homeless mentally ill people in Melbourne, Australia. *Hospital and Community Psychiatry* 41:1291–92.

Johnson, Jeffrey G., Patricia Cohen, Elizabeth M. Smailies, Stephanie Kasen, and Judith S. Brook. 2002. Television viewing and aggressive behavior during adolescence and adulthood. *Science* 295 (March 29):2468–70.

Kang, Bong W. 2000. A reconsideration of population pressure and warfare: A protohistoric Korean case. *Current Anthropology* 41:873–81.

Korbin, Jill E. 1981. Introduction. In *Child abuse and neglect,* ed. J. E. Korbin. Berkeley: University of California Press.

Krahn, Harvey, T. F. Hartnagel, and J. W. Gartrell. 1986. Income inequality and homicide rates: Cross-national data and criminological theories. *Criminology* 24:269–95.

Lareau, Annette. 2003. *Unequal childhoods: Class, race, and family life.* Berkeley: University of California Press.

Levinson, David. 1989. *Family violence in cross-cultural perspective.* Newbury Park, CA: Sage.

Loftin, Colin, David McDowall, and James Boudouris. 1989. Economic change and homicide in Detroit, 1926–1979. In *Violence in America,* vol. 1: *The history of crime,* ed. T. R. Gurr. Newbury Park, CA: Sage.

Mangin, William. 1967. Latin American squatter settlements: A problem and a solution. *Latin American Research Review* 2:65–98.

Meggitt, Mervyn J. 1977. *Blood is their argument: Warfare among the Mae Enga tribesmen of the New Guinea highlands.* Palo Alto, CA: Mayfield.

Mellor, John W., and Sarah Gavian. 1987. Famine: Causes, prevention, and relief. *Science* 235 (January 30):539–44.

Global Problems

Minturn, Leigh, and Jerry Stashak. 1982. Infanticide as a terminal abortion procedure. *Behavior Science Research* 17:70–85.

National Coalition for the Homeless. 2008. How many people experience homelessness? NCH Fact Sheet #2. http://www.nationalhomeless.org/factsheets/How_Many.html (accessed September 3, 2009).

Petersen, Larry R., G. R. Lee, and G. J. Ellis. 1982. Social structure, socialization values, and disciplinary techniques: A cross-cultural analysis. *Journal of Marriage and the Family* 44:131–42.

Rodwin, Lloyd, and Bishwapriya Sanyal. 1987. Shelter, settlement, and development: An overview. In *Shelter, settlement, and development*, ed. L. Rodwin. Boston: Allen & Unwin.

Rummel, Rudolf J. 2002a. Death by government. Chapter 1. http://www.hawaii.edu/powerkills/DBG.CHAP1.HTM.

Rummel, Rudolf J. 2002c. Statistics of democide. Chapter 17. http://www.hawaii.edu/powerkills/SOD.CHAP17.HTM.

Rummel, Rudolf J. 2002d. Statistics of democide. Chapter 21. http://www.hawaii.edu/powerkills/SOD.CHAP21.HTM.

Russell, Elbert W. 1972. Factors of human aggression. *Behavior Science Notes* 7:275–312.

Russett, Bruce, and John R. Oneal. 2001. *Triangulating peace: Democracy, interdependence, and international organizations.* New York: Norton.

Scientific American. 2005. Crossroads for Planet Earth. *Scientific American.* Special Issue, September.

Sipes, Richard G. 1973. War, sports, and aggression: An empirical test of two rival theories. *American Anthropologist* 75:64–86.

Straus, Murray A. 1991. Physical violence in American families: Incidence rates, causes, and trends. In *Abused and battered,* eds. D. D. Knudsen and J. L. Miller. New York: Aldine.

Straus, Murray A. 1995. Trends in cultural norms and rates of partner violence: An update to 1992. In *Understanding partner violence: Prevalence, causes, consequences, and solutions,* eds. S. M. Stith and M. A. Straus, 30–33. Minneapolis, MN: National Council on Family Relations. http://pubpages.unh.edu/~mas2/v56.pdf/ (accessed August 2002).

Straus, Murray A. 2001. Physical aggression in the family: Prevalence rates, links to non-family violence, and implications for primary prevention of societal violence. In *Prevention and control of aggression and the impact on its victims,* ed. M. Martinez, 181–200. New York: Kluwer Academic/Plenum Press.

Straus, Murray A., and Glenda Kaufman Kantor. 1994 (July). Change in Spouse assault rates from 1975 to 1992: A comparison of three national surveys in the United States. Paper presented at the 13th World Congress of Sociology, Bielefeld, Germany. http://pubpages.unh.edu/~mas2/v55. pdf/ (accessed August 2002).

Straus, Murray A., and Glenda Kaufman Kantor. 1995. Trends in physical abuse by parents from 1975 to 1992: A comparison of three national surveys. Paper presented at the annual meeting of the American Society of Criminology, Boston, November 18. http://pubpages.unh.edu/~mas2/V57.pdf/ (accessed August 2002).

Straus, Murray A., and Carrie L. Yodanis. 1996. Corporal punishment in adolescence and physical assaults on spouses in later life: What accounts for the link? *Journal of Marriage and the Family* 58:825–41.

Suárez-Orozco, Marcelo. 1992. A grammar of terror: Psychocultural responses to state terrorism in dirty war and post-dirty war Argentina. In *The paths to domination, resistance, and terror,* eds. C. Nordstrom and J. Martin, 219–59. Berkeley: University of California Press.

Textor, Robert B., comp. 1967. *A cross-cultural summary.* New Haven, CT: HRAF Press.

Torry, William I. 1986. Morality and harm: Hindu peasant adjustments to famines. *Social Science Information* 25:125–60.

UN Works. n.d. http://www.un.org/works/goingon/mongolia/lessonplan_homelessness.html.

United Nations Human Settlements Programme. 2003. The challenge of slums: Global report on human settlements, 2003. Nairobi, Kenya: Author.

U.S. Department of Justice. 1988 (November). Prevalence, incidence, and consequences of violence against women: Findings from the National Violence against Women Survey. Washington, DC.

U.S. Department of Justice. 1994 (April). Violent crime. NCJ-147486. Washington, DC: Author

U.S. Department of Justice. 2000. Children as victims. *Juvenile Justice Bulletin 1999.* National Report Series. Washington, DC: Author.

U.S. Department of Justice. n.d. Bureau of Justice statistics homi-cide trends in the U.S: Long-term trends and patterns. http://www.ojp.gov/bjs/homicide/hmrt.htm (accessed Sept. 5, 2009).

Wallace, Alfred Russell. 1970/1858. On the tendency of varieties to depart indefinitely from the original type. (Originally published in 1858.) In *Evolution of man,* ed. L. B. Young. New York: Oxford University Press.

Ward, Peter M. 1982. Introduction and purpose. In *Self-help housing,* ed. P. M. Ward. London: Mansell.

Whiting, Beatrice B. 1965. Sex identity conflict and physical violence. *American Anthropologist* 67:123–40.

World Bank. 2004. *World development indicators 2004.* Washington, DC: World Bank Publications.

Index